Harvard East Asian Series, 34

TRADITIONAL MEDICINE IN MODERN CHINA

---

*The East Asian Research Center
at Harvard University
administers projects designed
to further scholarly understanding
of China, Korea, Japan,
and adjacent areas.*

TRADITIONAL MEDICINE IN

MODERN CHINA

Science, Nationalism,
and
the Tensions
of Cultural Change

RALPH C. CROIZIER

Harvard University Press

CAMBRIDGE, MASSACHUSETTS

1968

The characters on the title page
are translated as "Chinese medicine."

To my parents,
Charles J. and Doris M. Croizier,
who showed the love and wisdom
to let their impractical son
steer by his own star

FOREWORD

Franz Schurmann, in his masterly *Ideology and Organization in Communist China,* dwells on a "contradiction" which the Communists dwell on lovingly themselves: the contradiction (sometimes), the tense relationship always, between "red" and "expert." There is never a mention of medicine, no reference to the "Great Leap" annexation of Chinese medicine (red, being "people's") as a body of stern lessons to the "experts." Mr. Croizier deals, in deep historical context, with the medical experts. They are the practicers of modern medicine, and as devotees of a universal science they (and their advocates) had been cultural revolutionaries of unimpeachable standing. Why should they be suspect in revolutionary China?

The same Chinese history that made medicine a germ of revolution gave it, unshakably, beneath the bland title of "modern," the blunt label of "Western Medicine." When the Communists came to police it, then, and to force it into association with the native medical tradition, were they reverting to an old xenophobia, anti-expert because anti-Western? Were they reverting to a Confucian cultural bias, anti-expert because anti-professional?

Foreword

Mr. Croizier, while treating comprehensively several shades of thought about "Chinese essence," writes history as process; he has no need of essence to relate the present to the past. He makes the elusive but vital distinction between cultural nationalism and traditionalism, that universal Confucian expression of cultural self-esteem. He demonstrates convincingly that "the West" is not a constant in Chinese history, even if hostility to the West—some kind of hostility —seems a once and future thing. The cultural West (with its science, including medicine) facing Confucian China is not the warm war political West facing Communist China. Science, however policed, is a Communist value, a Confucian dereliction.

It is not just that "scientific socialists" could hardly condescend to science like humanist literati. Marxists trade on the prestige of science, and they know quite well what was never true for Confucian China, that in everyone's modern world, in "bourgeois" countries and anti-bourgeois alike, science has prestige. And when the Chinese Communists put scientists down (medical experts among them), the Communists are acknowledging that prestige, not impugning it; its very universality, its seeming transcendence of ideology, is a threat to the masters of ideology. Medical science, all science, must be mastered by the ideologues, or their own occupation would be gone. In effect, the questionable reputation of the Chinese medical tradition gives the Communists a pretext for enhancing it; the very need for enhancement, for state decree of its scientific standing, makes the medical corps, reconstituted thus, more naturally subservient to its protectors.

For all the common "generalism" of the Communist cadre and the Confucian official, the latter never held what the former has to hold as an article of faith: that one of the reasons for demeaning expertise is the need to erase the distinction—a crucial *Confucian* distinction—between mental and physical labor. Just as the Confucianist, with his amateur ideal, had displaced the aristocracy, and then had taken on an aristocratic aura (with license to condescend to the technical professional), so the professional in the modern world, having broken the amateur ideal, has the status pride of the aristocrat today. Therefore, the Party must trim him down, to vindicate its own version of autocratic rule. This confirms the process of change toward a new world of pervasive specialization; it is no witness at all to the eternity of a Confucian-amateur essence.

Communist China's revival of pride in Chinese medicine, then, is appreciation of a heritage from a sub-Confucian culture, which lends it a "people's" identity. And it is "people's," too, as a pill for cosmopolitans to swallow. For the latter are the experts, associated in universal science with professional colleagues on the other side of national and ideological walls.

Still, the medical issue in modern China has its own nuances; it is more than a microcosm of the issue of science in general, the issue of tradition in general. Mr. Croizier starts just about all the possible hares, and catches them. He is extraordinarily subtle in following all the avenues of argument, and relating the logic to the psychology, the psychology to the history. He gives a brilliant demonstration of a tenet of intellectual history, that there are two nouns to consider: *thought* and *thinking*. Men's thinking is determined partly —indispensably, but only partly—by the intellectual persuasiveness of a given body of thought. And it is determined partly by an emotional preference (deriving from historical context) that the persuasion be congenial. There is the purpose of reaching truth, and there is compulsion *a tergo* to move in a certain direction—both a pull and a push, and not always on the same line. Men want satisfying conclusions, but satisfaction is ambiguous. One may satisfy the logic of argument. One may satisfy oneself. The "tensions" of Mr. Croizier's title, perhaps never so well disclosed as in this history of medicine in modern China, lie in the effort to force coincidence of intellect and will.

Joseph R. Levenson

PREFACE

In recent years it has become increasingly apparent that medicine is far too important to be left to doctors. Accordingly, social scientists of various disciplines and interests have been drawn to study the social and cultural aspects of medicine. In fairness to our medical colleagues, it must be added that they too have been active in furthering a fruitful cross-fertilization between the medical and social sciences. Physical anthropology, ethnology, sociology, psychology—all have been enriched by this process.

This book, however, takes a somewhat different tack, largely due to the basic fact that its author is by training neither a medical nor, strictly speaking, a social, scientist. My training and interests are in intellectual and general cultural history, and it is from this viewpoint that the book is written. This means that many questions about traditional medicine in modern China that are terribly important to the sociologist, anthropologist, or physician will not be answered. It also means that some rather different questions will be asked about the relationship of medicine to cultural and intellectual developments. It is hoped that these will provide something of interest to both medical and social scientists, China specialists and students of medical acculturation.

Preface

Similarly, in writing this book the author has drawn freely on the knowledge and kindness of scholars in varied fields and disciplines. But the genesis of this idea—that a medical topic could be illuminating for intellectual history—and its growth into a book owes more to Professor Joseph Levenson than to any other person. Of course, he is in no way responsible for any errors and distortions that may have crept into it, but the ultimate responsibility for opening to me the challenge and excitement of intellectual history is his almost alone. And for this my gratitude extends far beyond this one book.

Otherwise, the production of this book is largely a tale of two centers—the Center for Chinese Studies of the University of California at Berkeley and the East Asian Research Center at Harvard. During my graduate school days at Berkeley I enjoyed the support—moral, intellectual, and financial—of the Center for Chinese Studies and its staff. Professors Wolfram Eberhard and Cyril Birch were particularly helpful in commenting upon preliminary drafts of the manuscript. At Harvard—apart from the general stimulation and excellent working facilities of the East Asian Research Center—Professor John Fairbank, Ezra Vogel, and Sidney Liu have been most helpful in putting the manuscript into final shape.

It would also be most ungrateful of me not to acknowledge the invaluable assistance rendered by numerous librarians at numerous libraries in the United States and the Far East. Dr. Eugene Wu, formerly East Asian Curator at the Hoover Institution and now Director of the Harvard-Yenching Library, Dr. Alfred K'ai-ming Ch'iu, former Director of the Harvard-Yenching Library, and Mr. Stephen Kim of the National Library of Medicine deserve special thanks. All of these gentlemen, plus many scholars unnamed, made research into the very heterogeneous materials relevant to this study pos-

Preface

sible. I should also mention that a Foreign Area Fellowship in 1963-64 was vital to carrying out research in the Far East. To all the above individuals and institutions, my sincere thanks.

R. C. C.

CONTENTS

xv

Contents

Part Three
Science, Communism,
and "The People's Medical Heritage"

TRADITIONAL MEDICINE IN MODERN CHINA

INTRODUCTION

MEDICINE IN A CONTEXT OF

CULTURAL CONFRONTATION

In 1923 Hu Shih cogently remarked that "ever since the beginning of reform tendencies in China, there is not a single
person who calls himself a modern man and yet dares openly to belittle science." [1] While by no means all of China's
modern intellectuals accepted Hu Shih's ideas on what constituted science, there was indeed by the 1920's a general
consensus that "science" had to play a leading role in
twentieth-century China, if there was to be a China in the
twentieth century. With varying degrees of enthusiasm and
with varying interpretations of science, Marxist radicals, pro-
Western liberals, and conservative nationalists could all agree
on this one central fact.

Such had not always been the case. Only half a century
before, the influential scholar and statesman Wo Jen had
argued vehemently against those "self-strengtheners" who

wanted a measured dose of Western science and technology as a necessary preservative of Chinese Empire and Chinese culture. As a leading member of that Confucian holy of holies, the Hanlin Academy, he considered Western science irrelevant and dangerous to that quintessence of civilization embodied in the traditional culture of the Middle Kingdom. As for medicine, although it escaped Wo's specific scorn, there were plenty of other conservative scholars who saw no reason why China should abandon her millennia-old medical tradition in favor of the new "Western medicine."

But in the ensuing fifty years Wo Jen and his kind had clearly lost. The traditional state, society, and culture they had sought to preserve pure and untainted had crumbled before the onslaughts of the new civilization whose most obvious superiority lay in a superior command over nature, that is, in science. Small wonder, then, that by the 1920's intellectuals of all stripes wanted science for China. And, in the medical field, small wonder that the Empire's indifference to Western medicine had been replaced by official endorsement of modern medical education, hospitals, and public health.

But traditional Chinese medicine has not meekly disappeared with the triumph of the new culture and of scientism in modern China. It has, not surprisingly, survived in the countryside where the new intellectual currents ran weak indeed. More significant for our purposes, it has found numerous supporters among those intellectuals who belonged to Hu Shih's "modern men." Not merely cultural obscurantists and old-style doctors, but many of the most important intellectual and political figures in modern China have flocked to its defense. Herein lies our central paradox and main theme—why twentieth-century intellectuals, committed in so many ways to science and modernity, have insisted on upholding China's ancient prescientific medical tradition.

Introduction

There are several possible explanations for this seeming paradox. The most obvious is that Chinese medicine has real therapeutic value: it survives because in many cases it actually works. There is probably much truth to this contention, although most of the traditional medicine's remedies and diagnostic principles remain unverified scientifically. Nor is it the intention here to go into this highly complex and rather vexed scientific question. For our purposes it is sufficient to note that, even granting the real value of much in the native medical tradition, the persistent attempts to preserve it as a distinct system—and more particularly the rhetoric infusing those attempts—point to more than purely scientific considerations. Similarly, the very real difficulties in providing the large rural population with modern medical care (and in gaining its acceptance) do not explain the sources of traditional medicine's political and intellectual support. For these, it is necessary to examine some of the larger tensions of modern Chinese intellectual life as they relate to the medical question. Here, in fact, lies the central theme of this book.

It has not been psychologically easy for any of the great high cultures of Asia to accept the necessity of borrowing so much of Western technology, institutions, and values in order to survive in the modern world. This has been particularly true for those civilizations, like China, historically accustomed more to the role of disseminators of culture rather than borrowers. The sharp reversal of familiar roles was certainly one of the factors inhibiting traditional China's adaptation to the problems posed by the Western challenge. Moreover, even when her new leaders recognized the necessity for a Western-inspired cultural revolution, this did not erase a conscious or subconscious concern over the heavy indebtedness thereby owed to the West. For the pure traditionalist, the West had to be held off and China's age-old culture preserved; for the modern nationalist, heavy cultural borrowing was permissible and necessary, but it had to be shown that this did not constitute betrayal of his own unique national identity. In other words, in becoming modern, China must remain recognizably Chinese.

The acceptance of foreign-inspired cultural revolution thus has not removed anxiety over national cultural continuity.[2] Rather, the more sweeping the cultural changes, the more acute the concern for preserving one's own national identity. This tension is accountable for many of the seemingly paradoxical survivals in rapidly changing Asia. As modernization demands parting with the old culture, modern nationalism sanctifies and exalts much of it as the unique product of the national genius.

In China, where "culture" itself was the cement and hallmark of the traditional civilization, this modern concern has been particularly sharp precisely in the cultural fields. One sign of it is the persistence of a semantic dichotomy in many cultural spheres between, for example, "Chinese painting" and "Western painting," "Chinese music" and "Western music," "Chinese drama" and "Western drama." The common factor in all of them is a deep-grained concern to preserve distinctively Chinese cultural forms, or, if the two can be synthesized, to produce a new form which is still unmistakably, and self-consciously, Chinese.

Science, of course, has generally been free from such complications—except in medicine. Here, the same semantic dichotomy, "Chinese" and "Western," * reveals the same cul-

---

*The precise origin of these terms, "Chinese medicine" *(chung-i)* and "Western medicine" *(hsi-i),* is rather obscure. Wu Lien-te attributes it to the early nineteenth-century introduction of vaccination into South China: "It was heralded as a triumph of Western medicine, thereby introducing the term, 'Western' as against 'Eastern' or 'Chinese' medicine." Wu Lien-te, "A Hundred Years of Modern Medicine in China," *Chinese Medical Journal,* 50.2:152 (February 1936). References to "Western medicine" certainly outdate this, but it was only in the nineteenth century that the term

tural concern for preserving "our" indigenous tradition against the foreign. In this, medicine is unique among the scientific and technical fields. Nowhere else has it been possible to oppose, and defend, a Chinese tradition against the scientific developments of the modern West. Of course, one could praise the nation's historical achievements in the sciences and technology, and even stress earlier European indebtedness to China in this regard. But, in the present, no one could seriously argue Taoist alchemy against modern chemistry, "feng-shui" against geology, or, more pointedly, firecrackers against high explosives. Once China decided on the need for science, it had to be the most advanced, or it was useless. And the most advanced, regardless of science's universal applicability and ideally international character, was patently of Western origin. Chinese art, even Chinese ethics, could be clung to as a matter of cultural preference, but no such freedom of choice existed regarding the scientific command over nature.

Medicine, however, has been the exception. For, despite its indissoluble links with the enormous advances of modern physics, chemistry, biology, and the more directly relevant subsciences, such as bacteriology, radiology, and eugenics, medicine remains part of a particular cultural milieu as well as a universal science. On the one hand, it is among the proudest achievements of the scientific revolution. On the other hand, in dealing with human beings with all the complex human factors involved, it has not yet achieved the degree of precision and assured predictability which marks the

came into common use and with it the common use of "Chinese medicine" to refer to the native system. These terms still persist in common usage, despite the objections of modern-trained Chinese doctors. Following Chinese usage, we shall occasionally use these terms—Chinese medicine and Western medicine—without quotation marks wherever the context permits no ambiguity.

more purely natural sciences. It remains part science and part social science, or perhaps part cultural element.[3]

In modern China, this ambiguous position of medicine has both linked it to the prestige of modern science and involved it in the cultural controversy over Chinese versus Western. Since there has been some possibility of arguing the superiority, or partial superiority, of one system of medicine over another, cultural conservatives have seized on Chinese medicine as something which China must not surrender. More important, modern nationalists have seen Chinese medicine as proof of China's creative ability in at least this one scientific area. With science generally hailed as the key to national survival, and almost all that science of foreign origin, claims for the scientific validity of the native medical tradition have had a powerful appeal to cultural nationalism.

Interestingly, the closest parallel to this has been in India, also one of the great high cultures of traditional Asia and also possessing her own well-developed and theoretically articulated system of medicine. There, too, prominent politicians and intellectuals speak in favor of keeping the precious essence of the traditional medical system; hospitals, schools, and research centers (some with government support) are built to preserve it; and the organized old-style practitioners frustrate the attempts of modern health bureaus to impose legal restrictions on their practice.[4] Furthermore, the stress on Ayurveda (Hindu medicine) as an integral part of Hindu culture closely resembles the Chinese medicine advocates' emphasis on preserving their art as a central part of the "national essence." If Ceylon is considered part of the Indian culture area, it is difficult to find comparable movements outside of these two great culture areas of traditional Asia. Of course, there is medical conservatism and resistance to change in all modernizing societies. Even in Japan some of the traditional medical practices—notably acupuncture and moxibustion—still enjoy considerable popularity, despite the country's well-developed scientific medicine and generally high level of modernization. But the significant point is that there has been no sustained and intellectually respectable support for traditional medicine as a system. There has been no movement to preserve it as part of Japan's "national essence," nothing to deflect the Japanese government from systematic medical modernization. In any case, the Japanese term, "han-i" ("Chinese medicine"), has served as a reminder of its foreign origins, making this a most unlikely object for nationalistic praise.

Similarly in other Asian countries conservative peasants may cling to old ways, and modernized intellectuals occasionally point out that modern medicine might find some useful products in the native pharmacopoeia. But nowhere else has traditional medicine become such volatile fuel for modern cultural nationalism. For one thing, only Arabic medicine could approach the Chinese or Indian tradition in richness and sophistication. The fact that it has not assumed any vital role in modern Arab nationalism might be related to the different character of Islamic culture, or, more obviously, to the simple truth that Arabic medicine is closely related to pre-Renaissance European medicine, making it much more difficult to assert a unique value unknown in the West.[5] Throughout the rest of Asia the old medical systems have either been too rudimentary or too manifestly of earlier foreign importation to carry much weight in nationalist ideology. It is in China and India where perhaps the implications of foreign-inspired cultural revolution have cut most deeply, where we find the deepest nationalistic attachment to traditional systems of medicine.

In China, however, this medical manifestation of cultural nationalism has been a serious affront to other nationalists who saw China's salvation in a ruthless modernization which would sweep away all such "unscientific" rubbish from the nation's past. For these worshippers of science and advocates of "wholesale Westernization," even the compromise proposed in plans to synthesize Chinese and Western medicine was treason to the paramountcy of science and a subterfuge for harmful conservatism. In fact, it was their outspoken attacks on the old medical tradition which directly provoked most of the plans to reform and save it. This in turn touched off a long and lively debate which has raged intermittently ever since the early 1920's and has reached far beyond medical circles and purely medical questions. When national figures as disparate, and as important, as Ch'en Kuo-fu, Fu Ssu-nien, Kuo Mo-jo, Feng Yu-lan, Yen Hsi-shan, and Mao Tse-tung, can all be drawn into a debate at one point or another, there is obviously more than a narrowly medical question at stake. It is our task here to follow that debate and attempt to elucidate all that was at stake in it. This means that our major focus of interest is less on medical questions per se than on what the controversy over traditional medicine can reveal about modern Chinese thinking—more specifically, about attitudes toward science, progress, modernity, traditional authority, and cultural nationalism. The time span, going back to the first serious critics of Chinese medicine at the end of the nineteenth century, is almost seventy years, and during this turbulent period the grounds of controversy naturally have shifted. In following these shifts—the definition and redefinition of the issues, the different significance of familiar arguments in a new context—we must be sensitive to what they reveal of the larger concerns in modern Chinese thinking. It should then become apparent that, conceived as a cultural and intellectual problem, a medical topic can be significant for far more than purely medical history.

Yet we cannot dispense with a certain amount of medical background in order to set this controversy in its proper per-

Introduction

spective. Part One of this book will therefore be devoted to a discussion of some of the relevant features of traditional medical thought and practice, followed by a brief summary of how modern medicine has come to China. These chapters are by no means comprehensive, but they may provide useful orientation to a subject still somewhat esoteric in the West.[6] It will then be possible to examine in depth the tensions behind, and the issues expressed in, the controversy over Chinese medicine.

Part One
Traditional Chinese Medicine and the
Introduction of Modern Medicine

I

THE TRADITIONAL MEDICAL

SYSTEM

Contrary to the impression conveyed by its more enthusiastic modern supporters, Chinese medicine is not the world's earliest recorded medical system. Egyptian and Babylonian medicine outdate it by perhaps a millennium. But, as with Chinese culture in general, it is the oldest continuous surviving tradition, rivaled only by Ayurvedic medicine in India. The origins of Chinese medicine go back to the legend-shrouded culture heroes of antiquity who allegedly gave to the inhabitants of the Yellow River basin the fundamentals of what became distinctively Chinese civilization. Medicine was among their gifts, for to *Shen-nung* (traditional dates 3737–2697 B.C.) is attributed the first pharmacopoeia. Appropriately for the founder of agriculture, he tasted "the hundred herbs" to find which were beneficial for the people's illnesses and recorded his findings in the *Pen-ts'ao,* or "Herbal." His

13

successor, *Huang-ti,* the "Yellow Emperor," contributed a complete treatise on the principles of health and medicine, the *Huang-ti nei-ching* ("The Yellow Emperor's Inner Classic"). Both of these works are products of a much later period, probably the third or second century B.C., but their attribution to these civilization builders of legendary antiquity shows the integral position of medicine in the emerging culture of the North China plain.

CHINESE MEDICINE AS A RATIONAL SYSTEM

The actual origins of primitive medicine here, as elsewhere, must have been from two directions. First, there was the empirical experience with simple remedies for disease and injury, the use of herbs probably even outdating the origins of agriculture. Simultaneously, much of early medicine was closely connected with magic or supernatural beliefs. There is abundant evidence from Chou texts that as late as Confucius' time doctors and shamans were classed together as healers.[1] The etymology of the character for medicine, or doctor, shows the shamanistic origins of the healing profession. In its earliest form the character for priest, or shaman, *wu,* is an integral part, only later being replaced by the character for wine, *chiu,* as the application of drugs and medicines came to predominate over charms and incantations in the treatment of illness. That the early Chinese should have looked to their priests for succor against the mysterious ravages of disease is hardly surprising. The parallels to the priestly medicines of ancient Egypt, Babylon, or even Vedic India—all being somewhat similar agricultural civilizations—are obvious.[2] On the origins of this combination of rational and supernatural therapy, comparative anthropology is enlightening as to how practical empirical remedies are given supernatural significance and apparently pure magic can have a rational principle behind it.[3]

Yet, according to the pioneer sociologist of medicine, B. J. Stern, it is necessary that a "secular, scientific tradition" be separated from "the magico-religious, supernatural tradition" before a true system of rational medicine can be established.[4] By late Chou (700–200 B.C.) this process was under way in China as a class of secular physicians emerged clearly distinct from priests or sorcerers. The *Chou-li* is the earliest positive evidence of this, for it lists physicians, *i,* separately from religious functionaries.[5] Although the book itself is from Han times, it probably reflects a growing differentiation of the two before the end of Chou. Certainly during the Han (197 B.C.–A.D. 205) a distinct secular medical tradition and profession emerged.

This can be seen from the appearance of purely medical books in that period, some of them attributed to famous physicians who subsequently became patron deities of the Chinese medical profession. The most famous of these, Chang Chung-ching (c. A.D. 195), was notable for his careful clinical observation of disease symptoms, his greatest work, *Shang-han lun* ("Treatise on Fevers") being the classic of Chinese clinical medicine right down to the present. His rational clinical procedures and lasting fame have led modern observers to style him the "Hippocrates of China." Actually, the cross-cultural identification here is more suggestive than most such superficial comparisons. For, if Chang Chung-ching is taken as the prototype of the Chinese physician who emerged by Han times, and Hippocrates as the founder of secular medicine in Greece, it should be noted that the "Chinese Hippocrates" did not have to break with religious orthodoxy in the manner of his Western namesake. Hippocratic medicine was studiously secular in avoiding the healing cult associated with the temple to Aesculapius;[6] Chinese medicine, no longer magical or tied to the anthropomorphic gods of currently viable myths, clung to an identification with an

15

idealized historical past in attributing its *locus classicus* to the Yellow Emperor. Medicine was undoubtedly secular and rationalistic by Han, but this evolution from an earlier magico-religious stage had not, as in Greece, meant any sharp break with the past. In China the gods had become historical figures—sage kings or culture heroes of antiquity —and later secular wisdom was not vitiated by adding their imprimatur. Thus, although the several centuries around the beginning of the Christian era witnessed a medical revolution (from primitive, theocentric, or magical healing to a secular, predominantly rational written tradition) almost as profound as that inspired by Western contact in the last century, the transition was accomplished without any great cultural wrench.

This is apparent in the attribution of the great medical classic from late Chou or early Han, the *Nei-ching,* to the hoary figure of the Yellow Emperor.[7] The text, taking the form of a dialogue between the Emperor and his chief minister, Ch'i Po, is comprised of two sections; the *Su-wen,* or "Plain Questions," and the *Ling-shu,* or "Mystical Gate." It is concerned more with the general principles of health and the human body than specific therapeutics, clearly reflecting the more sophisticated thinking about the natural world, the universe, and man's place in it which had evolved by that time. As such, it laid a firmly rational theoretical basis for the accumulated empirical knowledge of Chinese medicine. However, while early Han cosmological speculation may have been naturalistic and rationalistic, as opposed to superstitious or supernatural explanations of the universe, it failed to establish a scientific method for observation and verification of data.[8] Thus the wedding of an evolving empirical tradition to the larger world view of classical China —a process which the *Nei-ching* both reflected and consolidated through its rapidly acquired status as a classic—while culturally understandable, was not an unmixed blessing from the purely medical viewpoint.

The central concept of Chinese cosmology since classical times has been the dual forces of *yin* and *yang,* whose continuous interaction lies behind all natural phenomena, including the constitution and functioning of the human body. The *Su-wen* section of the *Nei-ching* explains how maintenance of the proper balance of *yin* and *yang* within the body is essential for good health, and discusses the ways of obtaining this equilibrium. These range from proper conduct and mental hygiene—adumbrations of psychotherapy, but also traces of religious concepts—to dietary rules and acupuncture. Behind it all lies a stress on maintaining balance, or harmony, a concept central to the social and natural philosophy of the emerging bureaucratic-gentry society. This principle of harmony, which views disease as essentially due to its impairment through external or internal, physical or mental causes, has remained central to all of later Chinese medicine. Such homeostatic concepts of health and disease are not unique to China. The idea of balance, or equilibrium, is basic to the humoral pathologies of classical Greek and Hindu medicine. Nowhere else, however, has this simple idea been the foundation stone for so elaborate and sophisticated a body of medical theorizing.

On top of the concept of *yin* and *yang* were imposed other naturalistic ideas about the composition and working of the universe. The most important were "the five elements," which were conceived of more as qualitative phases of cyclic processes than physical substances, and a system of numerical concordances between various items in nature. Needham has shown how these ideas were originally a separate strain in late Chou thinking which became fused with the *yin-yang* concept by the Former Han.[9] They certainly were well combined by the time of the *Nei-ching* and in subsequent

Chinese medical thought. The five elements—wood, fire, earth, metal, and water—are linked to natural physiological processes and to specific internal organs. The heart, for instance, partakes of the element fire and therefore corresponds to the emotion of joy (which has fire as its element), a burnt taste, a hot climate, the planet Mars, glutinous rice among the five grains, and a host of other correspondences.[10] Other organs have similar concordances based on their respective elements. The order by which the five elements produce and subjugate each other (actually there are several conflicting theories of their proper order) explains the relationships between the various internal organs.

From this it can be seen how the anatomical and physiological principles of the *Nei-ching,* despite some precise knowledge of internal measurements apparently derived from earlier human dissection, tended to become exempt from empirical modification as they became philosophically more elaborate, so that they ended up true to their larger cosmological system but often far removed from material reality. There was, for instance, listed among the two kinds of internal organs (five solid organs and six hollow organs) a fanciful invention called the *san chiao,* "three burning places." Similarly, although certain passages suggest some appreciation of the circulation of the blood, it is never systematically explained, nor was this intuitive insight ever developed to give an adequate understanding of its physiological importance.[11] Of course, the difficult, elliptical, and frequently symbolic language of the *Nei-ching* makes a dogmatic assessment of its scientific value rather hazardous, but it can safely be said that this coordinative thinking, whereby all things were classified (often completely arbitrarily) into numerical groups, ultimately did a grave disservice to Chinese science. In medicine it led to the *Nei-ching's* concept of the human body as a microcosm of the universe. This was well suited to the over-all idea of harmony between *yin* and *yang* and between the individual and the cosmos.[12] By itself this was perhaps not inimical to science, and undoubtedly this entire system of coordinative thinking represented a great advance in organizing ancient Chinese knowledge about the natural world and in creating a satisfying picture of the universe. Joseph Needham in his monumental work, *Science and Civilization in China,* reaches the tentative conclusion that "there was little to choose between ancient European and ancient Chinese philosophy so far as the foundations of scientific thought were concerned, and indeed, . . . in certain respects the advantage lay with the Chinese." [13] It may be true that what he calls a biological, not mechanistic, "system of correlative organismic thinking," [14] had in it the potential for scientific growth. However, in the medical field it seems clear that its codification and canonization in a classic of supposed sage-king authority tended to retard major theoretical modifications in the light of clinical experience. Empirical medicine did not cease to develop—far from it—but subsequent development all took place within the general theoretical framework established under the aegis of the venerated Yellow Emperor.

MAIN FEATURES OF CHINESE MEDICAL PRACTICE

Perhaps a somewhat better idea of the actual character of the distinctive medical system that was established in China over 2000 years ago can be conveyed by examining briefly some of its main features and techniques. As noted above, Chinese have used medicinal herbs from the earliest times, and although they do not figure prominently in the more theoretically inclined *Nei-ching,* by Han times China had evolved a large and well-proven materia medica. The earliest surviving pharmacopoeia, the *Pen-ts'ao ching* attributed to *Shen-nung,* was probably compiled in the first century

B.C. It contains 365 drugs (the number corresponding to the days of a year being part of the Han system of numerical concordances), which are classified as "superior," that is nontoxic, "medium," relatively nontoxic, and "inferior," poisonous drugs used only to cure serious diseases.[15] About two thirds of these are of vegetable origin. Since then the pharmacopoeia has grown enormously. According to one estimate succeeding dynasties produced "at least thirty-nine kinds of *Pen Tsao*,[16] a process culminating in the monumental *Pen-ts'ao kang-mu*, "General Principles of Pharmacology," by the famous sixteenth-century pharmacologist Li Shih-chen.[17] The expansion of the materia medica since Han is shown in the 1871 substances Li discusses. A majority are still of plant origin, although there also are many drugs of animal or mineral extraction. Many of the drugs have been proved in modern times to be highly effective. This is hardly surprising, for the bulk of the pharmacopoeia doubtlessly was built up through centuries of empirical observation. There are, of course, as in medieval European materia medica, a large number of apparently useless and nauseating substances which may or may not, on closer examination, prove to have a rational basis. Some of this *drek apothek* clearly does not, but is included because of a belief in sympathetic magic or some concordance based on the five elements. The pioneer missionary doctor, Edward Hume, noted in Hunan the "almost universal acceptance of the idea that medicaments are potent not only because they produce measurable pharmacological effects, but because they correspond, in some mysterious way, to the patient's affected organs, and possess some magical power to drive harmful spirits away."[18] This points partly to the survival of some superstitious, irrational elements even in the best Chinese medical thinking, and partly to the influence of the system of correlative thinking. To give a simple example, the famous medicinal root *ginseng,* in part, was thought efficacious because its shape resembles a human figure. Its lasting popularity is probably more attributable to the ingredients it contains, but even Li Shih-chen did not entirely disassociate medicine from such irrational ideas.

Chinese pharmacology has long had pills and powders, but the characteristic method of taking medicine is in a boiled broth made from the crude ingredients. Sometimes simples are used for a specific malady; more often the doctor will prescribe a complex prescription of many ingredients suited to the exact nature of the patient's condition. In this it goes far beyond primitive herb medicine. The Chinese physician uses herbs as part of the entire system of Chinese medicine based on its store of empirical knowledge. He thus prescribes to make up a deficiency of *yang,* to aid the fire element against an excess of water, or to remove an impediment to the free circulation of *ch'i,* pneuma or vital life force. Of course, modern critics, both Chinese and foreigners, have insisted that everything beneficial in the traditional pharmacopoeia came from trial-and-error empiricism and that all the rest has nothing to do with medical efficacy. To understand traditional Chinese medicine, however, one must realize that it operated according to these principles. The herbs are part of a comprehensive medical system.

The importance of the ideas behind this system in its everyday practice becomes apparent when one considers the methods of diagnosis used by a traditional Chinese doctor. The *Nei-ching* lists four basic methods: visual observation, questioning about case history, auditory symptoms, and taking the pulse. The close attention to symptomology apparent in these methods tended, however, to be somewhat overshadowed by the great attention devoted to the last procedure. The *Nei-ching* itself has a fairly long explanation of the physiological principles behind the pulse symptoms, and after Wang Shu-ho's *Mo-ching* ("Pulse Classic") of the third century A.D., pulse-taking became the chief method for all diagnoses. It is certainly the most complex. Chinese pulsology recognizes three spots along the radial artery of each wrist that give pulse readings of the functioning of different internal organs. Morever, at these three spots each wrist has a deep and a superficial reading, giving a total of twelve different pulses in all. From these, the trained physician—and it is an art which requires long experience as well as great sensitivity—can diagnose malfunction in any of the internal organs or in the various physiological processes of the body.

Obviously this is entirely different from Western medicine's use of the pulse for simple cardiovascular measurement. The Chinese art, claiming to be able to learn much more from the pulse, or rather pulses, is grounded on the unique Chinese physiological principles outlined above. It cannot, therefore, be understood in terms of conventional Western physiological notions. Indeed, as yet there is no anatomical evidence for the connection of these twelve pulses to their respective organs. Absence of a plausible scientific explanation should not, however, obscure the fact that traditional doctors are frequently able to make diagnoses from the pulse alone which are confirmed by modern scientific apparatus.[19] The art is extremely complex, even mysterious, in its working.[20] In the twentieth century it has become one of the chief points of controversy between those who believe in traditional Chinese medicine and those who do not.

The other area of acute controversy, because it too cannot be divorced from the theoretical principles of Chinese medicine, is the ancient therapeutic art of acupuncture. It was fully developed by the time of the *Nei-ching*—almost all of the *Ling-shu* section is devoted to an elaborate description of the practice and its principles. Actually, there are two closely related practices, the insertion of needles into specified points of the body (acupuncture), and the burning of small cones of dried herbs on these points (moxibustion). Both operate according to the belief that through stimulating these points the functioning of internal organs can be affected. For there are, according to the physiological concepts first systematically described in the *Nei-ching,* twelve main channels, or meridians, running over the body close beneath the skin. Each of these is related to a specific organ, and so by stimulating certain points along these meridians a sluggish organ can be stimulated or an overactive one pacified. The process is by no means this simple, but rather operates according to exceedingly complex relationships between the various organs (based on their respective elements) and in stimulating the vital life force of *ch'i,* or restoring a balance of *yin* and *yang.*[21]

The therapeutic concept, restoring internal harmony, is thus the same as that behind Chinese herb medicine, even though the techniques employed differ widely. It should also be noted that specific disease categories, as such, do not figure very prominently in this theory. Certain diseases were recognized and their symptoms described in the earliest medical works, but the major stress has been on treating the human condition itself. Since disease arises out of a disequilibrium in the human organism, the basic cure is in restoring harmony.[22] Acupuncture is one of the main techniques for doing this, and it is therefore used on a wide variety of maladies, including what we would consider mental disturbances.[23]

Westerners generally regard acupuncture as the most bizarre branch of Chinese medicine, for existing physiological knowledge cannot explain its working. Moreover, the idea of sticking needles into the body often evokes emotion close to horror at what seems to be the epitome of the benighted practices of old, unscientific China. Certainly in the hands of ignorant practitioners it can be frightening, especially because of their lack of knowledge about infection.[24] It should be noted, however, that the needles are so fine as to do little serious damage, and the points of insertion are carefully chosen to avoid vital organs. Moreover, at least according to one school, it is thought unnecessary to insert the needles more than a few millimeters. At its worst, acupuncture cannot have been more harmful than the bleeding popular in Western medical practice. At its best, although conclusive evidence for even the existence of the meridians is still lacking, acupuncture may be able to stimulate the body to resist disease and strengthen itself. It has been variously suggested that this might be accomplished by raising the red corpuscle count, increasing blood circulation, stimulating the sympathetic and parasympathetic nerve system, or by provoking responses in the cerebral cortex which in turn react upon the respective organs. All such speculations remain unproved, but in the face of mounting evidence for its effectiveness, at least for certain diseases, perhaps it should not be dismissed out of hand. Although most Western medical specialists remain highly skeptical about the ancient art, it has won a few converts in the modern medical profession (especially in Europe), and even experts unmoved by its grander claims as a system of therapy admit the possibility of obtaining some specific neurological reactions through this procedure.[25] At any rate, acupuncture, and to a lesser extent moxibustion, which has attained more popularity in Japan, remain prominent features of Chinese medicine.

Although acupuncture may appear to be external medicine, it obviously is far more concerned with internal complaints. As for real external medicine, this has been another relatively neglected field in China. Certain manipulative arts, notably massage (which, again, goes beyond relieving sore muscles to setting the patient's entire mind and body at rest), reduction of dislocations, and bonesetting, have been carried to a high level of practical skill. But surgery itself has remained surprisingly crude, or rather simply undeveloped. There was, still during the formative period of Chinese medicine, one great surgeon in Chinese history, Hua T'o, who flourished during the romantic period of the Three Kingdoms. According to the *Hou-han shu* and other less reliable sources, he is alleged to have performed many remarkable operations, opening the abdominal wall to excise diseased organs and employing anesthetic powders. Probably his most celebrated case was the heroic treatment he gave to the great warrior Kuan Yü, afterward canonized as the God of War. Supposedly in treating an acute infection from a deep arrow wound, he opened Kuan Yü's arm to scrape the bone while the redoubtable general, spurning anesthetics and restraints, calmly played chess with the other hand. One need not take such stories literally to appreciate the considerable development of surgery in ancient China which they indicate.

This development soon stopped, however. Legend has it that Hua T'o ran afoul of the arch villain of the Three Kingdoms period, Ts'ao Ts'ao, the tyrannical ruler of Wei. Suffering from severe headaches he summoned the famous surgeon, who offered the trephine the skull. Evidently Ts'ao Ts'ao did not have much faith in even this famous surgeon's knife, for he flew into a rage and accused Hua T'o of wanting to assassinate him. The unfortunate doctor, already an old man, was thrown into prison where he soon died. His writings on all the various surgical techniques he had mastered were entrusted to a jailer who, fearing punishment himself, destroyed most of them. Only one operation survived and continued to be practiced until the twentieth century. That particular operation was indeed useful to the emperors of all succeeding dynasties, for it supplied their harems with suitable attendants. It was the technique for castration.

The later neglect of surgery was tied to a neglect of practical anatomy which has often been attributed to the Confucian abhorrence of dissection as a gross violation of filial piety. The sacredness of the body, based on the famous passage from the *Classic of Filial Piety*—"The body, hair and skin are all received from the parents; not to presume to injure them is the beginning of filial piety" [26]—both provided an impediment to anatomical investigation and encouraged reluctance to submit to serious surgery. Yet it is doubtful if the religious obstacle was any greater than in medieval Europe, where eventually it was overcome. The generally nonmartial character of later Chinese culture might also be noted as a factor in the neglect of surgery, since the surgeon's arts have usually made their greatest advances on or near the battlefield. Witness the earliest Egyptian nonreligious medical treatment, surgical repair of battle wounds;[27] or the emergence of Vesalius, the father of modern anatomy, and Ambrose Paré, the father of modern surgery, with the increased frequency of gunshot wounds in sixteenth-century Europe.[28] But it should be recognized that the low esteem for soldiers did not mean that China lacked its share of battles and potential victims for surgical experimentation.

The explanation probably should be sought elsewhere. It has been seen how the entire bent of Chinese medicine tended away from superficial, external therapy toward a preference for treating the root causes of disease internally. Of course, the reasons behind this philosophic preference for internal medicine have to be explained. Moreover, obviously surgical cases, as those from battle wounds, were left relatively uncared for. Here, the literati disdain for war may not be completely irrelevant. More basic, however, was the disdain for manual work of any kind. The doctor, mastering a body of classical texts and prescribing medicines for internal treatment, did not lower himself to perform manual, surgical operations. This same prejudice is very apparent in the physician of medieval Europe, who emulated the scholar in his reliance on texts, scholastic robes, and academic airs. Vulgar surgery—vulgar not only because it was crude and dangerous, but also because it was manual—was left to the barber-surgeon's guild.[29] In China we find the same social prejudices, only much stronger. As a consequence, surgery, since Hua T'o's era (which, significantly, saw the last flourishing of feudal martial values), has been left to crude quacks and charlatans who, not unnaturally, have been greatly distrusted. Hua T'o remained as one of the patron deities of medicine, but his art, except for its one very special function in the Imperial Palace, died with him.

SOCIAL POSITION OF MEDICINE

Not only in the special case of the nondevelopment of surgery, but in many other aspects as well, Chinese medicine can be understood only in relation to the social position of medicine and doctors in traditional China. This is neither simple nor unambiguous. Medicine, because of its benevolent aspects in serving suffering humanity, was not without honor. In the pantheon of apotheosized historical figures there were no less than seventy-eight physicians, a fact leading Castiglioni to remark in his history of world medicine that "no other people so frequently gave their physicians the honour of being included among the gods." [30] Since T'ang, the state has sponsored and given official sanction to ceremonies at temples to the three medical emperors (Fu Hsi, Shen Nung, and Huang Ti) where historical physicians were also worshipped.[31]

More important, the state recognized the importance of medicine for national welfare and, at least in theory, accepted responsibility for sponsoring and regulating medical practice. The *Chou-li* outlines a system by which a state medical department supervises and gives annual examinations to physicians in order to grade them according to their skill. Apparently this procedure was intended to extend beyond the Imperial Court, for it refers to State physicians, who are to treat the people, as well as to imperial physicians for the emperor's household.[32] Although the historical existence of such a system is most doubtful, this passage, in a semi-sacred text, does establish the concept of state responsibility for medical welfare. This is certainly how it was interpreted by later imperial bureaucratic centralizers, notably the famous Wang An-shih, who in his commentary on the *Chou-li* wrote, "That the treatment extends to the common people is clearly evident. Whether one refers to those in the administration of the country, or whether one speaks about the common people, both are being cared for." [33]

As a matter of actual historical fact, no dynasty, not even the Sung during Wang An-shih's period, lived up to this ideal. But there was a degree of state involvement in training and regulating physicians unmatched in Europe until modern times. Following the Han, there were official medical posts attached to the court bureaucracy and, at least since T'ang, medical instruction was given at an Imperial College of Medicine in the capital. Moreover, in 629 it was decreed that this be paralleled by medical colleges, complete with certifying examinations, in the provincial cities.[34] The medical examination system by Sung times closely followed in structure the regular civil examination system, and, in theory at least, the state undertook to assign medical officials as teachers and practitioners to the prefecture and district seats.[35] The system was intermittently maintained until Ming, after which it became confined to training court physicians.

Similarly, the idea of state-supported hospitals to care for the indigent is very ancient, the first references to government charity hospitals coming from the dubiously au-

The Traditional Medical System

thentic *Kuan-tzu* book, purportedly of the fifth century B.C. There are more reliable historical references to temporary hospitals for natural disaster victims in the first century A.D., and by Sung, officially supervised hospitals and dispensaries were relatively common.[36] Here too, however, the system had sadly declined by the time Western medicine reached China in the nineteenth century. Although one must distinguish between the ideal systems and their actual operation in earlier dynasties, there clearly was a retreat in the state's supervision and sponsorship of medicine. Concomitant with this, according to some modern Chinese authorities, was a lowering of the social status of medicine as a profession.[37] It is interesting to speculate whether this decline in prestige was related to the ascendancy of the gentry-literati class in later dynasties and the influence of their social-cultural values. At any rate, for much of Chinese history the state had accepted, even if only in principle, a certain social responsibility regarding medicine. This, and the sponsorship of the medical temples, show that the beneficent aspects of medicine were not unrecognized—medicine, of course, according well with the paternalistic concepts of the emperor's duty to see to his subjects' welfare.

As for the values of society in general, the idealistic concept of medicine fitted in with certain strains of Confucian humanism. Thus it is frequently referred to in scholarly writings as the "benevolent art," and many famous Confucian scholars can be cited in its favor. Chia I, who was one of those most instrumental in establishing the official position of Confucianism in the Former Han, is alleged to have remarked that the "superior man," if disinclined for official life, could practice medicine, for it too served the people. Many centuries later, Fan Wen-chung of the Sung dynasty echoed these sentiments: if he could not be a good official, he would be a good doctor.[38] On the level of more private virtue, it was important that the good, filial Confucian scholar possess some medical knowledge in order to care for his parents in their declining years. This ideal was given its most explicit expression in a famous book by Chang Tzu-ho of the Chin dynasty, *Ju-men shih ch'in* ("Confucian Scholars Care for their Parents"). Medicine was essential for the proper fulfillment of filial duties, and there was the highest approval of studying it for that end.

Yet if medicine was recognized as important and beneficial knowledge, the attitude toward its practitioners was something else again. The highest prestige belonged to the scholar who practiced medicine purely out of benevolent motives, without any kind of pecuniary reward. He would already be a person of approved social status (otherwise he would not have the leisure to pursue such studies) and of suitable scholarly attainments. His social position already established, he could earn approbation through the study and practice of medicine in fulfillment of Confucian virtues of benevolence and filial piety. This practice was usually confined to his immediate relatives or friends, although a particularly skillful doctor might attract much wider notice. The essential thing was that all his treatment was given as a personal favor, or out of charity, never for financial gain.

It can be seen how these moral associations of medicine permitted scholars of a more practical turn of mind to engage in a study which was not considered demeaning, as engineering or agronomy might be. Their medical work, however, by virtue of their social character, partook strongly of a literary bias. Most of their knowledge was acquired from classical medical texts, and their most prestigious activity was to write of their own experience, or an exegesis of an earlier classic.[39] It is therefore not surprising that they shared the general characteristics of Confucian scholarship. The name given them, *Ju-i,* or "Confucian doctor," was intended to

distinguish them from those who practiced medicine without
a literary background (both medical and nonmedical) or
with less altruistic motives.

Actually, many professional medical men emulated them
both in style and title, for the higher class of doctor also
was a medical scholar. His emulation of the ideal type of
Confucian doctor can be seen in many of the characteristic
features of Chinese medical practice: the neglect of surgery,
reverence for textual authority, disdain for manual operations. Yet as an occupation medicine had to be just that—
a vocation, a trade, something a gentleman did not do, at
least not to make a living. No matter how skillful or learned
he might be, the professional physician still had to be regarded as a kind of tradesman or artisan. One consequence
of such status was to minimize the benevolent aspect of much
of medical practice in favor of purely pecuniary motives.
The best of such physicians had frequently inherited their
calling; many more were scholars who had failed the civil
examinations.[40] Huc, in the nineteenth century, noted that
"the profession of medicine is considered an excellent con-
duit, or waste pipe, to carry off all the literary bachelors who
cannot attain to the superior grades, or pretend to the
mandarinate; and China is consequently swarming with
doctors."[41] What a fall this was in social and economic terms
is shown by the popular saying quoted in a Ming drama,
Ju pien i, ts'ai pien ch'i, "When a scholar becomes a doctor,
his table delicacies become onions."[42]

Not all professional doctors had to suffer economic dep-
rivation. There were famous doctors who prospered from
their fame. But they still could not really lay claim to scholar,
or gentry, status. Chu Hsi remarks of a famous T'ang physician: "Sun Szu-mo was a noted doctor of literature of the
T'ang dynasty, but as he practiced healing as a profession he
was relegated to the class of artisans. What a pity!"[43]

There were also large numbers of lower-grade doctors, apothecaries, "surgeons," itinerant medicine peddlers, and quacks of every description who usually fully merited the low esteem in which they were held. As everywhere, it was the common fate of the lower classes to fall into their hands in time of illness, and their performance probably justified the popular image of doctors as people who kill more than they cure.[44] It was, then, hardly surprising that superstitious and religious healing methods persisted side by side with, and often mixed into, popular medical practice. One particularly interesting example of the close connection between medicine and magic in everyday use was the dispensation of herbal prescriptions at temples, not by medical diagnosis of the patient, but through tossing joss sticks to find the corresponding slip with the correct prescription. This holy medicine was natural in composition, but supernatural in prescription.[45]

Popular ignorance and superstition bred even worse forms of charlatanism, which further lowered the reputation of doctors generally. Also, the special philanthropic concept of medicine probably exacerbated feeling against those physicians who in many instances were more concerned with their purse than their patient. This again is not a feeling peculiar to China. One has only to look at a contemporary description of the typical seventeenth-century English physician to recognize a universal complaint: "The best cure he has done is upon his own purse, which from a leane sickness he hath made lusty, and in flesh."[46] Writings on medical ethics in China constantly stressed an altruistic disregard for financial, or other, reward. For example, Ch'en Shih-kung, laying down five commandments for physicians in 1617, began with the exhortation, "Physicians should be ever ready to respond to any calls of patients, high or low, rich or poor," and ended with the injunction, "Prostitutes should be treated just like patients from a good family, and gratuitous services should be given to the poor ones . . . but physicians should not visit them again for lewd reward." [47] There was, then, in traditional China as elsewhere, a strong moral idealism attached to the medical calling. Doctors should be altruistic, and when—because they had to earn a living in a world which usually mistrusted them—they were not, they were resented all the more for their too common medical failures. Furthermore, medicine as a trade was intensely jealous in guarding its secrets. Despite the large medical literature, much of Chinese medical knowledge was the private possession of the individual practitioner, who might transmit it to his son or disciple but would certainly not share it with his professional rivals. Such a tradesman's view of medicine was not overcome in Europe until the rise of a modern medical profession where all members could benefit from a shared body of knowledge. [48] In China this did not happen until the twentieth century. The state schools, when they existed, and the philanthropic medical scholars shared medical knowledge as a benevolent act, [49] and this was considered the proper attitude toward medical knowledge. The fact that professional physicians often did not do so, besides retarding medical development, was another score against them in the eyes of their society. [50] Therefore it is not strange that in traditional China, although medicine was held in high esteem, doctors usually were not.

In view of this analysis of the social position of doctors, and particularly of their emulation of Confucian social virtues, something should be said about the frequent identification of Chinese medicine with Taoism. Certainly many of its techniques and practices clearly are derived from the Taoist tradition of "nurturing life." Among these are the breathing techniques of *ch'i-kung,* some forms of exercise (others are specifically of Buddhist origin), sexual hygiene, dietary principles, and alchemical experimentation with mineral drugs. Moreover, many of the central concepts behind

Chinese medicine are deeply tinged with Taoist ideas. All this is obvious, but it does not mean that strong Taoist influences were incompatible with striving for a Confucian social identification. It is suggested here that this social pressure was as important as any Taoist ideas in shaping the characteristic form, and even content, of Chinese medicine.

FAILURE OF SCIENTIFIC DEVELOPMENT—
SOME SOCIOCULTURAL FACTORS

In sum, Chinese medicine formed a complete and integrated medical system, even if the absence of enforced medical standards permitted the survival of a wide variety of dubious and superstitious practices, many of which were only loosely related to what might be called the scholarly medical tradition. The compatibility of its central concepts and practices with the cultural pattern of traditional China has already been noted. It was well—perhaps too well—integrated into its larger culture, for the same factors that inhibited scientific development in the culture as a whole acted to retard the further development of medicine. In any event, it would be unlikely that by itself medicine could have supplied the impetus for any substantial scientific breakthrough. Zimmer points out regarding Hindu medicine that it "was incapable of producing a revolutionary impulse out of itself, because, as is invariably true, medicine throughout its history is cautious and conservative when isolated from other sciences." [51] One has only to reflect on the influence of the mechanical and quantitative sciences on post-Renaissance European medicine to appreciate the validity of this generalization. Certainly it held true for China where, as Needham has noted, it was the "environing intellectual climate" and especially its social foundations, rather than any innate limitation on early Chinese scientific speculations or technological inventiveness per se, that frustrated a genuine scientific flight. [52]

In medicine the textual emphasis imparted by its Confucian

34

social emulation was particularly harmful in reinforcing a conservative, agrarian society's tendency to scholasticism and reverence for past authority. Of course, the picture of absolute stagnation since classical times, in medicine as in other areas of Chinese culture, is a gross oversimplification. One should perhaps mention the influence of Buddhism in enriching the pharmacopoeia with Indian and Central Asian products, the appearance of much more intensive and specialized medical monographs after the popularization of printing in the Sung, and the existence of at least five mutually opposed schools of Chinese medical thought in Ming and Ch'ing to correct this oversimplified picture of stagnant uniformity from Han on.

Yet Chinese medicine did come to form a closed and complete system within the confines of its traditional principles. This is nowhere more apparent than when it first encountered post-Renaissance European medicine in the seventeenth and eighteenth centuries. The Jesuits at Peking were good transmitters of the best Europe had to offer, which at that time was chiefly an anatomy and physiology far more accurate than the native concepts. Some translations were made, but Chinese scholars, and medical scholars in particular, were almost totally indifferent.[53] Even the bestowal of royal favor after a judicious application of the newly discovered cinchona bark to cure a fever in the K'ang Hsi Emperor, failed to change this. With the weakening of the Jesuits' position in Peking, Western medical influence disappeared almost without a ripple. When contrasted with the contemporaneous efforts of Japanese physicians, in the face of much greater practical and political difficulties, to grasp the meaning of Dutch anatomical treatises, the Chinese imperviousness to external intellectual stimuli becomes all the more striking.[54] Chinese medicine, alongside Chinese culture in general, took little interest in things radically new and foreign until faced with Western *force majeure* in the nineteenth century.

II

INTRODUCTION AND GROWTH OF

MODERN MEDICINE IN CHINA

1800–1949

During the nineteenth century it was almost entirely Western initiative, mainly in the form of the medical missionary movement, that brought Western medicine to a passive, if not hostile, China. Again, the speed and efficiency with which Meiji Japan adopted a complete system of modern medicine and public health stand in sharp contrast to official Chinese lethargy in this field. The medical missionary movement itself was, of course, closely tied to the exertion of Western military power which forced China to accept Western commerce, Western institutions, and eventually Western culture. This association may have contributed to Chinese reluctance actively to accept a new medicine which came more or less in the same package with an unwelcome religion and an unwelcome culture. Yet the earlier experience with the Jesuits suggests that the adoption of Western medicine would have to be part of a general cultural revolution. In any case, it is a moot point whether Western medicine could have been grafted onto the old culture. The fact is that Western medicine was an integral part of Western cultural aggression and ultimately of Chinese cultural revolution.

THE FORCED INTRUSION OF WESTERN MEDICINE—
THE MEDICAL MISSIONARY MOVEMENT

But if the association with Christianity harmed the reception of Western medicine in China, the social gospel of nineteenth-century Anglo-American Protestantism also provided a driving force to introduce Western medicine into China. True, surgeons of the East India Company at Macao and Canton had done some earlier work, notably the introduction of Jennerian smallpox vaccination, but this was a side line with them. The missionaries, on the other hand, recognized from the very first the advantages of medical work for their general evangelical enterprise. The great pioneer, Robert Morrison, although not a medical man himself, founded a simple dispensary for the Chinese poor at Macao in 1827. Soon after, in 1835, Peter Parker as the first full-time medical missionary established a small hospital and out-patient clinic in Canton, and three years later the Medical Missionary Society was formed to organize support for a systematic program of medical missions in China.[1] It was probably fortunate for both the missions and Western medicine that from the start it was decided that medicine should be brought to China by well-trained doctors, not presented simply as an adjunct to Christian charity. After the Opium War it was possible to expand medical missions to the four new treaty ports, and after the Treaties of Tientsin in 1860 the entire country was open to missionary and medical missionary work. By 1889 the number of hospitals and clinics had risen to 61; by the end of the century they had penetrated every province and every major city in the Empire.[2] The greatest growth of medical missions, however, came after the turn of the century, reaching a peak of 326 hospitals and 244 outpatient clinics by the early 1920's.[3]

Apart from giving treatment to individual patients, many of the medical missionaries recognized an obligation to spread the blessings of modern medical knowledge among the Chinese. For this it was essential that a new type of modern Chinese doctor be trained in the techniques and principles of Western medicine. The early medical missionaries began by training native assistants, more or less in the personal apprentice manner which was very familiar to China. The most famous of Peter Parker's assistants, Kwan Ato, became a competent surgeon in his own right, assisting and continuing Parker's work. Other pioneer medical missionaries, Lockhart in Shanghai and Macgowan in Ningpo, also engaged to teach a small number of students. Macgowan went beyond this by giving local Chinese-style physicians lessons in anatomy and Western medical techniques. Out of this individual medical instruction there gradually emerged the first modern medical schools in China, the earliest of these being inaugurated at the Canton Missionary Hospital in 1866. It was a small establishment with only a dozen students and three instructors, but it did offer a more systematic and specialized curriculum than previously available. This type of school, attached to a missionary hospital and training a small number of students under the supervision of the hospital chief, remained typical of the missionary medical schools up until the twentieth century. By the 1890's they had become quite numerous, yet they remained small, scattered, and hence rather poorly equipped and poorly staffed to offer first-grade medical instruction, despite the excellence of some of the individual teachers. The number of modern Chinese physicians trained also remained small. In 1897, only 300 had been graduated, and 250–300 were in training.[4]

There were also a few Chinese who were abroad to study modern medicine at its fount in Europe or the United States. The first small group of Chinese students sent back to the United States by missionaries included Wong Fun, who after middle-school education in New England took a medical degree at Edinburgh in 1853. Later he went back to China under the auspices of the London Missionary Society. Such cases were rare, however, and the Chinese government's hostility to students' going abroad prevented any significant number from seeking such training until the very end of the century. In the 1890's a small group of women medical pioneers studied in the United States under missionary auspices, thus introducing another dimension to the social revolution being worked by Western contact.[5] Despite conservative hostility to women playing such a role, these women doctors had remarkably successful careers in China, partly due to the reluctance of Chinese women, with their traditional ideas of Confucian propriety, to submit to examination by male doctors.

Besides training the first modern Chinese doctors, the medical missionaries were also instrumental in introducing modern medical literature into China. This started with translations of basic textbooks for use in their schools, but they reached an audience far larger than those small classes. The first series of textbooks on anatomy, physiology, surgery, pediatrics, and other branches of medicine were prepared by Dr. Benjamin Hobson in the 1850's. That his work was not ignored in the manner of the Jesuits' earlier efforts to explain Western anatomy is shown by Chinese republications of Hobson's texts. In succeeding decades a considerable literature of medical translations appeared, perhaps the most notable being the works published in the eighties by Dr. John Dudgeon at the government press of the *T'ung-wen kuan*.[6] In 1886 the newly founded Medical Missionary Association inaugurated its *China Medical Missionary Journal* which, although not in the Chinese language, was the first professional scientific journal in China.[7]

The importance of establishing this new scientific literature in China can hardly be exaggerated, even if the initial response of the educated classes was somewhat less than overwhelming, for it provided one of the main channels for the intellectual revolution of the twentieth century. In medicine, as in other areas, it was essential that a new scientific vocabulary be established and standardized if China was to assimilate Western knowledge. The foundations for this assimilation were laid almost entirely by medical missionary authors and translators in the second half of the nineteenth century.

INITIAL CHINESE RESPONSES TO WESTERN MEDICINE

But what of the Chinese response to this missionary activity in medicine? Certain of the more obvious benefits were accepted fairly readily by the patients—mainly from the poorer classes—reached by the missionaries' charity hospitals. Western surgeons and ophthalmologists, in particular, seem to have gained quick acceptance because of their ability to cope with problems beyond the skill of the native medical practitioners. The hospitals themselves, offering free or inexpensive care to all who needed it, also gained a certain popularity with the lower classes. In this, the humble buildings and crude wards of the early hospitals probably helped by not intimidating simple peasants with an alien and too antiseptic environment. It must be noted, however, that use of the missionaries' wards and dispensaries did not necessarily indicate a complete preference for Western medicine. Many of the persons who patronized missionary hospitals for certain complaints would also use traditional Chinese medicine for others; or perhaps they would try both to see which got the best results. This simple eclecticism obviously fell far short of total conversion from one system of medicine to another. But it was, and to some extent still is, an extremely widespread attitude.[8]

The medical missionaries' reception naturally varied from place to place. Generally, however, their greatest problem was gaining the acceptance and support of the gentry and official class. In the first place, the traditionally low social status of physicians was a disadvantage in approaching these key members of society. Moreover, as missionaries, even the charitable and benevolent aspects of their medical work could not remove the suspicions behind general anti-Christian and antiforeign sentiment. At times this came from special interest groups, as when the traditional doctors in Mukden circulated rumors that the new English medical missionary there was an advance spy for foreign invasion.[9] More often, it was part of the pervasive anti-foreignism, taking the form of horror stories about diabolic practices behind the hospital walls.[10]

Yet the medical missionaries, because of the charitable nature of their work and because of the demonstrable merit of their techniques, were probably the most successful of the missionaries in overcoming these hostile sentiments. The usual pattern was that sooner or later some of the more respected members of the community would seek help from the new-style doctor for some malady beyond the power of traditional physicians. Successes meant good will from the influential persons and favorable publicity for the foreigners and their medicine. In this regard, the traditional practice of presenting eulogistic ornamental plaques to the successful physician was a very helpful means of getting well-publicized testimonials.[11]

Apart from local gentry notables, among the higher officials who came into contact with the foreigners there were some who came to appreciate their medicine. As early as the 1820's Juan Yuan, Viceroy at Canton, an implacable foe of the opium smugglers, had written appreciatively of the recently introduced practice of vaccination: "The poison of opium has been brought to China, and although the most stringent means are used to prevent it, they do not succeed. But this foreign art of vaccination may be carried into all the provinces, for it will truly prolong life." [12] Here was obviously no blind antiforeignism, but rather a realistic appreciation of the mixed nature of foreign offerings. Their medicine, or at least this particular part of it, was clearly on the useful and benevolent side. Later, progressive officials accepted much more of Western medicine. Tseng Kao-fan himself was not quite prepared personally to use it, but he sanctioned calling foreign doctors for his family.[13] His son, Tseng Chi-tse, became totally convinced of the superiority of Western medicine,[14] and a most influential patron, Li Hung-chang, was won over when his wife was cured by Western doctors after traditional medicine had given up hope for her.

But if Western medicine had its successes in important quarters and could frequently overcome antiforeign prejudices, this in itself was insufficient to bring about any significant changes in the Chinese medical situation. The effective adoption of modern medicine required more than appreciation for individual cures; it required thorough government realization of the institutional, or organizational, basis of modern medicine—the hospitals, medical schools, and, increasingly, administrative machinery for effective public health administration. Admittedly, these institutional aspects were also something new in Western medicine. Hospitals had only in the late nineteenth century become really effective therapeutic centers where chances of survival merited public confidence in them. Large medical schools combining effective laboratory and clinical teaching were also recent phenomena. And public health, even in the most advanced industrial nations, was only just becoming a serious government concern. Yet all these institutional aspects were essential for any rapid absorption on a national scale of the best of modern Western medicine, and they were clearly beyond the scope of private individuals or even very well-endowed missionary societies.

The most conspicuous institution brought by the medical missionaries was, of course, the hospital. The philanthropic motive behind charity hospitals for the poor was not, however, entirely new to China. For example, donations by wealthy merchants or gentry to the missionary establishments fitted into familiar concepts of maintaining benevolent institutions for the care of the poor. Christian charity or Buddhist compassion—the motive and the institution were similar. In Shanghai, for instance, wealthy citizens sponsored a free dispensary of native drugs in order to show the new foreign missionary that Christians had no monopoly on benevolence.[15] But such private gestures, though significant for traditional attitudes toward charity and medicine, were by no means adequate to the growing institutional demands of modern medicine. Even in wealthy Western countries with large, well-established private and religious institutions for medical care, these have required state participation. In China, active government leadership, of the type provided by the Meiji government in Japan, was essential. But it was not forthcoming.

The enfeebled Ch'ing government was very slow to accept even the idea of supporting hospitals and medical schools to train modern Chinese doctors. There were many reasons for this: the cultural conservatism at court which distrusted all Western importations, including medicine; failure to appreciate soon enough the institutional requirements of modernization; a lack of energetic and efficient leadership. In principle, at least, the Taipings were much more receptive to new medical ideas. Hung Jen-kan envisaged a system of state-sponsored hospitals and actually set one up in Nanking. His program involved "establishing hospitals, examinations for physicians, concern for environmental hygiene, setting up first-aid stations, prohibition of prostitution and opium smoking." [16] All this could have come directly from Hung's association with missionaries. Probably it did, but there is also ample precedent for all these measures in the two thousand-year-old *Chou-li*,* and there is no indication of the extent to which Hung's program made use of Western medical techniques.

The Ch'ing court was much slower to accept these ideas, even in principle, but some of its leading statesmen were more progressive. Li Hung-chang, after his conversion to Western medicine, in 1881 established a medical school at Tientsin to train modern doctors for his Northern army and fleet. The school, run partly by foreign doctors, while small by Western standards, was the largest and best-equipped medical college in China at the time. But, more significantly, it was the only official effort to introduce Western medicine. The general neglect and apathy in official quarters is reflected in the fact that the first three graduates of a missionary established medical school in Taiwan all migrated to the British Straits Settlement because "they could not find suitable posts in China." [17]

CHINESE EFFORTS AT MEDICAL MODERNIZATION

It was only after the Boxer debacle that, in their tardy and faltering reform program, the Ch'ing began to move toward

* See Chapter I.

medical modernization. Yuan Shih-k'ai, succeeding to Li Hung-chang's position as Viceroy of Chihli, continued and expanded the medical school at Tientsin, renaming it the "Army Medical College." He also introduced the first government public health measures into China when he founded the "Peiyang Sanitary Service" in 1902. The central government, as usual, lagged behind, but it did move toward a partial acceptance of Western medicine in 1903 when a "Medical Profession Academy" teaching some modern and some traditional medicine was set up at the Imperial University.[18] Two years later it made another gesture toward assuming some of the public health responsibilities of a modern government by establishing a Sanitary Department under the Ministry of Police, made up of three divisions: quarantine, medical protection, and technical affairs. In reality, however, the department never was very active, although it did open a few charitable hospitals where both traditional and Western medicine were practiced. There was also one isolated, but quite remarkable, attempt to enforce examination and registration of medical practitioners. In 1908, Tuan Fang, the Viceroy at Nanking, revived an obscure Ch'ing law that "any person practising medicine without permission from the proper authorities" was subject to a fine. He thereupon held an examination for about 900 traditional doctors in Nanking, grading them into five groups. Those placing in the three highest grades received government licenses; the others were prohibited from practicing medicine.[19] The attempt soon proved unworkable, but it was another interesting case of both old precedents and new examples justifying what was certainly an innovation in official medical responsibilities.

At the very end of the dynasty, the great Manchurian plague epidemic of 1910–1911 provided a lesson in the importance of epidemic control and preventive medicine far more vivid than any modern doctors or Chinese reformers could give. This outbreak of pneumonic plague accounted for some 60,000 dead, including a specially selected group of eighty traditional physicians whose efforts to stem its ravages resulted only in their own deaths. Western medicine at that time could not cure this particularly virulent form of plague either, but it could and, under the direction of a young Cambridge-educated physician, Wu Lien-te, did provide the effective sanitary and public hygiene measures necessary to control the outbreak before it spread throughout North China.[20] This achievement made a considerable impression on official circles, leading the Ch'ing to set up as a permanent government organ the "North Manchurian Plague Prevention Service" as recommended by an International Plague Conference held in Mukden during April 1911. Unlike other paper reforms, this institution, under Wu Lien-te's energetic direction, was an effective public health organization. Whether, had there been time, the Ch'ing would have drawn further lessons from the experience of 1910–1911 is impossible to surmise. Its significance, however, had not been lost even upon conservative officials. Hsi Liang, the venerable and traditionally oriented Viceroy of Manchuria, remarked to the International Plague Conference: "The lessons taught us by this epidemic . . . have been great and have compelled several of us to revise our former ideas . . . if railways, telegraphs, electric lights, and other modern inventions are indispensable to the material welfare of this country, we should also make use of the wonderful resources of Western medicine for the benefit of our people." [21] Medicine was at last beginning to be included among the essential elements of Western material strength.

Although Western medicine was fully accepted by the early Republican government, the increasing political chaos made it impossible to implement any systematic plans. In

November 1913 Yuan Shih-k'ai gave explicit recognition to Western medicine in a Presidential decree legalizing dissection, and two years later Western medicine was adopted exclusively for the officially approved medical curriculum.[22] The government thus gave official recognition to modern-style doctors only, but without explicitly banning the traditional practitioners. In 1922 the legal situation was somewhat clarified by Ministry of the Interior regulations defining two types of doctors, the traditional physicians clearly assigned to a separate and lower category. The Peking government also acknowledged its responsibilities in the field of public health by maintaining a Public Health Office under the Ministry of the Interior, which in 1916 issued regulations on preventing infectious diseases. But, apart from the Central Epidemic Prevention Bureau, which did do some useful work in North China, almost all such plans and regulations remained largely on paper. What little pioneering public health work was undertaken in these years came from municipal governments in the larger cities. Canton, as early as 1913, had a working public health and sanitation department; Shanghai and Peking were experimenting with civic health departments by the mid-1920's.[23]

For its net effect on health conditions in China as a whole, all of this, like the Republic itself, was little more than a declaration of intent. The increase in Chinese-sponsored hospitals and medical schools, on the other hand, while completely inadequate for the needs of the country, did have a significant effect on the medical situation. A number of hospitals were built and run under Chinese auspices, either government or private. The most notable of these was the Peking Central Hospital, a model civil institution built mainly by private subscription but with the assistance of a central government appropriation.[24] Of the military hospitals, with which the more prosperous and ambitious warlords began to supply their forces, Chang Tso-lin's Mukden Military Hospital was probably the best. There was also a considerable growth in Chinese-run medical schools, mostly established by provincial (that is, warlord) governments. Although they were generally much inferior to the missionary institutions, they did serve to increase the small number of Western-style doctors in China. They were also another indication of growing recognition of the need for modern medicine.

Yet, despite the greater efforts by various levels of Chinese government, the lack of any strong central direction made the country still heavily dependent upon foreigners, mainly missionaries, in building a foundation in modern medicine. By the 1920's Chinese finally constituted a majority of the modern doctors in China, but most of the leading medical establishments were still foreign-run.[25] Most important, the largest and best-equipped medical colleges—training ground for China's new medical elite—were all missionary institutions. These had come into being after 1900 when, as a direct reflection of the revolution in medical education in the United States, it was generally recognized that the scattered, poorly equipped hospital schools of the nineteenth century had to be consolidated in the interests of efficiency and better medical training. The ensuing growth of Union Medical Colleges, of which Peking Union was the prototype, reduced the number of missionary medical schools to nine, located in Peking, Shanghai, Canton, Mukden, Changsha, Chengtu, Hangchow, and Tsinan.[26] Several of these became outstanding institutions, but the most important by far was Peking Union Medical College which in 1915 was chosen by the Rockefeller Foundation as a pilot project in establishing a first-rate medical research and teaching center in China. The objective was to place the very best that modern medical science could offer in one strategic location, with the hope that it would both help train the nucleus of a native medical leadership and serve as an example to other institutions.[27] The goal, quite frankly, was quality, not quantity, for the College, with its superb plant and staff, never turned out a large number of graduates. It did, however, give excellent training to those who did graduate or take postgraduate work there and Peking Union did succeed in becoming a symbol and pacesetter for high-level medical education and research in China. The other colleges, still dependent on the less munificent support of missionary boards, were somewhat less impressive, but they too generally decided on high standards and small numbers in medical training. The rationale behind this deliberate decision to concentrate on producing only well-trained, thoroughly qualified modern doctors was that, although by lowering standards more doctors could be produced more quickly, the missionary schools could not under any circumstances begin to meet China's quantitative needs for modern doctors. But, by offering an example of excellence in modern medicine, they might be able to stimulate and provide the native leadership for China herself to do this.[28] Thus, they trained a cadre of very competent modern physicians and specialists, but they did not rapidly expand the total number.

RISE OF A MODERN CHINESE MEDICAL PROFESSION
AND ITS PROBLEMS

Yet the number did grow considerably with the opening of more Chinese-managed medical schools and the influx of students to Japan in the decade 1905–1915. As early as 1910 there had been suggestions that the nascent modern Chinese medical profession should organize its own national medical association apart from the missionary organization.[29] This idea accorded well with its own interests and with the growing swell of nationalist feeling. In 1915 a small group of twenty-one doctors, most of them foreign-trained, took the occasion of the China Medical Missionary Association's annual meeting to create their own organization under the name, "National Medical Association of China." [30] Within a year it had grown to 232 members, and at its first national meeting in 1916 began an annual custom of passing resolutions urging more active government leadership in promoting modern medicine and public health. The association also published the *National Medical Journal,* with a Chinese edition, to further professional unity.

The emergence of an indigenous modern medical profession was perhaps the most significant medical development during these years of political chaos. Its membership was not large, but it possessed a national organization, plus several specialized or regional associations, and shared a rapidly growing medical literature in the proliferating new medical journals of the early Republic.[31] This new medical profession —new not only in its medical knowledge, but also in the very idea of a profession with established standards, shared technical knowledge, and common ideals of service—was a powerful force for medical modernization.

It was, however, also beset by problems. One of these was a tendency toward the formation of separate factions, based upon country and language of medical training, which impaired the unity of the modern medical profession as a whole. Part of this division came from uneven standards of technical competence within the profession. The doctors trained in Europe or America or in the large missionary colleges were generally much better prepared than those who graduated from second-rate Japanese medical schools or from the inferior provincial medical colleges set up after 1911. Thus, there tended to be created a small medical elite of the foreign-trained and a larger body of lower-grade modern practitioners who did not have the linguistic skills or thorough scientific training to keep up with the top level of international medical science.[32] This lower-level physician was not usually active in the larger professional causes championed by the National Medical Association, whose leadership remained exclusively with those educated in England and America.[33] Moreover, even among the foreign-trained elite, there was a division between physicians of the Anglo-American school, who were strongest in the missionary-run institutions, and those of the German or French school, who ran many of the government medical colleges. The differences in curriculum, teaching methods, and language of instruction that they had acquired from their foreign education tended to be passed down to their students in China.

Like an emerging profession anywhere, the new Chinese physicians' association was also much concerned with fixing and maintaining standards. This, obviously, was very difficult in the uncertain state of medical training, without a strong central government to enforce prescribed qualifications. The very first resolution of the National Medical Association in 1915 had called for government registration of doctors and clinics according to fixed standards,[34] and subsequently the modern medical profession kept up a continuous agitation for such measures. This, of course, led it into direct conflict with traditional doctors, who could not meet these modern qualifications; nor was it very popular with poorer quality modern doctors. There is no doubt, however, that some kind of government regulation was desirable, for apart from the manifold fraudulent and harmful medical practices of traditional China, the modernization process itself afforded new opportunities for quackery. On the one hand, it brought a new medical lore, isolated parts of which ingenious charlatans could adopt to present "modern" cures to an unsophisticated public. On the other, it provided a much broader platform from which to extol the wonders of all sorts of nostrums and miracle remedies through the introduction of the popular press. Shryock has noted how the golden age of quackery and patent medicine in the West followed upon the mass circulation newspaper and the patent law.[35] The same phenomenon can be noted in twentieth-century China, except that there such mass advertising partook of both kinds of medicine, new and old. From ancient herbal elixirs for sexual potency to "Dr. Williams' Pink Pills for Pale People," modern Chinese newspapers and magazines have been happy hunting grounds for the credulous customer. The modern medical profession fought these practices, especially those that might lower the prestige of modern medicine, but without effective government machinery little could be done to check them.

Similarly, lack of an effective government also prevented the most rational use of China's scarce medical resources for the general social good. Without a comprehensive state medical system, medical practice was usually purely private. Pursuing the profit motive, physicians concentrated in the large urban centers where such opportunities were best. The result was to leave the poorer areas and—except for the help they received from the missionaries—the poorer classes, without modern medical care. The higher costs of private Western medicine thus tended to confine it to wealthy urban dwellers.[36] The League of Nations investigating committee summed up the situation:

> Most of the graduates are attracted by the pecuniary benefits of private practice. So-called private hospitals, which are, in fact, paying clinics, abound, particularly in the greater cities and foreign concessions, and the exercise of medicine is rapidly becoming commercialized . . . The appeal of social service in public health, which calls for heavy sacrifice, perhaps to a higher degree in China than

elsewhere, has been felt up to the present, by only a small number of workers.[37]

It was somewhat paradoxical that medical missionary teaching, the purpose of which was social service, should turn out a profession which often ignored that aspect of medicine. But in the absence of positive state direction and in view of the economic opportunities for private practice, this was probably inevitable.

THE NATIONAL GOVERNMENT AND MEDICAL MODERNIZATION— HOPES, PLANS, AND FRUSTRATIONS

The Nationalist revolution and the establishment of the Nanking Government created, it was hoped, the conditions for such state leadership. Through the very process of the revolution itself, even more of this responsibility had fallen into Chinese hands when antiforeign zeal had forced many of the missionary schools and hospitals to suspend or terminate operation.[38] Some of them, including Peking Union Medical College, because of these events, were put under partial Chinese control. Others continued as missionary enterprises, but the revolution clearly had shifted the main responsibility for China's medical future from the missionaries to the new Chinese government.

The National Government, with strong support from China's own medical leaders, tried to meet this challenge effectively. In November 1928 it established a Ministry of Health at Nanking with five departments (administration, medical administration, health and sanitation, epidemiology, and vital statistics) and several attached institutes such as the National Hygienic Laboratory, the National Epidemic Preventive Bureau, and the National Midwifery Board.[39] In 1931 the whole organization was incorporated into a National Health Administration under the Ministry of the Interior, but with no reduction of its plans to provide China with a complete modern public health and medical system. To this end, the National Government enlisted the cooperation of the League's Health Commission, which sent an investigation committee to China in 1930. It recommended establishment of a Central Field Health Station in Nanking to lead and coordinate eventual establishment of *hsien* health centers throughout the country. During the 1930's these plans were implemented in a few special pilot project districts, *Tinghsien* in Hopei being the best known.[40] Simultaneously, at the urging of the modern medical profession, the government attempted to regulate medical practice, but in this it ran into strong opposition. No effective regulations were ever enforced.

All such public health plans depended on an adequate number of modern-trained physicians. In 1927 there were fewer than 3000 in all China.[41] Professor Knud Faber, a League of Nations expert sent out to investigate medical schools in China, saw this as the fundamental problem facing the government: "Preventive medicine can succeed only when the country possesses a medical profession capable of recognizing diseases. A primary need of preventive medicine is therefore the training of physicians."[42] He recognized that there were some good medical schools in China, including the ones at the National Universities, but considered it imperative that the number of medical graduates be increased many fold. To do this Faber recognized that it was impossible to maintain the high standards of the best schools and so argued for a separate kind of "Special Medical School" to give a four-year training course to many more students.[43] The goal he aimed for was 5000 graduates a year as compared to less than 200 in 1929. Although the medical colleges in the National Universities were expanded, this goal was never approached. By 1937, the year of the outbreak of the Sino-

Japanese War, the number of registered modern physicians in China totaled just over 9000. Although this meant approximately a 300 per cent increase in the decade since 1927, in absolute terms it was entirely inadequate to change China's basic medical situation.[44]

The war required a major reorganization of the national health services, with much more emphasis on military medicine.[45] It also meant a severe disruption of medical education and serious dislocation of all the National Government's health plans. The *hsien* health center system was partially implemented until by 1944 three quarters of the districts controlled by the National Government supposedly were covered.[46] In reality, the critical shortages of personnel and supplies strictly limited medical work of all kinds. The Army, with only about 2000 trained doctors to fill the need for 30,000 medical officers, resorted to short term training in "Emergency Medical Services Training Schools," [47] but for the most part, such shortages simply could not be repaired. After 1945, renewed civil war and accelerated disintegration of the National Government further retarded progress.

By 1949, then, the ambitious health plans of the National Government remained largely unfulfilled. Medical facilities and trained personnel, especially outside the coastal cities, continued to be woefully inadequate for the needs of China's huge population; the de facto practice of medicine was still almost as unregulated as during the Ch'ing; only a start had been made on preventive medicine, sanitation, and vital statistics. But there was a core of excellence in the major medical centers which could supply the medical leadership for a vigorous national health program. When the Communist Party (whose medical policies will be discussed later) established the first really effective national government in a century, it thus inherited a situation where old-style medicine still prevailed over most of the country, but it also inherited from the hated missionaries and the despised National Government a nucleus of very high-grade modern medicine.

It is against this background of the slow, painful, but irresistible introduction of modern medicine that the twentieth-century controversy over traditional Chinese medicine has taken place. Here we have outlined some of the central features of the indigenous medical system and touched upon some of the political, social, and cultural factors involved in its clash with modern medical science. The following chapters will examine in depth the clash as reflected in the thinking of modern China's intellectual leaders.

Part Two
Medicine as a Cultural
and Intellectual Issue, 1895–1949

"There are two aspects to preserving the race: one is study in order to preserve its mental power; one is medicine in order to preserve its physical constitution."—Liang Ch'i-ch'ao

---

III

MEDICINE AND NATIONAL STRENGTH

IN A SOCIAL-DARWINIST CONTEXT

Before a "Chinese medicine question" could arise, China's intellectual leaders had to realize, not just the advantages Western medicine offered over the native medicine in individual therapy, but also the importance of medicine to society and the nation at large. This awakening to the challenges and opportunities of modern medicine proceeded slowly, especially on the official level. It was only after the Japanese (who had since early Meiji adopted Western medicine and public hygiene) administered the shocking lesson on modernization of 1895, that among the new reformers there finally emerged important voices arguing for medicine as an area of state concern—a vital element of national strength in the struggle for survival.

K'ang Yu-wei's famous "Ten Thousand Word Memorial" of 1895 already contained references to the need for a modern medical and public health system.[1] Two years later Liang Ch'i-ch'ao supported and joined a group founding a "Charitable Medical Society," *I-hsüeh shan hui*. The title, with *Shan* full of traditional associations with philanthropic good works, smacks of familiar benevolent organizations—scholars helping to relieve the sufferings of the common people. Indeed, for this, the society wished to set up a charity hospital. But its purpose went far beyond familiar philanthropic motives. As Liang explained in an introduction to the society's objectives, it was concerned about the poor quality of medicine as practiced in China and its deleterious effect on the nation's health. Its basic purpose was to improve, or reform, medicine in China as an essential step in strengthening the race and, through it, the nation.

This stress on racial strengthening for survival (with its strong Darwinian overtones) comes through clearly in Liang's discussion of the society's purposes. In order to avoid extermination, the physical as well as the intellectual condition of the Chinese people had to be improved. Medicine had a vital role to play, for "preserving the people must start from medicine." [2] Moreover, looking to the modern nations of the West, he saw concern for advancing the medical sciences and promoting public health as foundation stones for national prosperity and power. But in China the government ignored medicine, neglected public health, and disregarded the parlous state of medical practice in the country. Liang castigated this indifference, not only on humanitarian grounds for the countless number of unnecessary deaths each year, but also for its long-range effects in debilitating the Chinese race and even reducing its numbers. As with Sun Yat-sen thirty years later, he somberly viewed demographic stagnation or decline in the face of rapid European population expansion as a threat to racial survival.[3]

China, he warned, had to correct the habits of thought

which traditionally had despised the medical calling as beneath a scholar's notice. Nothing was more important to
national survival: "Today the practice of medicine is the
noblest profession in the world . . . and the writing of
eight-legged essays the basest." [4] Here again is an echo of
traditional sentiments, Confucian or Buddhist, in the approbation of relieving human misery; but the basic values behind such a statement are radically new. Medicine, vital to
preserving the race, is eminently useful in the new world of
desperate struggle for survival between competing nation-
states, while the old knowledge which formed the basis for
the eight-legged essays is now useless. Liang is not repeating
here age-worn complaints against examinations as demeaning the body of Confucian knowledge. Rather, focusing on
the race as the unit of survival and exalting medicine as
vital to that concept, he has banished the old knowledge, culture, and values to the limbo of uselessness. Whatever honor
he and his master, K'ang Yu-wei, might still pay to Confucianism, Liang's preoccupation with national survival conceived primarily in terms of race has clearly carried him far
beyond the Confucian world. Mastery of the knowledge
and values of that world, as legitimatized by its institutional
machinery, has now become "the basest of professions."
Liang and those like him have moved into an entirely new
world of values, not just a new medical world.

Among the other reformers of 1898, T'an Ssu-t'ung shared
at least some of Liang's feelings about the need for active
state interest in medical improvement. Discussing general
modernization of society, he mentioned in a private letter
the need for public hygiene and a hospital system. [5] K'ang
Yu-wei himself had much grander ideas of the role medicine
should play in the ideal society. In his vision of the "Great
Commonwealth" (*Ta T'ung*) K'ang assigned to physicians
the highest role in the "management of things" which would

ensue after society was put in perfect natural working order.[6] With their responsibility for administering daily medical check-ups and supervising all phases of human life, he asserted, "the power of physicians will be the greatest." So great, in fact, that K'ang counseled "rigorous laws" to prevent the rise of a medical Napoleon who would usurp total power and plunge the world back into the political dictatorship of the ages of disorder.[7] Whatever one may think of the "Great Commonwealth" (which did not appear in print for several decades) it clearly reveals K'ang Yu-wei's keen appreciation of the social role of medicine and the state's responsibilities in this field. Here, once more, we may see shades of the old, dating back to the *Chou-li,* but the source of inspiration is again clearly the modern medicine of the Western powers.

On a more mundane level, K'ang, in his annotated bibliography of Japanese books, *Jih-pen shu mu-chi,* made invidious comparisons between medical development in Japan and China.[8] This was to become a favorite theme of Chinese medical progressives—contrasting Japan's rapid adoption of Western medical science and efficient public health measures with the slow progress in China. K'ang clearly found the contrast a source of national shame, but he was quick to absolve the original spirit of Chinese civilization from any blame. The ancient sages (Confucius and Mencius) had started China on the correct principles for medical development by stressing natural human feelings and physical preservation of the parent-bequeathed body. Later Confucianists, however, had obscured and neglected those precepts, while the Buddhist disregard for life and neglect of the body had led China fatally astray.[9] Thus, later accretions, not the primordial spirit of Chinese culture, were at fault.

K'ang Yu-wei had been impressed by Western medicine ever since it had cured him of a serious illness in his youth,[10] and remained a lifelong adherent.[11] Neither he nor any of the other reformers, however, condemned all of traditional Chinese medicine out of hand. The purpose of Liang Ch'i-ch'ao's "Medical Reform Society" was clearly syncretic—to combine the best of Chinese and Western medicine. In his words, it would "examine the best points in Chinese and Western methods." [12] This was clearly not the call to wipe out everything in the old medical tradition which would be sounded in the May 4th period. Similarly, it was not consciously contrived to preserve a Chinese identity threatened with extinction in a massive flood of Westernization. Liang belonged to an earlier generation which in medicine, as in other fields, was striving to introduce the new without real awareness of all this would imply for Chinese cultural continuity. The real emergence of the "Chinese medicine question" awaited the full-scale cultural and intellectual revolution which would bring these issues to life.

There were, however, in these years around the turn of the century already some telling criticisms of China's native medicine from those seriously influenced by Western science. The small number of modern, foreign-trained physicians generally were too disdainful of the native medical tradition to give it much attention, but there was beginning to appear a new type of doctor acquainted with both kinds of medicine. This medical hybrid never became numerous in China, at least until the Chinese Communist Government made it deliberate policy to train them. There was no institutional counterpart to the Indian Army medical service, which had as early as the eighteenth century started unwittingly to produce medical assistants who grafted rudiments of Western practice onto traditional Aryuvedic medicine, thereby creating a new school of Westernized Indian medicine or naturalized modern medicine.[13] The Ch'ing's half-hearted attempt at teaching both systems of medicine in the

Peking Imperial University after 1903 showed very meager results, and under the Republic modern medicine completely took over the government-approved medical curriculum.

Yet some Chinese did, through individual effort, acquire enough Western medical knowledge to question much of the native tradition without actually becoming Western-style doctors. The most famous example was Ting Fu-pao, a young scholar with a good classical education (*hsiu-ts'ai* in 1896, and a pupil of the conservative Hunanese scholar Wang Hsien-ch'ien),[14] who in the years after 1898 turned to the study of the new sciences—mathematics, chemistry, and medicine. After teaching mathematics and physiology at the Imperial University in Peking, in 1906 he began publishing medical books and commenced a long and famous private practice in Shanghai. At this time he visited Japan for a brief study tour of medical institutions in that country. Ting's copious writings in the next decade made it clear that he found much to be criticized in traditional Chinese medicine. From his knowledge of Western biological sciences he was able to demolish the ancient notions of anatomy and physiology, even ridiculing the pulse lore upon which its entire system of diagnosis was based.[15] Others, like Wang Ching-i and Liu Ch'eng-cheng, were similarly critical of the traditional anatomy after seeing Western books.[16] Outside of the medical world, and writing only in private correspondence, the prominent *Ku-wen* scholar and educational reformer, Wu Ju-lun, upheld to friends the clear superiority of Western medicine over Chinese medicine in almost every sphere.[17] This he attributed wholly to the scientific basis which traditional Chinese medicine lacked. Yet even he, perhaps the boldest critic of his time, stopped short of totally rejecting the native product, for Wu Ju-lun did envision great benefits ensuing from the scientific analysis of traditional pharmaceuticals.

The other critics conceded far more to the old medicine. Ting Fu-pao established in Shanghai a "Chinese and Western Medical Research Council" with a regular publication, *Chinese and Western Medicine*. The Council, unlike Liang Ch'i-ch'ao's group a decade earlier, was openly and self-consciously eclectic in its purposes. Ting's 1910 book, *Combining Chinese and Western Drug Prescriptions,* clearly outlined the goal of connecting or combining the two medicines. The preface, written by Ho Ping-yuan, is very specific about this.[18] The goal he outlined is a progressive synthesis using modern scientific concepts to explain and rationalize Chinese medicine, but not discarding it *in toto*. This book was accordingly a lesson to diehards of both medical schools who refused to learn from each other. In medicine nothing except a perfectly objective eclecticism that ignores national boundaries should be acceptable. Yet the subjective attachment to what is peculiarly Chinese has already begun to creep into this formulation. After defending the practical value of Chinese medicine based on its long experience, Ho praises this book for "preserving the national essence." With this identification of the indigenous medical arts (which for millennia had been useful techniques pure and simple) with the essence of what is Chinese, we see creeping into the Chinese consciousness new compulsions to hold onto and to glorify what is uniquely theirs—in a field which traditionally no one would have bothered to claim. The May 4th cultural revolution was still a decade away, but by the end of the Ch'ing there are occasional signs in the medical literature of the transvaluation of values that was to come.

The appeal of the synthesis formula put forward by Ho Ping-yuan and Liang Ch'i-ch'ao reached beyond progressives struggling to introduce modern science. In a slightly different form the more conservatively oriented could offer it as a defense to preserve the integrity of Chinese medicine against the new challenge from the West. Here, however, the dynamic function of science was ignored in favor of a simple combination of the best of both schools. Further, this synthesis usually implied some condescension toward the foreign element. For instance, Wu Tou offered a combination based essentially on Western "form," *hsing,* and Chinese "spirit," *shen.*[19] Shen T'ung-sheng and Huang Ch'ing-teng put it in the more common form of Western for external medicine and Chinese for internal medicine.[20] The suggestion, of course, frequently was that Chinese was more central in such a synthesis, Western being merely a useful addition according to the familiar *t'i-yung* pattern.

At least one of these synthesizers became openly hostile to Western medicine. T'ang Sung-hai, a traditional physician with some knowledge of modern medicine, wrote a number of books in the 1900's attempting to combine the two medicines. Basically, however, these contained little more than traditional explanations for some new medical concepts.[21] Apart from his superficial acquaintance with Western medicine, T'ang also considered it inferior to the basic teachings of Chinese medicine. He readily admitted that the present state of medicine in China left much to be desired, but explained this as coming from later mistakes which had distorted the original principles put forth in the ancient medical classics. This is vaguely similar to K'ang Yu-wei's comments about having lost the sages' meaning in later historical times, but it differs radically in emphasis and intent. T'ang Sung-hai and later medical conservatives were arguing the absolute superiority of a definite body of knowledge contained in the medical classics, not just a vague principle or direction in development which had gone astray. Unlike K'ang, who was essentially bolstering Chinese willingness to accept something new, these medical conservatives were defending the continued existence of the old. Thus, after the 1911 revolution, T'ang Sung-hai in the *Ch'ing-shih-kao* defended Chinese herbal prescriptions as superior to vulgar surgery and upheld the *Nei-ching* over Western anatomical charts.[22] In the 1900's, however, he was willing to concede Western medicine a role in helping to clear away the excrescences which had besmirched Chinese medicine. He also, in keeping with the national concern for self-strengthening, pointed to the great benefits in national prosperity and well-being which could spring from such medical reform.

This concern for medicine's potential contribution to national strength was indeed growing in the decade since Liang Ch'i-ch'ao's abortive "Charitable Medical Society." In 1905—more than coincidentally the year of Japan's second dramatic demonstration of efficient modernization—the important new journal *Tung-fang tsa-chih* ("Eastern Miscellany") ran two anonymous articles on the subject. The first, in April, was entitled "The Relationship between Medicine and Society." [23] The writer argued strongly in Social-Darwinist terms that racial strength was the key to national survival. For the race to be strong it was essential to have good medicine; to have good medicine it was essential that government and society awaken to their medical responsibilities. The modern Western nations all had comprehensive systems of public health, hospitals, and medical improvement which made their citizens fitter for every kind of activity. China, on the other hand, ignored medicine with devastating effects on the vitality of its people. If this "national self-weakening of its people" continued, the writer foresaw ultimate national extinction at the hands of stronger and fitter races.[24] The key to self-strengthening, therefore, had to be sought in awakening society to the role modern medicine could play in improving the nation's biological resources.

A second article, in June, pointed out the importance of

medical reform for national progress.[25] Though not quite so Social-Darwinist in tone, the argument was essentially the same—that good medicine was a foundation for national prosperity and progress. The author also saw modern medicine as an effective agent in introducing scientific consciousness by dispelling the old superstitions.[26] He did not, however, completely repudiate traditional Chinese medicine. Instead, he presented the familiar rationalization about degeneration from the excellences of antiquity. Very few were yet ready to dismiss Chinese medicine altogether, but more and more intellectuals were coming to realize the social significance of medicine which, because it now had the key to epidemic prevention since Pasteur's and Koch's discoveries, usually meant Western medicine.

At about the same time, yet another anonymous article, in Liang Ch'i-ch'ao's *Hsin-min ts'ung-pao,* put the case for "state medicine" in even stronger terms.[27] Evidently by the last years of the Ch'ing this concern for the nation's health was beginning to be rather widely diffused among progressive thinkers. It was not quite yet a frontal attack on traditional medicine per se, although the type of social or preventive medicine being advocated drew its inspiration from Western science and medicine. To thinkers of this bent, the government's lethargy in medical matters was only one more score against the Ch'ing. Dr. Edward Hume, the pioneer medical missionary at Changsha, tells how, soon after the revolution of 1911, a local notable complained to him: "But they (the Manchus) never turned a hand to improve the health of the nation. Every other country has health departments in all its great cities. What have we here in Changsha?" [28]

The early Republican government did at least make gestures in the direction of medical modernization. Although these were in fact little more than declarations of intent, as such they were significant in showing a new official awareness of the government's medical responsibilities and a greater appreciation of modern, scientific medicine. Thus, in 1914, when a group of traditional practitioners approached the Minister of Education, Wang Ta-hsieh (former ambassador to England) about government recognition for a traditional medicine association, he told them bluntly: "I have decided in future to abolish Chinese medicine and also not to use Chinese drugs." [29] Alarmed at the now obvious threat to their very existence, traditional doctors took the decidedly untraditional step of organizing in defense of Chinese medicine. A "Chinese Doctor's Committee to Petition for Saving Medicine from Extinction" approached the Ministry of the Interior in the hope of overruling the modernists in the Ministry of Education. Here too, however, they were completely unsuccessful.[30] Whatever the limits of its power, the government had set a course toward science and medical modernization with no concessions to traditional medicine. A new mentality and a new generation were emerging that saw no need to compromise with something so obviously unscientific, backward, and outdated.

IV

MEDICINE AND CULTURAL

ICONOCLASM IN THE

MAY 4TH ERA

One of the most remarkable features of the intellectual revolution in modern China has been the rapidity and decisive-
ness with which twentieth-century intellectuals have rejected
those traditional values which their nineteenth-century forebears fought so stubbornly to preserve. The ground had been
prepared for this rejection ever since the more perceptive of
the late nineteenth-century thinkers began to understand
that Western material superiority had nonmaterial roots.
Once it was realized that Western institutions, ideas, and values were all essential elements in any meaningful self-
strengthening, the hitherto sacrosanct culture and value
system subsumed under the rubric "Confucianism" was al-

70

ready on the slippery slope to oblivion. The pioneer transmitters of Western ideas (Yen Fu, K'ang Yu-wei, and Liang
Ch'i-ch'ao are the most prominent examples) had undercut
far more of the traditional culture than they had ever intended. So long as the ethnically alien Manchus occupied
the dragon throne, revolutionary political agitation could
divert attention away from the cultural implications of the
new ideas. But once both Manchus and dragon throne disappeared while China's parlous condition became worse instead of better, full attention was focused on the nonpolitical
sources of China's weakness. The traditional culture, no
longer shielded by anti-Manchu nationalism, then came
under full attack. The two-thousand-year Confucian cast
of the Chinese mind was not just broken, but smashed.

By the end of World War I the Chinese intellectual world
was dominated by a new generation of Western-oriented,
modern-educated intellectuals who were fully prepared to
denounce every aspect of the traditional culture, including
medicine. From these ruthless cultural iconoclasts of the May
4th era came the first real assault on Chinese medicine. The
shock troops were by no means all medical people, for the
old medicine also drew the fire of the new cultural iconoclasts who saw the fight for a new medicine as an integral
part of the general fight for a new culture and a new China.
What might be considered the opening shot in their attack
on traditional medicine came in the first issue of their leading organ, *Hsin ch'ing-nien* (New Youth). There, in his
famous broadside against the old culture and society, "Call
to youth," Ch'en Tu-hsiu raked Chinese medicine for its fundamental incompatibility with science.[1]

Our doctors don't know science. They don't understand
human anatomy and what is more don't analyse the nature of medicine. As for bacteria and communicable dis-

eases, they haven't even heard of them. They only talk about the five elements, their production and elimination, heat and cold, *yin* and *yang,* and prescribe medicine accordingly to the old formulae. All these nonsensical ideas and reasonless beliefs must basically be cured by the support of science.

The issue was thus squarely joined—science versus Chinese medicine, with no room for compromise.

The intensity of feeling on the part of radical young cultural iconoclasts toward traditional medicine is perhaps best conveyed in the new literature, and nowhere better than by its greatest spokesman, Lu Hsün. In the preface to his first collection of short stories, *Na-han,* ("War Cry"), he tells how as a youth studying at the Kiangnan Naval Academy in Nanking his interest in medicine was aroused by seeing modern physiology texts. Reflecting on the harm done to his countrymen by the ignorant old-style physicians and on the role Western medical science had played in the "Japanese Reformation," he determined to go to Japan to study medicine. On his return he planned to cure the sick, help his country as an army doctor in the event of war, while, in his own words, "at the same time strengthening my countrymen's faith in reformation." [2] The humanitarian, nationalistic, and reformist attractions of the new medicine are all apparent in this summary of his motives. In Japan, however, Lu Hsün decided that the basic illness of China was more of the spirit than of the flesh, and that literature could prove a better cure. The incident which provoked this decision came during the Russo-Japanese War when he saw pictures of a Chinese "spy" being executed by the Japanese military in Manchuria. Apart from the disgrace of the war being fought on Chinese soil, Lu Hsün felt deeply the shame of the other Chinese who had gathered indifferently to watch the spectacle. "They were all strong fellows but appeared completely apathetic." [3] After this, he recounts, "I felt that medical science was not so important after all. The people of a weak and backward country, however strong and healthy they may be, can only serve to be made examples of." [4] While some were reading the lessons of those times in terms of racial strengthening, Lu Hsün gave first priority to strengthening, or rather revolutionizing, the spirit of the people.

He had not, however, lost his faith in modern medical science, nor his contempt for the old-style practice. In one of his short topical essays in *Hsin Ch'ing-nien* in 1918, he ridiculed traditional notions of physiology, such absurdities representing for him the burden of ancient superstitions against which science had to struggle. [5] His short stories presented an even more damning indictment of Chinese medicine. The famous story, "Yao" (Medicine), written in 1919, draws a powerful picture of the disgusting, superstitious old medical practices, heightened by the tragedy of a child's death and his mother's grief. [6] In his next story, "Tomorrow," we see a traditional physician at work. [7] He is ignorant and callous, brushing off the anxious queries of a widowed mother with empty phrases about "obstruction of the digestive tract" and "fire overpowering metal," in order to pocket his fee and be rid of her. After taking his prescription, the woman's son dies. Again a child's death points to the tragedy of the old society, bringing to mind Lu Hsün's famous plea of 1918, "Save the children." [8]

In both of the stories traditional medicine is seen as an integral, representative part of all that is backward, inhuman, and disgusting in the old society. This becomes even clearer in his somewhat later (1926) autobiographical story "Father's Illness." [9] There the old-style physicians are even more ignorant and avaricious; their "wonder-working" medicines even more weird, disgusting, and ridiculous. In all of these stories the author's sense of outrage lies close beneath the surface.

But it is a controlled fury, tempered by the genius of an artist who makes his devastating points against the old society and the old medicine in a mordant satire which strengthens, rather than dilutes, a truly Swiftian indignation.

Some of the other literary giants of the new age expressed somewhat similar attitudes in their fiction, but none with quite the same devastating skill. Pa Chin has a comparable incident in his autobiographical novel, *Family*.[10] When the patriarch falls ill a parade of ignorant physicians, priests, and sorcerers are called in to try their skills. None has the slightest success, and the author clearly regards the doctors as little better than the demon-expelling sorcerer. All are superstitious dregs of the old culture. Lao She has a short story, "Grandma takes Charge," which exposes the folly and disaster in following the old beliefs about childbirth.[11] Here, however, there is an alternative in the modern hospital which the young people, despite their knowledge, refuse to take in deference to the authority of their ignorant elders. The real cause of the tragedy here lies in the old values which obstruct science and progress. Yeh Shao-chun, similarly attacking these old values in his story, "A Man Must Have a Son," also has an infant's death as the key to his tragedy.[12] Again the traditional medicine is worse than useless. The cumulative impression from these authors is completely negative. Not one good word is said for Chinese medicine or the men who practice it. The rejection of the old medicine, as with so much of the old society, is total.

The underlying basis for this disgust and total rejection has already been suggested. It can be found more explicitly expressed in an essay on medicine and jurisprudence appearing in the journal *New Education* (*Hsin Chiao-yü*) for November 1919. The writer, T'ang Erh-ho, in discussing some of the more obnoxious and irrational practices of the old medicine, commented: "These kinds of conditions are representative of a society in general." [13] It was precisely this association of the old medicine with the old society at large that lay behind the fervor of the new radical's condemnation. It stood as representative, or symbolic, of all that was backward, irrational, and superstitious in the old society. Moreover, to a generation so completely committed to science as the panacea for national ills, the continued existence of this unscientific nonsense in the scientific field of medicine was intolerable. Since the late Ch'ing reformers, consciousness of China's need for modern medicine and science had been growing. But in the new men after May 4th there is a haste, a passion, a ruthlessness toward the past which marks them off from their predecessors. This is evident in their attitudes toward medicine as well as much else. They have totally committed themselves to science and progress.

There is a much fuller explication of this in the more formal essays on the subject. One of the clearest, by Niu Jung-sheng, appeared in the liberal, Western-oriented review *Hsien-tai p'ing-lun* for February, 1927. [14] Taking a firm stand on the paramount value of science, Niu dismissed Chinese medicine as "basically incompatible with science" and hence doomed to extinction. [15] Since the fundamental principles of the old medicine were completely alien to a scientific way of thinking and the whole philosophy behind it hopelessly conservative, there was no use talking of any compromise or reform. Continuing opposition to complete adoption of Western medicine he compared to earlier conservatives' superstitious resistance to such other Western innovations as railways. Such stupidity, in a field so vital to human life as medicine, Niu asserted, was all the more reprehensible, for "How many hundreds and thousands of Chinese die each year due to this?" [16] But even above these deaths, the greatest harm in preserving Chinese medicine was its general effect in retarding science: "I believe that science is in its infancy in China. To protect, cultivate, encourage and promote it is essential. It is not right to obstruct its development." [17] Identifying Chinese medicine with non-science, Niu, and those like him, could give no quarter.

A similar attitude among the post-May 4th youth can be found expressed in a series of essays on "Old Style Versus Modern Medicine" sponsored by the Shanghai Council on Health Education for 1926.[18] The four published prize-winning essays, two by university students and two by middle school students, all unreservedly reject the old in favor of the new. This result might be expected from the nature of the contest, but the arguments and tone of the essays are nonetheless revealing of prevailing attitudes. By far the most eloquent and the most vehement of these essays was written by one Chang Tsung-liang, a twenty-two-year-old student at Fukien Christian University. Typical of the new youth, he passionately denied the authority of tradition and antiquity: "The very rock of ages upon which they (traditionalists) are depending has proved itself nothing but a medical iceberg melting now under the brilliant sunshine of science." [19] And now that this "brilliant sunshine" had fallen on China it was absurd to deny its blessings. "Everybody knows that modern China needs science. Modern medicine is a branch of science, whereas 'old style' medicine is but a fool's philosophy." [20] The other essayists, although making some concessions to useful products in the traditional pharmacopoeia, similarly welcomed scientific medicine and dismissed the native tradition as a "fool's philosophy." [21] There was nothing coolly scientific about their rejection of the old. They hailed the dawn of science and scientific medicine with the passion of converts; they rejected Chinese medicine with the indignation of polemicists.

Much of the bitterness in this rejection came from the

larger context in which the militant modernists of the 1920's viewed Chinese medicine. They saw it as symbolic of the dead past. But, more than that, in organized attempts to revive and preserve traditional medicine, it appeared as part of a past that would not die. Medical iconoclasm was to many an integral part of the struggle against the still visible forces of political, social, and cultural reaction. In a private letter dated 25 August 1928, Chou Tso-jen expressed this view.[22]

> The struggle between a new and old medicine is, I believe, not merely a professional question, but is a part of the reactionaries' flood of reviving the old. Therefore it cannot be minimized. In other aspects new forces already have been suppressed, because at any time they may be struck with the label "Communist." Already they lack power to resist. The struggle for new medical science still goes on.

Chiang Shao-yüan, liberal professor at Peking National University, agreed with Chou by identifying propaganda on behalf of traditional medicine with the traditionalism cultivated by Northern warlords as a counter to Kuomintang ideas.[23] It was this context of an ongoing struggle that sharpened the attacks on Chinese medicine and made many progressives unwilling to see any value in it. For in their minds "science" (however imperfectly understood in practice) stood as a paramount value in behalf of which they had broken with their own cultural tradition and through whose extension into all realms of Chinese life the deadly weight of that tradition would be cast off. In this prevailing scientism of the 1920's even the suggestion that science might not provide the answer to all the problems of man and society had been hooted out of court in the famous "science and the philosophy of life" debate in 1923.[24] In a field so obviously scientific as medicine, to suggest that the native tradition might (in part or as a whole) be preserved was an even greater affront to the sensibilities of these cultural revolutionaries. Throughout the next decade, growing attempts to save something of Chinese medicine called down upon it increasing scorn from determinedly "scientific" intellectuals.

Apart from these liberal, nontechnical intellectuals who staffed the legions of the new scientism, the new medical profession occasionally added its voice to the assault on the old medicine. The new-style Chinese doctors' hostility was perfectly natural in view of their scientific training and professional rivalry with the old-style practitioners. Generally, however, the two chief modern medical associations condescendingly ignored traditional medicine as something certain to disappear with the growth of scientific medicine in China. Yet there were times when some offensive act of the traditional doctors provoked a hostile outburst from individual members of the modern medical profession. One such incident was the summoning of traditional physicians to Sun Yat-sen's deathbed.[25] A certain Dr. Hou Tsung-lien, writing in the *Republic Medical Journal,* felt that this was an insult to Dr. Sun's scientific training and progressive orientation.[26] With indignant sarcasm he denounced these ignorant charlatans for their presumptuous claims to be able to cure cancer when modern medicine had failed.

In this same year, 1925, another doctor, Yang Chi-shih, wrote a long denunciation of traditional medicine: He related how he, too, had once asked: "Why should we struggle with Chinese medicine? In time it will perish of its own accord." [27] But, he continued, "As today the tide of promoting Chinese medicine becomes worse and worse," he realized the need to wage active war against it. His full fury was turned against the opposition to modern medicine which, because it was grounded in the sciences, should be the only medicine for modern China. To cling to the old, instead of adopting the new was immoral as well as stupid: "You worthies who promote Chinese medicine, what a responsibility you bear for the deaths of your fellow country-men!" [28] Thus, on account of the cultural and intellectual conservatism which would not let old-style medicine die the natural death it deserved, it was necessary to combat these reactionary efforts and actively promote the country's "still inadequate understanding of and faith in science." [29]

The person who most consistently and most forcefully took up this task in these years was Yü Yün-hsiu, a doctor who like Ting Fu-pao, had started wth a traditional medical education, but unlike Ting, had later acquired a modern medical degree and had completely changed his allegiance. His writings on traditional medicine and medical modernization are voluminous and express a continued determination to see Chinese medicine, as a separate system of medical thought and practice, eradicated in favor of modern scientific medicine.[30] But, knowing the traditional pharmacopoeia much better than his nonmedical compatriots, he was willing to concede some merit to the old herbs and a future role for them once they had been subjected to scientific analysis and refinement. Although overshadowed by the outpouring of criticism in the post-May 4th era, this view of Chinese medicine was already present in modern medical circles by the early 1920's and was to become more popular in the next decade. Indeed, as early as 1916, an article "Discussing the Preservation of Old Medicine" in the *National Medical Journal* had put forth essentially this argument.[31] It implied no weakening of faith in science, and especially in the case of Yü Yün-hsiu, no concession of scientific validity to the old medical system.

Not all modern doctors took it upon themselves to wage

open war on the traditional medicine with pen as well as scalpel, but, as medical conservatives organized to uphold Chinese medicine, gradually more and more Western-style doctors were drawn into the fray. One issue on which they could all unite, along with nonprofessional scientific modernists, was the fallacy behind this "Chinese" versus "Western" terminology. Yang Ch'i-shih denounced it vehemently. Later in 1925 another modern physician, Huang Sheng-pai, argued the same question in some detail.[32]

> Formerly ignorant persons wrongly coined the term "Western Medicine" and then this bunch took to themselves the name "Chinese Medicine." Today medical people of our generation follow this practice. This is very wrong. From this mistake in naming has followed the nationalistic nonsense of this generation.

Although these names reflected more of basic cultural attitudes than Dr. Huang would care to admit, there is a certain justice to his plaint: "We Chinese who have studied and practiced scientific medicine should be called Chinese doctors," not Western doctors.[33] With science a universal value and the unit of identification national rather than cultural, this perhaps should have been the case. But the persistence of these adjectives, "Chinese" and "Western," reflected that continuing psychological pressure to reaffirm a Chinese identity which has persistently bedeviled the medical question in modern China. Thus, though Huang and many others would repeatedly insist that "there is no so-called Chinese or Western medicine, only old and new,"[34] the name—and the reality—would remain.

"The biggest reason offered for opposing Chinese medicine is that it is unscientific. As I see it, this is entirely too arbitrary."—Ch'en Kuo-Fu

"The learning of Huang-ti truly constitutes an important part of Chinese culture."—Chiao I-t'ang

V

NATIONAL ESSENCE

AND NATIONAL MEDICINE

With the radical young intellectuals violently attacking all of the old culture (including the old medicine), there were naturally those who sprang to its defense, rallying behind the cry, "Preserve the national essence." But, for all these conservatives' devotion to China's traditional culture, the very use of this new slogan, "national essence," betrayed the essential modernity of their central concerns. To modern nationalists—often not deeply immersed in the traditional culture but loath to spurn what seemed the essence of Chineseness—such devotion became increasingly more traditionalistic than traditional, more romantic than genuine.[1] There were also, of course, genuine devotees of the old culture—men for whom the "Way" was still more important than the nation —but they were already becoming irrelevant in a modern world whose demands the old cultural values could no longer meet. And in speaking to a new situation, entering a new dialogue, even these "pure" conservatives became increasingly more traditionalistic than traditional. For instance, the commitment to a Chinese national essence was in itself a far cry from their forebears' complacent assumptions about the universal validity of Confucian culture as the only expression of true civilization. The nationalization of this culture was, in a sense, another sign that the old Chinese cultural world had passed.

A further sign was the inclusion of medicine in this epitome of Chinese culture, the "national essence." This in itself was a modern phenomenon. Traditionally, the guardians of China's high culture had hardly held so lofty a view of medicine, which, for all its scholastic pretensions and humanitarian virtues, was still demeaned as a craft. But in the general attack on traditional culture, Chinese medicine suddenly became a very important part of that cultural tradition. To defend it became part of the defense of Chinese culture. And, more subtly, as the value of scientific achievement permeated modern China, even traditionalists began to esteem China's medical riches (whether real or supposed is immaterial) far more highly than ever before. The tradesman's art of traditional China became a national treasure to latter-day traditionalists, an integral part of the "national essence."

THE WANING VOICE OF TRADITION

The modern defenders of this new-found "national essence" were a heterogeneous lot, and their arguments varied widely in intent and sophistication. At one extreme were obscurantist old-style doctors and cultural traditionalists who neither understood modern medicine nor would make any concessions to it. Their usual rejection of Western medicine was couched in the familiar terms of spiritual versus material values which marked the death throes of a deinstitutionalized Confucianism. According to a prominent Chekiang traditional doctor, Tu Tzu-liang, Western medicine was crude and materialistic.[2] The foreigners' anatomy and surgery were not so valuable as Chinese medicine's concepts of *ch'i* (vital force) and *ching-shen* (spirit); their germ theory was inferior to the principles of the five elements and six vapors. In grand old Confucian terminology, Western medicine used the *pa tao* (Way of Force, or Way of the Tyrant)—Chinese medicine used the *wang tao* (Way of Virtue, or Way of the True King).[3]

Similar sentiments were expressed in an article entitled "Comparing Chinese and Western Medicine," written for the November 1923 issue of the traditionalist journal *Hua-kuo*.[4] The author, Lu Ching-sui, doggedly upeld Chinese medicine's superiority over anything the West had to offer. Even surgery, where most traditionalists were willing to grant Western superiority, was belittled as something which China had had in antiquity (references to Hua T'o's miraculous feats) but had abandoned in favor of more subtle and effective drug therapy. Lu did, however, concede the prevalence of bad Chinese doctors who gave their art a bad reputation, causing people needlessly to abandon their own medical tradition in favor of Western medicine. This would subsequently become a major theme of Chinese medicine's supporters: the medicine was good in itself, its practice needed reforming. In Lu's case it did not imply any need of Western techniques or Western science. The human-based diagnoses of Chinese medicine were better than the West's reliance on mere machines; there was no need for Chinese to sell their national identity in becoming mere "Westernizers." [5]

Here Lu Ching-sui still betrays himself as a post-May 4th phenomenon just as surely as Chou Tso-jen and Lu Hsün, although his arguments seem purely traditional in terms of reverence for antiquity and total rejection of Western medicine. His entire tone is belligerently defensive against the forces of science and iconoclasm which are overwhelming traditional medicine and Chinese tradition in general. The indignation with which Lu condemned advocates of Western medicine was a measure of the uncertain ground on which he stood. With the onrushing tide of science and progress sweeping all respect for antiquity before it, one posture was to shout defiance until swept under. But, with so much of the old culture and its institutions changed or changing, and science so manifestly essential in an unavoidably modern world, this was only a posture, or gesture, of cultural despair. Wo Jen might have declared against admitting modern science fifty years earlier, but in those intervening years it had come in irreversibly. In 1923, Hu Shih wrote: "Ever since the beginnings of reformist tendencies in China, there is not a single person who calls himself a modern man and yet dares openly belittle science." [6] To belong to modern Chinese history and not become just a relic of an irretrievable past, everyone—both friend and foe of Chinese medicine—somehow had to come to terms with this thing called science.

A favorite method of staunch medical conservatives was to lay claim to the new value of science by proving that it was already there in traditional Chinese medicine. This had been a standard defense of late Ch'ing conservatives against almost all foreign innovations.[7] In the 1890's, for instance, the Cantonese scholar, Wang Jen-chün, had found surgery in the *Shih-chi,* chemistry in the *Nei-ching,* and anesthesia in the *T'ai-p'ing kuang-chi.*[8] By so stretching the content of ancient texts, justification for a total rejection of Western medicine could be found: Why look abroad for something we already have, or already have rejected? This reluctance or inability to face up to what modern science implied was still extant, though hardly prevalent, thirty years later. One

Nieh Tsung-k'uan, writing in the journal *Contemporary National Medicine* in 1931, provides a good example. What, he asked, was this "science" which had become the universal cry? It was not some wonderful mysterious secret of the foreigners, but only plain truth based on reality and proof. And this, of course, is exactly what underlay Chinese medicine—concrete reality and proof. Moreover, China not only already had a completely scientific medicine, but had one even more scientific than Western medicine which, "inclining toward the material is too formal. That is only one part of science." [9] Chinese medicine, combining the spiritual and the material, was more completely scientific.

SYNCRETISM, THE MODERN CULTURAL CONSERVATIVE'S SOLUTION

Such a crude equating of empiricism with science, compounded with overtones about spiritual superiority, was typical only of the real obscurantists. For anyone at all in tune with the main currents of twentieth-century intellectual life such arguments were hopelessly out of date. More and more, those who wished to preserve a distinct Chinese medical tradition came to argue its validity in terms of the same science that was being used to attack it. In claiming science for their own, they could at times approach a Nieh Tsung-k'uan type of defiance toward things Western, but customarily they approached Western medicine and science in a more conciliatory manner. The argument became not so much that Chinese medicine needed nothing from the West, but rather that Chinese medicine was compatible with science and thus both worthy of and amenable to scientific reform. The ultimate aim became syncretism, not rejection.

Such syncretic solutions to the confrontation between Chinese and Western medicine were, of course, hardly new. The initial impulse of medical reformers in the late Ch'ing had been mainly in this direction, and even earlier Li Hung-chang had talked somewhat loosely of combining the strong points of Western and Chinese medicine.[10] Then, however, it had been essentially a progressive position for introducing modern medical science. By the 1920's, after the cultural radicals' total rejection of traditional medicine, it became a conservative's device for maintaining a Chinese identity in medicine while simultaneously absorbing the modern scientific values of Western provenance. The upholders of such a solution were by no means obscurantists. All of them, to a greater or lesser degree, accepted science as the basis of a thorough reform of traditional medicine. But at the same time all of them remained convinced that Chinese medicine possessed a unique value, and that the final syncretism must produce something still Chinese in character. The maximum modernizers, although some of them may have acknowledged the possibility of adopting scattered elements from Chinese medical experience, had felt no regret over Chinese medicine disappearing before the advance of universal science. To the modern nationalists the traditional culture meant nothing for only the nation mattered. Yet the syncretists—no less modern and no less nationalist—felt a new compulsion to hold onto something of a Chinese identity here, not out of ignorance or blind loyalty to the past, but simply because this was a Chinese heritage. To reform and preserve it could, in an age where China had borrowed almost everything in the realm of science from the West, reaffirm the national creative ability in at least this one scientific area. It could salve a much-bruised national pride.

As a clearly formulated and organized program, the prototype for this solution to the clash between Chinese and Western medicine was worked out by that conservative modernizer, or perhaps modernizing conservative, Yen Hsi-shan. Although hardly one of the profound thinkers of modern China, Yen was unique among his warlord confreres in that he was concerned about social and cultural problems beyond the next battle or gaining control over the finances of the next province. Moreover, as effective ruler of Shansi, he could, unlike the intellectuals who argued over the elimination or preservation of Chinese medicine, do something to implement his ideas.

In 1919 Yen founded in Taiyuan a "Research Society for the Improvement of Chinese Medicine" with himself as President. The chief purpose, as set forth in its charter, was the transformation of Chinese medicine into "a high-class, unified branch of learning." [11] For this, modern science was to serve as the foundation for systematic research into the traditional medical literature and practices. The society was to manage a school, hospital, and medical publishing house.

Yen was himself deeply impressed with the scientific precision and efficiency of Western medicine and its formidable apparatus.[12] He contrasted all this with the current state of Chinese medicine, drawing the crude but suggestive analogy of a locomotive compared to a cripple. Yet the burden of his criticism was really on the practice of Chinese medicine, on its practitioners rather than its underlying nature. As Yen expatiates on the reasons for this sorry state, it becomes apparent that, for all his harsh words, he is not totally discarding Chinese medicine. The defects are many: secrecy and jealous preservation of knowledge, bad medical ethics, numerous frauds and charlatans, lack of progress or cooperative research. But the solution is not its abolition. In the first place, China's enormous medical needs could not be met by the handful of Western-style doctors available. Yen estimated that the country required 800,000 physicians and that it could take fifty years to train them in modern medical schools. Besides, it was doubtful that the impoverished masses could afford the high cost of Western medicine. Clearly, Chinese medicine had to survive for some time and therefore it should be improved. In these two arguments—immediate medical needs and cost factors—Yen set the tone for many subsequent hard-minded, practical reformers of Chinese medicine. The traditional medicine was all the common people were likely to have for a long time and all they were likely to be able to afford. So, instead of shouting for its abolition, make the best of it until modern scientific medicine could reach the masses—a position apparently acceptable on strictly scientific grounds.

But beyond these hard-headed realistic arguments Yen revealed a softer attachment to the traditional medicine. He was reluctant to see it simply "perish according to the principle of survival of the fittest." [13]—an end the cultural iconoclasts fervently urged. For Yen and many like him, however, the demise of a national tradition was not cause for celebration, and while accepting modern science, they tried to find an innate value in Chinese medicine that would permit it more than a stopgap survival. Yen groped for but did not very clearly work out a convincing solution. Chinese medicine, he argued, had a precious central core of practices and concepts which, because they tended to the spiritual or philosophic, were difficult to standardize and transmit. Still, he was hopeful that modern science could penetrate to the core of Chinese medicine, put it in order, and combine it with the best features of Western medicine to produce a new Chinese medicine. It would then be possible "to announce to the modern medical world that Chinese medicine can take its place along with Western medicine in the modern world." [14] The nationalistic appeal of such a triumph is obvious.

In theory this vital scientific research into traditional medicine should have been entrusted to well-trained modern scientists. To this end, Yen Hsi-shan planned to send students abroad for high-level scientific training who should, on their return, carry out this research. In fact, however, most of the society's work seems to have been in the hands of old-style physicians, and those not the most progressive.[15] Modern critics of Chinese medicine had nothing but scorn for the Taiyuan groups and its reform plans. Chiang Shao-yuan devoted one of his essays, "Chinese Reactions to Western Medicine," to a point-by-point repudiation of Yen's program.[16] Dr. Huang Sheng-pai, another leader in the fight against traditional medicine, considered it a distortion of science and progress even more harmful than outright traditionalism. He sarcastically dismissed the research society as "one of the trappings of the model province." [17]

Whatever the limitations of Yen Hsi-shan's understanding of both science and the nature of traditional medicine, he clearly valued both and saw their reconciliation in a progressive synthesis of the two medical traditions. The problems, logical and scientific, inherent in such a synthesis were just beginning to appear. However, the psychological appeal of this formula was undeniably strong to a wide range of medical conservatives and cultural nationalists, giving Yen many comrades who, as individuals or in organizations, would seek to implement it.

THE "NATIONAL MEDICINE" MOVEMENT

In some ways Yen Hsi-shan's program was ahead of its time, for in the tumult and chaos of the early Republic there were no other systematic attempts to realize the ideal of a reformed, or scientific, Chinese medicine. But after the establishment of the National Government in 1927 these ideas were spelled out in much greater detail—especially their nationalistic implications. Yen had not used the term "national essence" for medicine, but by the late 1920's this term had been appropriated by more than just the hidebound traditionalists. Further, in their struggle against hostile advocates of modern medicine, the more influential supporters of the traditional system increasingly adopted the term *Kuo-i,* "national medicine."

One of the earliest and most interesting groups to attach this name to a program of synthesis and reform was the "Shanghai Academy of National Medicine," founded in 1929. It took as its Honorary President, Chang Ping-lin, the veteran Kuomintang revolutionary and a leading cultural conservative. Chang's own position, although never set forth in great detail, seems to have been well within the general syncretic formula. He was undoubtedly deeply interested in traditional medicine and believed firmly in its contemporary, as well as historical, value.[18] Among his medical writings (which in true Confucian fashion were entirely an avocation with him) is a 1924 article on Chang Chung-ching's classic Han dynasty treatise on fevers, *Shang-han lun.* Showing great knowledge about its theories and textual history, Chang Ping-lin praised the medical classic as "more precious than a piece of exquisite jade."[19] Later, in the Shanghai Academy's new journal, he acknowledged that because of its superior anatomical knowledge Western medicine was better for organic illnesses, but Chinese medicine, because of its close attention to environmental factors, was best for "seasonal illnesses."[20]

Just as Chang Ping-lin was essentially more culturally conservative than Yen Hsi-shan (and much more deeply immersed in the traditional culture), the Shanghai National Medical Academy appears to have been more conservative, or at least more explicitly nationalistic, in its aims than the Taiyuan group. In the new Academy's official declaration of purpose, Hsü Heng-chih, presumably a traditional physician, defined it in syncretic terms: "to explain old theories and unite them with new knowledge."[21] In by now thoroughly familiar fashion for traditional medicine reformers, he criticized the vulgar practices which had come to obscure the vital essence of Chinese medicine, causing modern scientists to reject it as valueless. The current task was to use science to expose this precious essence for all to see. Half-baked attempts at joining the two schools without a real understanding of modern science were only harmful to this end. Yet, despite his appreciation of certain parts of Western medicine, Hsü's proposed syncretism still weighed heavily in favor of Chinese medicine: "Joining Chinese and Western (medicine) also must not cause Chinese medicine to become an appendage of Western medicine and form a new Western medicine." [22] Few of the modern synthesizers would put it as baldly as this, but it was the underlying motive beneath many of their statements about combining Chinese and Western—the final product must still be Chinese. The central impulse of such groups was to preserve the "national essence," not lose it in the process of reform.

This became abundantly clear when in February 1929 the National Government's newly established Ministry of Health convened a special conference of modern medical and public health leaders to consider the problem of traditional medicine. One would scarcely expect such a body to be well-disposed toward the old-style medicine, and indeed it was not. The conference adopted a resolution, largely drafted by Yü Yün-hsiu, entitled "The abolition of old medicine in order to clear away obstacles to medicine and public health." [23] This would require traditional doctors to register with the government and to attend government-sponsored "supplementary classes" in order to continue practicing. They were not to be allowed to organize schools, advertise, or spread propaganda through traditional medical societies. In sum, Chinese medicine could exist only on sufferance and could not propagate itself. The final goal was clearly its complete abolition.

Galvanized into action by this direct and immediate threat, the traditional medicine groups hurriedly summoned a national conference to deal with the emergency. It met in Shanghai where, on 17 March 1929, 281 representatives from seventeen provinces and 242 *hsien* formed a national association to mobilize public opinion against the threatening resolution.[24] The date of March 17 was subsequently celebrated as the "day of deliverance" for Chinese medicine. It did indeed mark a significant innovation in the organization of the traditionally diffuse old-style medical profession. With this, the organization of "National Medicine" also became national in scope. More to the point, the association was able to exert enough influence on public opinion and important political leaders to have the resolution killed.

Encouraged by this success, the traditional doctors and their sympathizers proceeded to organize a permanent national body. In March 1931 the *Kuo-i kuan* (Institute for National Medicine) was formally inaugurated. A central institute in Nanking served as coordinating center for a network of affiliated branch institutions, forming a rallying point for Chinese medicine in the major cities and even in overseas Chinese communities.[25] The entire organization, rather ponderously named the Institute for National Medicine Medical and Pharmaceutical Improvement Society, would meet semiannually, while an elected executive committee carried on the regular work of the central institute. The branch institutes were run on a similar basis.

As defined in its constitution, to which each branch had to subscribe, the central institute's purposes were avowedly reformist. The first article read: "This institute has the objective of choosing scientific methods to put in order Chinese medicine and pharmacy, improve treatment of disease, and improve methods of manufacturing drugs." [26] It was hoped that the *Kuo-i kuan* would provide part of the necessary institutional framework and, even more important, the leverage to reverse government hostility to Chinese medicine. In this regard it was infinitely better connected politically than any of the earlier traditional medical societies. The President of the *Kuo-i kuan* was Chiao I-t'ang, a prominent member of the right-wing Hu Han-min faction in the Kuomintang, and concurrently chairman of the legislation drafting committee in the Legislative Yuan. Even more important for its political influence, Ch'en Li-fu and Ch'en Kuo-fu—whose twin political star was very much on the rise in the inner party circles—were both on the institute's board of directors.

What this political influence meant for the developing of Chinese medicine will become apparent later. Here it is worth examining in some detail the arguments used by the institute's leading spokesmen, for they represent the most articulate and most coherent exposition of the modern cultural conservative's views on traditional medicine's place in modern China.

In making their claim for preserving and developing Chinese medicine, the *Kuo-i kuan's* spokesmen often produced the kind of practical, reformist arguments that Yen Hsi-shan had used over a decade earlier. For instance, Ch'en Kuo-fu could be even more devastating in his criticisms of the existing organizational state of Chinese medicine.[27] And, why not, since its institutional defects could serve as a scapegoat for the obvious shortcomings of traditional medical practice, sparing medical concepts themselves? Similarly, arguments about shortages of modern medical personnel and the high cost of modern medicine were just as cogent in the 1930's, for the supply of modern doctors was still woefully inadequate and the rural masses still too poor to support a costly modern medical system.

But these arguments, though relevant, were not at the heart of their concern, which was to show why a distinctively

"Chinese" medicine should survive beyond its immediate usefulness in a poor, backward country. For this, at least the leading theoreticians of the *Kuo-i kuan* saw the necessity of reconciling Chinese medicine with Western medicine. Of course, there were still many traditional doctors for whom this was not a philosophical problem. They could maintain a dogged medical particularism: Chinese medicine, evolved in China to meet Chinese conditions, was best for Chinese. At times, even more sophisticated spokesmen, like Ch'en Kuo-fu, flirted with this theme: "So it is not certain that drugs which foreigners can rely on can be suited to the constitution of Chinese." [28] Generally, however, he drew back from such scientifically dubious and psychologically ambivalent claims. Ch'en, after all, wanted to prove Chinese medicine's scientific basis rather than cut it off from science.

Less sophisticated, or less "modern," proponents of the old medicine could also take refuge in the well-worn "spiritual–material" dichotomy, or a slightly more refined "philosophical–scientific" distinction. According to this, Chinese "philosophical" medicine was different from scientific medicine in its approach, but not necessarily inferior.[29] The approach could be quite conciliatory—not demeaning Western material science but offering a Chinese philosophical or spiritual complement.[30] But respect for the omnicompetence of science was becoming too pervasive in China to give this a wide appeal. More militant traditionalists simply continued to defy Western medicine and deny the need for Western science. As Tseng Chüeh-sou, head of the Hunan branch of the *Kuo-i kuan,* explained in a letter of 27 February 1935, Chinese medicine differed fundamentally from Western medicine. But it was not inferior. Taking the "philosophy of ethics" as its basis, it too was grounded in nature and hence in science. To adopt Western names and Western theory in any proposed synthesis would make "Western medicine the main body and Chinese medicine an appendage."[31] He was opposed to leading Chinese medicine to its own extermination through this unnecessary pursuit of Western science. The traditional system could exist on its own merit without need of copying and worshipping the West.

But for the Ch'en brothers, Chiao I-t'ang, and others like them, such a position was no longer tenable. As modern nationalists, they were concerned with national strength as well as "national essence." And, unlike their traditionalist colleagues, they realized science was essential for building that strength. Ch'en Kuo-fu, for example, could speak as fervently about the nation's need for a modern public health program and the blessings of science as any modern doctor, while at the same time insisting that Chinese medicine must be an important part of such plans.[32] They wanted, then, to have both—the obvious advantages of modern science and a uniquely "Chinese" medical identity. The only solution must be some kind of synthesis between the two medical systems, one that would incorporate the values of science without invalidating the "Chinese" character of the final product. This rather facile formula was not, of course, anything new in the medical field. In the form of a simple eclecticism between the strong points of Chinese and Western medicine it went back to the late Ch'ing. Nor was it peculiar to medicine, for rather imprecise talk of combining the best of Western and Chinese, modern and traditional, permeated every area of Chinese culture from painting to philosophy. But in medicine, as Yen Hsi-shan and other earlier synthesis theorists had discovered, the problems, both intellectual and practical, in working out a meaningful medical synthesis—one that would not violate the integrity of science and yet would still satisfy the psychological commitment to Chinese cultural identity —were especially intricate.

The key phrase in the *Kuo-i kuan's* approach to this syn-

95

thesis was the "scientification (*k'e-hsüeh hua*) of Chinese medicine," that is, to make traditional medicine scientific so that it could survive in the modern world without abandoning its distinctive Chinese features. Basically, the idea of scientification rested upon two assumptions: one, that in principle Chinese medicine, if not scientific, was compatible with science; two, that it possessed real empirical value accumulated over its long history. Even some of the scientific modernizers would grant at least part of the second assumption, as evidenced by their interest in the native pharmacopoeia. The first, however, was another matter, for here its opponents generally brought up the conceptual unfitness of traditional medicine for survival in the modern age of science. Since the turn of the century the old theories of *yin-yang*, five elements, and the rest, had been dismissed by those imbued with western science as entirely fallacious. "Mystic theories" (*hsüan-hsüeh*), was the favorite epithet, mysticism being the antithesis of the cold, clear light of science. The modern-minded apologists thus had to show how the acceptance of a scientific viewpoint would not invalidate the very basis of Chinese medicine. The easy way out was to dismiss all the theory as so much mystic mumbo jumbo (as the Western medicine advocates did), but this would undermine the nationalist's insistence that there was more worth preserving in Chinese medicine than a few useful herbals. National pride demanded that somehow the principles behind these herbals be explained, or explained away.

One of the favorite rationalizations for the principles of *yin-yang* and the five elements was that they were really symbolic terms for perfectly natural physiological functions. Chang Ping-lin had interpreted the five elements as a sort of medical algebra having no relation to the actual substances of wood, water, earth, fire, and metal: "The references to the five elements are just like a mathematician's use of the digits 1, 2, 3, 4, 5 to represent numbers." [33] Ch'en Kuo-fu agreed that they were symbolic of natural processes and added an explanation of *yin-yang* theory in terms of positive and negative electrical charges. Modern medical investigators' failure to realize these naturalistic concepts behind the rather esoteric terminology had led them to reject Chinese medicine without really trying to penetrate the deeper meaning of its principles.[34] Chiao I-t'ang gave this charge an extra twist by commenting that much of the fault for these misunderstandings lay in the modernists' poor command of the classical language of the ancient medical texts. [35] In any event, all agreed that despite surface appearances the "names are different from science, but the realities are the same."

There is implied in this statement a certain appeal to practical results divorced from empty theorizing. This, too, became a common theme in such writings. From true medical conservatives it could be a denigration of the theory behind both medicines, science and *yin-yang* alike.[36] The sole test should be practical value—which works the best. More often, however, it meant nothing more than explicit recognition that the theoretical foundations of Chinese medicine were underdeveloped, coupled with a reaffirmation of the real value it possessed in curing people. A common phrase was to the effect that Chinese medicine knew the results of certain effective therapeutic techniques but did not know why these worked (*Chih ch'i jan, pu chih ch'i so jan*). Thus an article, "Discussing the Abolition of Chinese Medicine," in *Hsin wen pao* after the 1929 conference, openly admitted that there was nothing to traditional medical theory, but since it could actually cure people, the task now was to use science to study the old medicine, not just abolish it.[37] Another example of this view was an article, "Chatting about Chinese Medicine," in the journal *Hua-nien* for December 1932.[38] The writer, Yu Hung-jen, was certainly receptive to science and explicitly denounced any *t'i-yung* formulations which tried to belittle its importance. Yet he did not see the development of modern science as eliminating Chinese medicine. Rather, it should illuminate the value which traditional medicine had accumulated through actual experience. The basis of Chinese medicine was empirical; the theory had been added later in mistaken efforts to explain why it worked. *Yin-yang,* five elements, and *ch'i* could all be expunged, therefore, without damaging the real essence of Chinese medicine; modern science could be grafted on to a body of empirical knowledge without eliminating the national character of Chinese medicine or belittling its achievements.

The danger in such a view, however, was that Chinese medicine might be reduced to a collection of specific remedies to be swallowed up in the universal sea of science. This could hardly please those to whom its preservation as a distinct medical tradition was important. Thus, there were a number of attempts to find in the ancient medical writings discoveries which anticipated later Western medical developments. Superficially, this may resemble earlier traditionalists' rejection of Western medicine on the grounds that China had had all of these techniques—surgery, for example—long before, but had rejected them in favor of better ones. It also resembles some modernists' condescending praise for Chinese medicine's historical achievements, while dismissing them as having no current value. But both these positions are far different from claiming that Chinese medicine had in embryo the essentials of modern medical science which could now be developed along scientific lines without abandoning anything that was particular to the national genius. This position (with shades of K'ang Yu-wei's reformed Confucianism) can be found very well expressed in an article by a sympathetic Western-style doctor, Chang Meng-chung.[39] According to Dr. Chang, the ancient theories, if properly understood, were identical with modern science. He cited as one example the *Nei-ching's* description of the channels, or meridians, as anticipating the discovery of the circulation of the blood. There was, then, no problem at all in effecting the desired synthesis. His own words sum up this position beautifully:

> Although Chinese and Western methods of treatment are different, their principles are the same . . . The most ancient theories of Chinese medicine and Western medicine's most recent discoveries, are, I venture to say, eminently compatible. Hence there is hope for a fusion of Chinese and Western. Chinese medicine's theory is commonly considered removed from reality. Actually this theory is identical with the recent discoveries based on reality.

The important factor here (and in all the other rationalizations about symbolic terminology or empirical foundations) is that modern science is accepted as the basis for preserving Chinese medicine, not rejected as its enemy. The defense of Chinese medicine has become, based almost entirely on modern (that is, scientific) values.

CULTURAL NATIONALISM AND CULTURISM:
SIMILARITIES AND DIFFERENCES

Yet if the modern values of science have triumphed among almost all parties in the medical controversy, the equally modern value of cultural nationalism continues to sustain the defenders of Chinese medicine. When they praise the value of Chinese medicine or cite cases of it surpassing Western medicine, there are certain resemblances to traditional assumptions about China's cultural superiority. But beneath this superficial similarity there lies, quite literally, a world of difference between the traditional Confucian scholar and the modern cultural conservative. The latter, indeed, belongs to a different world, and if his rhetoric at times rings in familiar tones, his central impulse is not the traditional conservative's opposition to change per se, nor the obscurantist's dismissal of everything foreign as inferior. He has accepted the need for change and reform (in medicine, reform of a very considerable magnitude), but also insists on a loyalty to what is uniquely Chinese, just because it is Chinese. With so much of foreign origin being accepted, he feels that to retain a Chinese national identity in a world of unique individual entities—rather than the traditional assumption of China as the only worthwhile entity beyond which all is barbarism—modern Chinese must strive to retain the products of their own culture wherever possible. In the case of medicine, this compulsion is tempered by the new respect for the universal values of science, and the same nationalistic compulsions which draw him to his own culture also make him stress that this necessary science must be universal so that China can share its benefits.

Nevertheless, the force of particularistic cultural attachment obviously operated in the medical question. This does not mean that modern supporters of Chinese medicine have had no real confidence in its merit apart from the fact that it was Chinese. Obviously, they did, and obviously there is some basis for this confidence. Yet, just as clearly, cultural and intellectual factors have played a key role in shaping attitudes toward Chinese medicine. The adherents of Chinese medicine, no less than its critics, have been part of the larger world of modern China, and the medical controversy has taken place in the context of that world's assumptions and pressures. The popularity of *kuo-ts'ui* ("national essence") in their rhetoric is only the most obvious sign that it belongs in the larger cultural controversy. At times—as in Yen Tu-chiao's equation of medicine with calligraphy, painting, and art work as "national essence"—it has openly been placed in that context.[40] More often there has been a realization that medicine is a special part of the "national essence," and for that reason all the more precious. Finally, the very name chosen for the *Kuo-i kuan* reflected the identification of traditional medicine with nationalist sentiment. Instead of *Chung-i* (Chinese medicine) the phrase was *Kuo-i* (national medicine)—the particular possession of the Chinese nation. The name, "Chinese medicine," had itself been a modern product of the Western impact; "national medicine" put the particularistic, the modern, attachment to what is peculiarly Chinese even more plainly.

Chinese who rejected traditional medicine were thus, in the heat of the polemic, often charged with rejecting their Chinese identity, losing national consciousness in an excessive worship of things foreign. Liberal, Western-oriented intellectuals were, of course, the prime target for such charges, and it is worth noting that these accusations could come from both the left and the right in China's political spectrum. After 1949 this "bourgeois" prejudice against things Chinese figured prominently in the indictment of pro-Western intellectuals; here in the 1930's Chinese conservatives condemned them in much the same terms. Fu Ssu-nien, a prominent liberal intellectual and bitter opponent of Chinese medicine, was thus rebuked:[41]

> Generally Mr. Fu's education was all American-style education and except for the yellow color of his face and his external appearance (although he wears foreign clothes, these things as a Chinese he cannot change) the rest—thought, life and habits—all are completely transformed into American. Suppose all Chinese study Mr. Fu's example, I fear China's independent spirit will quickly be basically shaken. All of China, will I fear, from the equality of opportunity of the open door, go further and become purely an American colony.

Chiao I-t'ang, certainly no Marxist, explicitly attached a class basis to such an attitude. "Those who believe in Western medicine and use Western drugs are, however, only an extremely small section of the bourgeoisie."[42] And Ch'en Kuo-fu himself lamented the loss of confidence in the national creative spirit attendant upon such excessive "superstitious belief" in things foreign.[43] Many years later, Ch'en reminisced that government discrimination against Chinese medicine had prevented the progressive synthesis he and others had worked for. This he attributed to the control of the Ministry of Public Health by foreign-trained doctors and their foreign-acquired prejudice against Chinese culture.[44]

Such sentiments should not, however, be confused with a traditional antiforeignism. They were expressions of concern over loss of national identity rather than a rejection of all things foreign. At the same time, the supporters of Chinese medicine were quick to note with pride any signs of foreign interest in the national medical arts, for this could be cited against the native opponents of Chinese medicine as evidence of the true worth of the national product they were so ready to discard. The European interest in acupuncture was a particular source of delight to patrons of that esoteric art, which had come under some of the heaviest scientific criticisms.[45] Even more interesting, however, is the medical conservatives' use of the Japanese example as a source of inspiration. Since the reform generation of the 1890's, Japanese medical work had served as an inspiration for Chinese medical reformers. In view of the Japanese government's own adoption of exclusively modern medicine and refusal to grant doctors' licenses to traditional practitioners, the Chinese medical conservatives' espousal of Japanese methods may appear rather odd. What they applauded, however, was the very considerable amount of research the Japanese were carrying out on the traditional Chinese materia medica. Taking this as evidence of modern Japan's interest in Chinese medicine, without mentioning the anti-Chinese medicine regulations, they could sadly contrast this with China's feeble efforts in studying her own medical legacy.

Often, even what seem to be purely traditional arguments in favor of Chinese medicine, upon closer examination betray their modernity by a nationalist's concern with what is particularly Chinese. For example, some medical conservatives could write quite uncritically about the early culture heroes, Shen Nung and Huang Ti, but they departed from real traditionalism in that their primary concern was to reaffirm a Chinese creative ability by citing ancient historical achievements rather than justify this antiquity as the font of all medical wisdom. They defended the historical authenticity and achievements of these hoary figures, not so much as universal blessings for mankind, but rather as Chinese possessions under foreign attack. Thus, Chiao I-t'ang writes of the shadowy figure of the "Yellow Emperor": "The learning of Huang-ti really constitutes an important part of Chinese culture." [46] Not of foreign culture, not of culture generally, but "of China's culture." [47]

Similarly, the familiar traditionalist plaint about a decline from the excellences of antiquity is also a fairly common theme among modern adherents of Chinese medicine. But increasingly the burden of this complaint has been about stagnation, lack of progress and development, not an absolute fall from the pinnacles of antiquity. Again Chiao I-t'ang, after praising the nation's "rich medical history," sadly notes that in the past thousand years a serious stagnation had set in, becoming most evident by Ch'ing times. [48] Even where this decline is put in terms of absolute deterioration—not simply failure to sustain earlier creativity—the point of view has shifted to one which expects continuous progress rather than one that attempts to recapture the golden age of antiquity. Modern critics of Chinese medicine frequently charged its supporters with wanting to *fu-ku,* "restore antiquity." However, this venerable Confucian slogan was not only rejected; it did not really fit the case. For the large majority of Chinese medicine adherents, the "golden age" had become just that, a glorious epoch in the national history, but not the repository of the final truths in medicine. Although they might talk of removing later excrescences which had obscured the original value of Chinese medicine, the dominant attitude was, with the help of science, to go forward instead of backward. The values of the modern medical conservative are typically modern—science and progress. In this, and in the real focus of his loyalty—to China, not to antiquity—he is essentially as modern as his iconoclastic counterpart who rejects all traditional medicine in the name of those same values—science, progress, and nationalism.

"The incompatibility of this so-called National Medicine with science is an obvious fact. As for those who advocate reforming Chinese medicine, are they prepared to accept modern physiology, pathology, and bacteriology? If not, what kind of reform is this? If they do . . . where is there any 'Chinese' medicine?"—Fu Ssu-nien

VI

SCIENCE AND MODERNITY: THE

REJECTION OF "NATIONAL MEDICINE"

In January 1935 a group of ten university professors published a "Manifesto for Cultural Construction on a Chinese Basis" (*Chung-kuo pen-wei to wen-hua chien-she hsüan-yen*).[1] It was not so much an argument for cultural conservatism as an expression of disquiet over the oft-asserted need for "complete Westernization" and what this would mean for China's cultural identity.[2] The manifesto explicitly rejected any ambition to "restore the past" (*fu-ku*) and certainly did not question the benefits of science. It did, however, argue that China's "cultural construction" could only proceed according to her own "spatial and temporal characteristics." Blind conservatism must fail, and so must blind imitation of different Western countries. Critically selecting the best from her own tradition and the best from the West, modern Chinese had to stand on the "Chinese basis" in reconstructing their nation's culture. In the process China would regain her lost cultural creativity and again "make valuable contributions to a world culture." [3]

The syncretic formula here was an old tune by now. But the response to this appeal on behalf of some vague "Chinese basis" (*pen-wei*) reflected a continuing widespread concern about the national identity of China's new culture—so widespread that Hu Shih felt compelled to attack the manifesto as "a very fashionable expression of a currently prevalent reactionary mood." [4] To him, true cultural change could proceed only on the basis of "survival of the fittest," and deliberate concern over any "Chinese basis" was only a "smoke-screen of compromise" for cultural conservatism. The "Chinese basis" was rooted in the Chinese people and would in any case remain; China's new culture "should humbly accept the scientific and technological world culture." [5] In other words, Chinese culture should have no particular claims on China's new culture.

Although the original manifesto had made no reference to medical questions, let alone arguing for any "national medicine," there soon appeared writers who did argue the applicability of "Chinese basis" to the Chinese-Western medicine debate. Usually it came up as a case in point in the modernists' argument for cultural construction based solely on science. For example, Li Mai-mai admitted that there might be elements worth selectively preserving from the past culture, but such a selection could only be made after the country had Europeanized and modernized: "This several thousand year-old Chinese medicine, although it contains some medical and pharmaceutical experience, must await the development of China's new medicine before that experience can be investigated." [6]

In the medical world, Chiang Hui-ming reached almost identical conclusions in an article in the Chinese Medical

Association's Journal. To him, "Chinese basis" smacked of the conservatives' agitation for "special Eastern cultural characteristics" or even outworn *t'i-yung* theories. Such nonsense was incompatible with building a modern scientific medicine in China.[7] Sung Ta-jen, President of the much smaller Medical Research Society of China, put it in even stronger terms. Citing Hu Shih's opinions with approval he too called for complete Westernization:[8] "if the Chinese people want to come up to the world's progressive peoples, the first step is to raise the level of the people's scientific culture, that is, Europeanize." For the medical field, he indignantly rejected the proffered synthesis of the national medicine proponents as more of the "smoke-screen of compromise" Hu Shih had warned against. Why, Sung Ta-jen demanded, should modern scientific medicine accept this marriage proposal from such a "lazy, stupid wife with bound feet wrapped in yards of smelly bandages?"[9] Science, and scientific medicine, would stand alone in the new China.

Thus the debate over a Chinese basis for cultural construction and the medical controversy overlapped, although they had been wholly separate in origin and differed widely in scope. Yet there was in this insistence on a "Chinese basis" something of the same particularistic attachment to what is Chinese, tempered by respect for science and willingness to modernize, that impelled much of the "national medicine" movement. Similarly, in denying this attachment, Hu Shih and other modernists were taking the same position as the opponents of national medicine. Some, as we have seen, explicitly connected the two battles. This was logical, for indeed medicine had become part of the larger cultural controversy; but in medicine the conservative nationalists' interference in what was seen as manifestly a scientific field provoked an even more bitter reaction on the part of the science-oriented "complete modernizers."

Perhaps most basic to the modernists' rejection of the *Kuo-i kuan* and all it stood for was the deep offense given to their sense of the universality of science by this insistence on national distinctions and "national medicine." It has already been noted how fundamental science had become to the modern Chinese nationalist's hopes and plans for the future of his country. For those who, in the iconoclastic spirit of the May 4th movement, deliberately repudiated all ties with China's past in order to defend her future, there was no intellectual problem in accepting the simple dictum that "science knows no national boundaries." It was not quite so easy for those other nationalists who, while seeking all the benefits of national strength, prosperity, and modernity involved with science, still felt an emotional impulse to preserve what was unmistakably Chinese. The attempts to do this by reconciling Chinese medicine with modern science have been described. In these, it is noteworthy that the temptation to defend Chinese medicine in highly particularistic terms (what is best for foreigners is not best for Chinese) was usually overruled by the consciously or subconsciously felt need to affirm that science was universal in character and hence accessible to all. This compulsion was naturally much stronger, and more strongly expressed, by those outright modernists who felt no regrets in parting with "Chinese medicine," or Chinese anything else, so long as China itself survived.

To people of this mind, concern with "national medicine" only weakened China's claims to participate in the world of modern science, while actually hindering and diverting attention from the urgent task of building scientific medicine in China. It was on these grounds that they joined battle with the entire "national medicine" movement—frequently in medical journals, occasionally in more general scholarly periodicals, and most commonly in the weekly medical supplements which became regular features of the leading newspapers. The latter media, of course, reached a far wider audience, to some extent carrying the controversy beyond the bounds of purely intellectual or professional medical circles.[10] Hence, a Western-style doctor who regularly contributed to the *Ta kung pao* medical supplement under the pseudonym *Yu Hsien* challenged the purport of Ch'en Kuo-fu's position as "resisting the world-wide modern scientific medicine, looking on it as the private possession of foreigners."[11] This was not Ch'en Kuo-fu's intention, but the point was that by clinging to a "Chinese" medical identity he was in effect assigning modern scientific medicine to the exclusive possession of foreigners, thereby denying China access to it.

This was why the adherents of modern medicine so adamantly denied national character, or origins, any role in China's medical construction. One Chou Shao, discussing in 1933 the "standpoint" from which China's medical revolution must be viewed, argued simply: "What is compatible with science should live, what is not, should die."[12] For modern China, then, science should become the sole standard of value. Other critics of traditional medicine unanimously echoed this condemnation of a "national medicine" philosophy, which at best could only be a misguided patriotism and at worst a cover for reactionary conservatism. Among the prominent liberal, Western-oriented intellectuals of the May 4th era, Fu Ssu-nien was probably most outspoken in his denunciation of Chinese medicine and the type of thinking that supported it. With regard to the term "national medicine," he noted that, apart from the absurdity of denying the international character of medical science, it could hardly fit traditional Chinese medicine, which itself was far from being purely indigenous after heavy borrowings in historic times from Indian, Central Asian, and Arab sources.[13] The present logic, as well as the historical accuracy, of this term was also severely tested. An anonymous writer in *Chung-yang jih-pao* asked why, if the old medicine was to be kept as "national medicine," the donkey cart could not also be retained as the "national cart," or the oil lamp as the "national lamp." In fact, the exponents of this type of muddled medical thinking should be preserved as the *kuo-nao,* "national brain." [14] Others asked why this should not extend to sorcery, divination, and other occult arts, which were certainly every bit as "national" historically, and had also been used from time immemorial to combat sickness in China. Why not a "national fortune-telling" or, more seriously, in the realm of political philosophy, why not remain satisfied with the teachings of Confucius and Mencius instead of seeking to implement Sun Yat-sen's three principles? [15]

Behind the irony and indignation in these attacks there lay the insistence that particularistic factors had no place in a scientific field such as medicine, and that they were generally harmful to progress and modernity. Accordingly, any attempts to assert that the science of Western medicine, as distinct from its social practice or organization, was not wholly applicable to China were vigorously resisted. Science had to be universal. Any arguments to the contrary—either in terms of Chinese medicine's particular suitability to the Chinese constitution, or in terms of its being "one kind of science" whose mysteries were beyond the ken of modern Western science—were inadmissible: "This kind of talk really is too mystical. This is just like that used by those medical practitioners of several thousand years ago who were without techniques, methods, or reason." [16] Science and modern medicine were universal in character and hence they rightfully belonged to modern China just as much as to anyone else.

With this conviction about the need for science, the modern

medicine supporters could give a different twist to the name "national medicine." In terms reminiscent of Lu Hsün's classic remark on "national essence," [17] Yu Hsien pointed out that only that which could preserve the Chinese nation deserved the title "national medicine." Traditional medicine clearly could not do this nearly so well as modern, scientific medicine, which should accordingly become the nation's medicine.[18] Other critics bluntly demanded why the "national medicine" should not be the medicine that best served China. The Japanese bombing of Shanghai in early 1932 gave them a case in point. On February 17 an unsigned article in *Ta kung-pao* asked if those partisans of the old medicine who were forever citing Japan as a strong nation which respected tradition, including traditional Chinese medicine, could not now see that it was respect for modernity, not tradition, that formed the basis of Japanese national power which China was feeling so painfully. From their modern bombs and airplanes it was clearly the latter, and this was what China herself must use to resist, not traditional arts like *t'ai chi ch'uan*. Similarly, in medicine, national survival required the latest and best—"He who follows the times lives, he who goes against the times dies." [19]

Here lay the real basis for the vehemence with which medical modernizers condemned Chinese medicine or national medicine advocates. Their insistence on "national essence" was seen as a cover for the same type of conservative mentality that had hindered China on every step of the road to modernization. While paying lip service to ideals of science and progress, the "national medicine" group allegedly was, in fact, opposing those values that were so essential to China's survival. This was harmful not just to medical and public health work; the effects of such a mentality extended into every aspect of the national life. Repeatedly, critics of the *Kuo-i kuan* castigated it as "a severe blow to the entire country's scholarly thought,"[20] and "a poisonous drug stupefying the thought of youth."[21] In its wider context, they saw the entire "national medicine" movement either as part of a reactionary scheme to restore the authority of a dead past or, at the very least, a manifestation of the stubborn tenacity of this outworn authority.[22]

If the syncretic plans of the "national medicine" group were unacceptable on scientific grounds, so was their version of "scientification" of Chinese medicine. Modern medicine advocates were quick to point out that once Chinese medicine was truly made scientific it would become one with universal, international science and would no longer be a "Chinese" medicine. "The day Chinese medicine is scientificized is precisely the day it becomes cosmopolitanized."[23] Talk of "scientification" to preserve a distinct Chinese medical identity was dismissed by the modernists as a contradiction in terms.[24] Similarly, they had no confidence in the will or ability of the "national medicine" partisans to carry out genuine scientific research. In explaining why he had rejected proffered membership in the *Kuo-i kuan,* Yü Yün-hsiu cited two basic reasons: the organization was based on an emotional, unscientific appeal, and in any event, it lacked the proper equipment and scientific ability to conduct meaningful research. Such research could only be carried out by competent scientists, and this was the only type of "scientification" worth talking about.

Instead of a distinction between Chinese and Western medicine, the modernists insisted that since science is one and universal, the only valid distinction could be between unscientific and scientific (or old and new) medicine. To illustrate this, the more theoretically inclined drew up various series of stages in universal evolutionary progress in medical history. The stages, depending on the individual theorist, could be spiritual–empirical–mystical–experimental, or in-

stinctual–religious–mystical–scientific, or some other variation.[25] In all of them, China was placed at an arrested mystical or empirical stage, roughly comparable to pre-Renaissance
Europe. To talk of synthesis, then, was absurd. The only
road in science was that of universal progress, upon which
all nations must travel. If China remained far behind on the
journey, the urgent task for contemporaries was to catch up,
and theories of synthesis were as relevant to this as proposing
to combine the best points of the ox cart and the locomotive.
Yu Hsien summed it up:[26]

> From religious medicine forward to mystical medicine,
> from mystical medicine forward to scientific medicine, is
> to follow the universal path which the evolution of human
> knowledge must take. There are no divisions of Chinese
> and Western, no partition of the globe.

Perhaps this formulation was not especially flattering to
China's cultural self-esteem, and for that reason many cultural nationalists boggled at it. But it did open the way for
China to take the latest and most modern without any nag-
ging doubts about source of origin and without any feeling
of betraying what was particularly Chinese. As modernists
insisted to the supporters of Chinese medicine, these ancient
arts were nothing special to China, but rather the type of
primitive knowledge which people everywhere had accumulated and later discarded as science progressed.[27] With the
latest and most modern felt to be essential to national survival,
this stress on temporal over spatial distinctions served ad-
mirably to dissolve old cultural loyalties. China, in joining
the front ranks of the modern world, was being true to the
law of universal progress, not false to her own culture.

The new, progressive views of history also found expression
in a generally iconoclastic attitude toward China's high antiquity. With the medical conservatives still treating antiquity

with a great deal of respect—even if its position as a source of final authority had been weakened—it was hardly surprising that their modernist opponents wrote articles exposing the medical sages of antiquity as mythical creatures and their teachings as primitive knowledge. P'an Leng-feng, for example, in the *Ta kung pao* medical supplement, disputed the historical authenticity of these figures, lumping Shen Nung with obviously implausible mythical beings such as Lei Kung, the God of Thunder.[28] He also drew attention to the close connection between this very early medicine and supernatural elements, prayer, divination, and fortune-telling. In a similar spirit, Yu Hsien gleefully seized upon a historical article alleging that the sanctified great Han dynasty surgeon Hua T'o, was only a Chinese version of a Buddhist religious myth from India.[29]

> Seeing Ch'en Heng-ch'üeh's conclusive essay, one truly can neither laugh nor cry. Hua T'o, this great doctor who was revered so long as China's great surgeon was just a myth . . . Thus, our compatriots of the old medicine world also lose a paper tiger.

The writings from the Chou-Han era—those "medical classics" which had been revered for two millennia—were similarly dismissed as crude and superstitious gropings, later transformed into a bizarre philosophical system having no contact with reality. The *Su-Wen* ("Plain Questions") section of the *Nei-ching,* for instance, was described as a very simple, primitive book "not worth preserving except as material for medical historians."[30]

What had been the wisdom of antiquity had become to the new generation of "antiquity doubters" merely primitive knowledge. Huang-ti had fallen from sage king to historical myth; his book, from revered classic to "material for medical historians." Here, of course, is one aspect of that great sea change in modern Chinese intellectual history—the displacement of antiquity by progress. The transition to a progressive viewpoint in the medical field also comes out in revealing phrases, as, for example: "The comparison of old and new medicine can thus be considered as a comparison between a child and an adult." [31] The new and modern was now no longer the child looking to its ancestors for guidance, but had become the adult building on the simpler knowledge of medicine's childhood. Traditional critics who rejected modern medicine as too new, too unproven, too infantile, were accordingly rebuffed with the assertion that the new medicine was even more infantile, that is, at an earlier stage of development. [32]

In all traditional societies the rise of modern science has been a powerful solvent of ancient pieties, a great force for liberation from the authority of traditional culture. This has been especially marked in China which was par excellence a society of the "Word"—the written word preserving eternal truths from antiquity for all ages. Science, with its stress on unfettered inquiry, experimentation, ever-expanding knowledge, and skepticism of prevailing doctrine, has been profoundly subversive of the core values of that society. Even more than in Europe (where a revealed religion has had more scope for adjustment to the implications of science and has been able to preserve a philosophical or theological sanctuary against those anti-authoritarian tendencies), science has been shattering to a more secular Confucianism which derived its authority from respect for historical tradition. This larger iconoclastic, anti-authoritarian potential of science in modern China had been implicit in much of the writings against Chinese medicine. At times it became explicit, as when Chou Shao dismissed all authorities other than science: "No matter though they come from respected fathers, from intimate friends, or revered teachers, we must all, basing ourselves on science, deny and reject them." [33] Another article attacked the "authority of the teacher" which had fettered Chinese medical progress. [34] This was attributed to the general Confucian emphasis on established authority and unquestioning acceptance of past knowledge. The link to the medical world could be seen in the highest honor paid to a traditional physician—the accolade of *ju-i,* "Confucian doctor." Since progress could only come from the struggle of new against old, such reverence for established authority could only be harmful to science and to China. Therefore, the present task was to "destroy the feudal and ancestor system of teacher's authority" both in the disciple system and in the mentality behind it. [35]

Generally, the advocates of Western medicine shared a type of late nineteenth-century European optimism about the progress of science and its implications for society. Yet this on occasion could give away to a deep pessimism over the future of science in China and China's own future. Fu Ssu-nien expressed their dismay at the recrudescence of traditional forces under the guise of "national medicine" when he referred to it as a symbol of the "defeat" of thirty years of modern education in China. [36] Yü Yün-hsiu, in one of his more pessimistic moods, gave voice to doubts over the usual modernist's assumptions that the growth of science in China would dispel such forces of darkness and ignorance. [37] He noted that it was a universal phenomenon that, as scientific knowledge becomes more complex it becomes more incomprehensible to the layman, thereby opening a widening gap in knowledge and viewpoint between the scientist and society at large. The problems this can pose in a modern society with a long tradition of respect for science have in recent years received increasing attention. [38] In a traditional society, where modern science is an alien innovation, these problems are further complicated by conservative resistance to change and nationalist insistence on preserving what is salvageable of the indigenous culture. Thus, Yü Yün-hsiu complained that insufficient knowledge of science led many modern Chinese to a "fence-sitting" position in the medical controversy whereby it was felt that Chinese medicine could not but be abolished, and yet, at the same time, could not be completely abolished. Such a conservative rationalization, he said, had no logical basis, but to the nonscientifically educated, caught in a crisis between general awareness that the old must change and ignorance of the scientific reasons why it must change, it had a powerful psychological appeal. Yü feared this would grow as science further expanded beyond the layman's comprehension. In China it obstructed necessary progress and reinforced innate conservatism, nowhere more than in the medical field, for out of such a mentality came all the various schools of medical synthesizers. Ignorant of science, and intellectually dishonest in their formulations, these people were only obstructing real scientific progress in their meaningless attempts to combine old and new.

Such hostility to these efforts was standard among modern doctors and advocates of science in general. Most interesting here, however, is the suspicion that the advance of scientific knowledge, rather than acting as a beacon to light the way to social progress, might, by the very brilliance of its beam, blind the public at large to its importance. Such pessimism was unheard of in the scientific euphoria of the May 4th spirit. It was rare a decade later, but perhaps not insignificant in revealing a growing awareness among scientific modernizers that China's path to science was not so smooth as had once been hoped.

Perhaps a better appreciation of the attitudes of the modern, "Westernized" intellectuals who led most of the agitation against Chinese medicine can be gained from a brief glimpse at two of their most famous figures. Fu Ssu-nien, it has already been noted, was violently opposed to everything about traditional medicine, especially to its revival under the cover of "national medicine." In 1934 he wrote an article in *Tu-li p'ing-lun* condemning "so-called national medicine" as a fraud and an affront to science and modernity in China.[39] This provoked a running feud with proponents of old medicine, during which Fu, who was noted for his temper and outspokenness, proved himself a master in the art of vituperation. A not untypical string of adjectives on Chinese medicine ran, "ignorant, nonsensical, blind, babbling."[40] To him the old medicine represented all the forces of conservatism, superstition, and ignorance with which science and enlightenment must struggle. It was impossible to find any good in it. He is widely reputed to have made the statement that he would rather die than take any Chinese medicine.[41]

What, then, of Hu Shih, a close colleague of Fu, who shared his friend's general philosophic outlook and zest for controversy, though not his choleric temper? It might be expected that Hu Shih would be wholly on the modern side in the medical controversy, and indeed he was a forceful proponent of China's medical modernization, serving as a member of the Board of Trustees for Peiping Union Medical College. But, unlike Fu Ssu-nien, he never directly expressed his views on Chinese medicine. True, in a commencement address to the graduating class of Peiping Union Medical College for 1931 he referred to the old-style medicine as a profession which "will sooner or later be replaced by modern medicine."[42] He also made some caustic references to the national medicine movement without specifically condemning it. Reviewing a translated Western medical history, he traced the course of Western medical evolution up to the rise of the modern scientific spirit since the sixteenth century.

This account of scientific progress would, he hoped, cause Chinese readers to ask, "What position does our own *yin-yang,* five elements 'national medicine' occupy in this history of the development of scientific medicine?"[43] Again, on the subject of the "Chinese basis" he lumped "national medicine" with the "read the classics, revere Confucius" campaign and other harmful manifestations of cultural conservatism.

Yet, at the very time when he was most active in fighting the cultural battles, Hu Shih did not join in the *Kuo-i kuan* debate. Silence in itself of course, proves little about his attitude. Many prominent intellectuals had nothing to do with the public medical debate, although in their private lives they too had to make some kind of decision about the respective merits of the new and the old medicine, and these decisions often reflected much of their general cultural attitude.[44] In Hu Shih's case, however, his silence may be more significant. There is a widespread story that during the winter of 1920–1921 he was suffering from a serious diabetic condition.[45] This was before insulin, and the Peking Union Medical College could not help him. In his extremity he took a friend's advice to consult the famous Peking herbalist, Lu Chung-an. Using herbal medicine, Lu completely cured him. In gratitude, Hu Shih is reported to have presented Dr. Lu with a painting, "Studying the Classics in the Autumn Pavillion," upon which Hu himself wrote a laudatory inscription dedicated to Lu Chung-an and Chinese medicine in general. In it he expressed the hope that "if the results of chemical analysis can cause the world's medical scholars gradually to understand the value of Chinese medicine and Chinese herbs, what a great contribution this will be for Mr. Lu."[46]

If this story is true—and besides the sources already cited, it is known that Hu Shih was one of those who summoned the same Dr. Lu Chung-an to Sun Yat-sen's deathbed in

1926[47]—it raises some interesting questions about why Hu Shih never publicly endorsed Chinese medicine, or openly condemned it. It seems probable that, despite his initial enthusiasm for the "contribution" Chinese medicine could make to world science, in the context of a general cultural struggle between old and new medicine, he found it impossible to give overt support to the medical conservatives. Yet his own personal experience, whatever his philosophic commitments, inhibited him from taking an open stand against Chinese medicine. Such instances of tension between personal involvement in the old cultural milieu and intellectual acceptance of new values are familiar enough in situations of rapid cultural change, and Hu Shih's dilemma here was not uncommon to many of his generation. The fact that Hu apparently felt this dilemma strongly enough to keep him out of any participation in the medical debate seems, therefore, rather significant for his times. In these circumstances his silence was as revealing of the modern intellectual's attitude toward Chinese medicine as Fu Ssu-nien's vituperative eloquence.

MEDICAL MODERATES AND THE SEARCH FOR A MIDDLE GROUND

Although such attitudes were prominent among modernists of the post-May 4th era, open hostility or an embarrassed silence was not the only possible position on the subject. There were some, no less modern in their goals, who could find kind words for Chinese medicine in the past, while seeking to abolish it in the present. For them, China's early achievements in medicine were legitimate subjects for national pride, and the only shame lay in losing the progressive spirit which had animated those times. The modern disgrace to the ancestors was not in supplanting their contributions with something better, but in the failing to carry forward their achievements: "If our ancestors could see what their descendants have come to, think how painful this would be to them." [48] This historical relativization of China's ancient medical accomplishments had begun somewhat earlier. In 1925, one S. C. Wu wrote an article on "Chinese Medicine" in the Chinese Recorder, an English-language journal for the "Christian Movement in China." [49] Although the writer was unmistakably an advocate of modern medicine, he warmly praised the ancient achievements of Chinese medicine. Yet in praising the *Nei-ching* for anticipating Harvey's discovery of circulation of the blood by almost 2000 years, he was not saying that the *Nei-ching* should replace modern physiological texts. The ancestors could be praised for their past achievements but that did not mean that one must accept them as guides for the present. Thus, so thoroughly modern a scientist as the Japanese-trained pharmacologist and member of Academia Sinica, Chao Yü-huang, could claim that seventy to eighty percent of the products used in modern herbology had originated in the Chinese *Pen-ts'ao*, without making any claim for native herbals over modern drugs. [50] Or, even more relevant, he could cite the myth of Shen Nung testing the various herbs as evidence of an original experimental spirit which modern Chinese should emulate. [51] There was no traditionalism in any of this. It was the spirit, not the product, which should be cherished, and this spirit pointed to progress and new values. Wu Lien-te, a founder of the National Medical Association and one of the outstanding figures in building modern medicine in China, had a keen interest in his country's medical history. [52] In an article significantly called "The Renaissance of Medicine in China," he discussed ancient times and concluded: "From the above we can know that China was a place of origin of medical science and that science is not the sole possession of one place." [53] The ancients could accordingly be called upon to sanction science and innovation as well as to preserve the existing order.

If the patron saints of Chinese medicine could thus be

spared from wholesale condemnation, similarly some of the products of native medical experience (as opposed to Chinese medicine as a system of medicine) need not be totally scorned. Many of the most determined opponents of Chinese medicine were anxious to see the traditional materia medica subjected to careful scientific research. Sometimes, one suspects, this was partly in order conclusively to disprove the native medical world's claims to wondrous miracle-working properties in these drugs.[54] But usually it was a sincere belief that much of use to modern scientific medicine could be discovered in the enormous native pharmacopoeia. This implied no concession to traditional medicine's claims for continued survival as a medical system. Its theoretical principles were still anathema to modern science, and even popular therapeutic techniques like acupuncture and moxibustion were generally regarded as beyond the pale of scientific respectability. Unlike the national medicine reformers, who put great stress on re-examination of the vast corpus of traditional medical writings, they also had little use for such literary research. Yü Yün-hsiu complained that these writings were generally worthless, for the ingrained literary habit of covering ignorance with verbose explanations was the root defect of Chinese medicine—"Their thought is fuzzy, their theory inexact, knowledge incorrect, and scholarship unprogressive." [55]

Native herbals, on the other hand, were a legitimate field for scientific research. Yü Yün-hsiu himself had urged such work since the early 1920's.[56] The early years of the National Government also witnessed several proposals to set up modern government facilities for these purposes. An unsigned article in *Ta kung-pao* for 10 May 1930 lauded the achievement of Dr. Ch'en K'e-hui (Kenneth Ch'en), formerly of the Peiping Union Medical College, for his work in refining ephedrine out of the native herb *ma-huang*.[57] It was a source of considerable national pride: "This can somewhat alleviate our melancholy over this 'sick man of Asia,' letting foreigners know that China also has this kind of talent and cannot be looked down upon." [58] It was a source of shame, however, that Dr. Ch'en had had to go to the United States to continue his work because China generally neglected setting up facilities for scientific research.

Thus, while proponents of saving Chinese medicine through "scientification" flocked together under the banner of "national medicine," some modern medicine supporters were urging the government toward scientific research on Chinese drugs. [59] Their motives, of course, were very different, as were their methods. There should be no commitment to preserving any national distinctions, and the work should be assigned to modern-trained scientists rather than old-style doctors. Opinion differed on whether traditional herbalists might serve as consultants, but in any case the type of work envisaged was mainly chemical analysis of medicinal properties, examination of their physiological effects, controlled clinical testing, and refinement, standardization, and extraction of the effective ingredients for more efficient conversion into modern pharmaceuticals. Japanese achievements in developing modern pharmaceuticals out of the old materia medica were frequently cited as evidence of what the support of a modern, scientifically oriented government could achieve while China's own private research successes with ephedrine and other drugs served as a source of domestic inspiration. None of this, however, was to be construed as sanctioning preservation of a separate Chinese branch of medicine. "Those all are the achievements of scientists' research and not the work of Chinese medicine." [60] The eminent pharmacologist, Chao Yü-huang, defended this type of work against any suspicions of medical conservatism. "Chinese drugs" (*Chung-yao*), unlike "Chinese medicine" (*Chung-i*), referred solely to their place of origin and not to any body of knowledge separate from modern science.[61] Naturally, modern Chinese should examine their own native products, for, apart from their potential contribution to economic self-sufficiency, these could be of the greatest value in building a modern science of pharmacology in China.

Such views were actually more popular among scientific and medical specialists than among the non-professional "science worshippers" who had led the "new culture movement" in the 1920's and 1930's. For these cultural radicals, science often stood more as a symbol than as a well-understood body of knowledge, and it was natural for them, putting the medical question in symbolic perspective, to maintain a root-and-branch hostility to the old medicine. Professional scientists could evidently be somewhat more tolerant.

But the growing popularity of such a position—Chinese drugs, but not Chinese medicine—extended beyond scientific circles by the late thirties. In it can be seen something of a toning down of the May 4th antitraditionalist rejection of anything that touched on the old medicine, or perhaps a searching for some middle ground in the controversy between traditional medicine's new defenders and their modernist critics. On a superficial, naive level, this could lead to a literal acceptance of Chinese drugs without concern about their scientific analysis and processing. Even an unimpeachable modern like the jurist and university professor, Mei Ju-ao, could declare that pharmacy, as opposed to medicine, was not an international science, but merely the sum of a country's botanical products. Hence, to use Chinese drugs was simply to choose a native product over a foreign one, like wearing Chinese silks instead of foreign fabrics.[62] The scientific community and many nonscientists, of course, had more sophisticated views about the role science must play in determining the use of these products. One writer suggested that, since modern pharmacology had to form the basis for such research, a suitable slogan would reverse the old *t'i-yung* formula to read, "Western drugs for substance, Chinese drugs for use." [63]

Something like this (if not quite in these terms) appealed to some influential figures, including the famous philosopher, Feng Yu-lan. Commenting on the heated debate over Chinese medicine in the Political Consultative Conference of 1941, Feng took something of a middle position.[64] In the philosopher's grand manner, he pointed out that the two propositions—that Chinese medicine was scientific and that it was unscientific—need not be mutually exclusive. Chinese medicine (*Chung-i,* the theoretical principles) was indeed unscientific; Chinese drugs (*Chung-yao*) were certainly based on empirical observation and could cure diseases. Therefore, rectifying the names, one should use *chiu-i,* "old medicine," and *Chung-yao,* "Chinese drugs," meaning the pharmaceutical products derived from the Chinese environment. He ended with a familiar conclusion. The former could be discounted as outworn; the latter should be studied with the aid of modern science to develop their full value. It was a suitable position for a modern thinker whose understanding of science ruled out "national medicine" arguments, but who still felt there must be something useful in the country's medical tradition. Moreover, it fitted the practical needs of a backward and war-torn economy, as well as squaring with the common experience many of the modern intellectuals had had of old drugs that actually worked.

Such sentiments about Chinese drugs were reinforced by vaguely expressed ideas about adapting a modern, scientific medicine to its Chinese environment and establishing national self-respect by scientifically studying the country's own medical experience. This can be seen in the speech of the Shanghai Kuomintang Party representative to the opening meeting of the Chinese and Western Medicine Society, in which he warned against the tendency to ignore Chinese products in learning from the West. Again Japanese research on traditional herbals was cited as an example of what China should do in order to "completely become a medically independent country so as to avoid having others laugh at us as free loaders." [65] Verging on but not quite reaching medical particularism, such sentiments also appeared in occasional articles calling for a Sinicization of Western medicine to match the scientification of Chinese medicine. This did not necessarily mean a different kind of medicine for China. It did, however, reflect a type of nationalist self-assertion in medicine similar to the demands for a distinctively "American medicine" in nineteenth-century United States medical journals.[66] This would still be scientific in content, but better adapted to the peculiar social, economic, and natural conditions of its native country. Thus, when a respected Western-style physician like Sung Kuo-pin called for "medical adaptation to the particular country," he did not mean to negate the universality of science itself.[67] Such themes did, however, give greater scope to meeting practical needs and adopting modern medicine to China's special conditions, the existing medical tradition being one of those conditions.

Thus during the war there emerged more suggestions that the native drugs and even native-style doctors could be of some use in meeting the country's urgent medical needs. The idea of retraining and using traditional physicians was not altogether novel. It had been broached by modern medical people earlier, but generally had been drowned out in the clamorous debate between advocates of national medicine and their opponents. The wartime emergency gave such appeals a somewhat better hearing, but paradoxically it was the Communists who went furthest along this line. Yet the suggestion itself was indicative of a generally more tolerant attitude, at least in some modern circles, toward the old medicine and its practitioners.

This was also apparent in the wartime writings of some modern medical theorizers about the form of China's new medicine. Huang Wen, a Cambridge-trained physician, in his book *San Min Chu I and Medicine*,[68] had some moderate praise for "the medical learning handed down by our ancestors," especially as a subject for scientific research. Another foreign-educated doctor, Kao Te-ming, was more explicit on the need for "nationalization" (*min-tsu hua*) of Western medicine to accompany the "modernization" (*shih-tai hua*) of Chinese medicine.[69] His meaning was different from any "national medicine" proposal. "Nationalization," the phrase borrowed directly from Sun Yat-sen's Three Principles, was simply a dramatic way of emphasizing that in its adaptation to Chinese conditions, modern medicine must take these conditions into consideration. Only then could it become China's modern medicine—not American, British, or German medicine in China.

All of these were essentially modern viewpoints by men basically committed to science and modern medicine. Yet none of them showed the active hostility toward traditional medicine which had animated many earlier modern intellectuals. Such hostility still existed, but the sharp polarization of opinion over Chinese medicine which had characterized the preceding decades was further disintegrating. One possible reason for this trend could have been that, although China's scientific construction had only begun, the battle to have science and its values accepted in intellectual circles was almost won. Accordingly, uncompromising hostility to Chinese medicine was perhaps no longer so significant as a touchstone of loyalty to science.

CONTINUATION OF CONTROVERSY—DR. KUO MO-JO TO THE ATTACK

Despite the modernists' willingness to make greater allowances for Chinese peculiarities and the more realistic traditional medicine supporters' acknowledgment of science, there still remained a huge gulf between the basic viewpoints of the two schools. This became apparent as soon as one went beyond rhetoric about respecting science or national characteristics to face concrete problems of what was to be done about preserving, improving, or eliminating traditional medicine. The key to their differences can be seen in the various interpretations of the much-used slogan, "scientification of Chinese medicine." An editorial in the *Journal of the Medical Research Society* in 1936 had pointed out at least three basic opinions regarding this scientification: the view held by staunch traditionalists that Chinese medicine did not have to become scientific either because it already had science or did not need it; the belief of modern conservatives (with Ch'en Kuo-fu at the top of the list) that Chinese medicine could become scientific; and finally the contention of some that it could not become scientific and still remain "Chinese medicine." [70] The real issue, by the 1930's, was between the last two groups. Exposed to modern science and scientific research, could Chinese medicine survive as a distinct medical system? Or, granting the desirability of synthesis, would the ultimate product in any meaningful sense still be recognizably Chinese?

The cultural nationalists still hoped so and tailored their "scientification" programs to that end; the modernists—even those interested in research on elements of traditional medicine—adamantly denied the possibility of such a synthesis. This continuing tension was still apparent after the National Government had retreated to its wartime capital in Chungking. Although the *Kuo-i kuan* had by then fallen on lean days, its viewpoint was still put forth in a journal *New China Medical Monthly,* sponsored by Ch'en Kuo-fu and Ch'en Li-fu, among others.[71] The program of scientific reform and

synthesis with Western medicine remained the same. Its
writers remained convinced that "China's ideal new medicine" was not far away.[72]

On the other side, there were still prominent intellectuals
who interpreted scientification to mean elimination of the
old medicine. Toward the end of the war, Kuo Mo-jo provoked a flurry of familiar controversy with a "Proposal for
the Scientification of Chinese Medicine" in the *New China
Daily*.[73] From his modern medical training as a youth and
his generally progressive viewpoint, it could be expected that
this type of "scientification" differed rather markedly from
that favored by the Chinese medicine advocates. To begin
with, Kuo called for an end to this continuing name nonsense about "national medicine" and "Western medicine."
Moreover, he was very patronizing about the supposed value
of Chinese medicine and its drugs, while bitingly critical of
the theoretical defects. The numerous claims of effective
cures he summarily dismissed: "The diseases Chinese medicine can cure, anyway, are diseases which can cure themselves." [74] The only useful ingredients in these herbals were
probably vitamins, but he conceded the need for honest
scientific research on their properties, as opposed to the nonsensical theory behind their use.[75] The old doctors could only
be allowed to practice after a scientific re-education in modern
medicine. Thus, Kuo Mo-jo hardly stood forth as a friend
of even the most progressive of the traditional doctors. The
basis of his hostility could, once again, be traced directly
to concern with the larger issues of science and cultural
conservatism. He still saw the two, science and traditionalism, as mortal enemies: "We have been slaves to the so-called
national essence for several thousand years. Today in every
quarter of the country the degree to which we are slaves to
science is still insufficient." [76]

The contributors to the *New China Medical Monthly* could

scarcely be pleased with these opinions from such a noted intellectual figure. Their first replies, perhaps out of deference to Kuo's stature, were extremely respectful, even in disagreeing with some of his points and conclusions.[77] Ch'eng Laoliang, a doctor who had had experience in both kinds of medicine and had visited the Soviet Union, complimented Kuo on retaining the fighting spirit of his twenties, but thought he had gone too far in condemning almost everything about Chinese medicine.[78] Most of the harmful practices Kuo so rightly condemned came from poor practitioners of Chinese medicine, rather than from the medicine itself. Ch'eng entirely agreed on the need to stamp out such harmful quacks, but this was more a social than a scientific problem. In conclusion, he rather wistfully commented on the efficiency of socialized Soviet medicine in such areas. At the time, 1945, simultaneous admiration for Soviet and traditional Chinese medicine seemed rather anomalous; within a few years it would become commonplace.

There were others who disagreed with Kuo Mo-jo in less respectful terms. Yen Kung-i, a young Chinese-style doctor, showed little restraint in rebuking Kuo for a typically ignorant, biased, and unfair approach to the question of reforming Chinese medicine.[79] Admittedly reform was necessary, but this kind of slanderous attack would discourage necessary scientific research rather than stimulate it. Of course it could be expected that any traditional doctor would react with hostility to such open threats to his profession, but there were other factors as well in the concern expressed by Yen: "We must not become too slavish to Europeanization and lose our self-confidence." [80] From all of this it is clear that by the end of the war the medical question could still arouse some passion. The issues involved were still alive, and in them still rang familiar echoes of "Chinese basis" and "complete Westernization" from the 1930's.

"Chinese and Western medicine each has its strong and weak points, and there are diseases which Chinese medicine can cure where Western medicine is helpless. Therefore, we propose setting up an Institute of National Medicine which will use scientific methods to put in order the art of Chinese medicine."—T'an Yen-Kai, Hu Han-min, Ch'en Li-fu, and others.

"Chinese medicine represents the old force in the medical world, and also is a sign of the Chinese people's conservative viewpoint."—Wang Ching-wei

---

VII

GOVERNMENT AND

CHINESE MEDICINE—TENSIONS

WITHIN THE KUOMINTANG

So far we have focused on the various arguments about Chinese medicine and the intellectual tensions manifested in the debate. But medicine, unlike philosophy and perhaps even art, is not just an abstractly intellectual part of a nation's culture. The intellectual concerns discussed above have been far from irrelevant to the actual development of Chinese medicine. Yet, to see how these ideas about scientific reform, institutional reorganization, and medical synthesis have affected the form and content of traditional Chinese medicine, it is necessary to come down from this intellectual plane to look at concrete developments. Here the work of the various reform organizations—the Taiyuan group, the Institute for National Medicine, and others—was important. But, as the attempted modernization of traditional medicine proceeded, it became apparent that the role of the government was even more important.

GOVERNMENT REGULATION OF CHINESE MEDICINE

As noted previously, health and the state of medical practice became one of the concerns of the new government in China's efforts to build a modern state structure. This involved several areas: sponsorship and encouragement of scientific research, promotion of hygiene and public health, medical education, and supervisory control over the practice of medicine. Not all of these, of course, were entirely novel areas of state supervision in China, but in their modern form they certainly did represent considerable innovation. They were, in fact, one more aspect of the country's general modernization.

One of the areas most directly relevant to the fate of traditional medicine was the new governmental concern about supervising and controlling the practice of medicine. The early Republic took this seriously enough to set up a public health office under the Ministry of the Interior, but the central government was so ineffective that it posed little threat to the existing medical practices. There was, especially after the May 4th Movement, a rising demand for government regulation and restriction of the old-style practitioners. In February 1920 a conference of modern doctors meeting at the newly built Peiping Union Medical College petitioned the central government "to regulate the practice of the doctors trained in the traditional way with a view to the unification of standards required of medical practitioners." [1] The following month the Ministry of Education informed the National Medical Association of its intention "to regulate the practice of doctors trained in the traditional way with a view to the unification of standards required of medical practitioners." [2] However, the medical regulations issued by the Ministry of the Interior in 1922 did not establish this "unification of standards"—a unification which necessarily meant disqualifying traditional doctors from legal practice. Instead, it provided licenses for two types of practitioners with different standards of qualification, based respectively on a modern or a traditional medical education. Lack of educational standards in the traditional medical world was to be overcome by requiring applicants to pass an examination administered by local police officers.

This was the first attempt to regulate the practice of Chinese medicine on a national level. It did not set up modern, scientific medical training as the only standard for legal practice; it did make an attempt to set some sort of standard for those who were entitled to practice traditional medicine. The compromise pleased neither modern medicine advocates nor traditional doctors, who believed they had been given an inferior status and suspected it was the beginning of legislation to restrict and abolish their practice. In the chaos of the 1920's the regulations were in any case no immediate threat. It was only after the Kuomintang had, at least theoretically, unified the country and set up an energetic, modern-minded National Ministry of Health in Nanking that the hope, or threat, of effective medical regulations became a possibility.

On 15 January 1929 the Ministry of Health drew up "Provisional Regulations for Physicians" which ended the dual medical status of 1922 by referring only to modern-trained physicians.[3] The following month it convened the public health conference whose resolution on "Abolishing Traditional Medicine" so alarmed the Chinese medicine world. The national organization of traditional doctors which arose to combat this proposal has been described. In this context it is important to examine the means by which they brought effective political pressure to bear on the hostile health authorities. Partly it was through propaganda efforts to mobilize "public opinion" (mainly various private cultural or social organizations) against the threat to the "national essence." More direct, and probably more effective, however, was the personal pressure exerted at the Kuomintang's Third Party Congress.[4] There a delegation received assurances from Party secretary Yeh Ch'u-chuang that the government had no intention of attacking Chinese medicine. Members of the delegation also received promises of support from T'an Yen-k'ai (then President of the Executive Yuan), Li Shih-tseng, Chang Ching-chiang, and Ch'en Kuo-fu. The public health conference resolution was accordingly dropped. Moreover, in 1930 the "Provisional Regulations for Physicians" were reissued to apply specifically to Western-style doctors.[5]

These striking successes and the involvement of prominent political figures in the subsequent organization of the Institute for National Medicine revealed considerable sympathy for the claims of Chinese medicine (especially in its scientific, reformist guise) among important elements of the ruling Party. The pattern of this support soon became clear. Figures from a wide range of the Kuomintang political spectrum, although generally tending toward its right wing, could be enlisted by the culturally nationalistic appeals of the national medicine group. In 1930 seven members of the Kuomintang Central Political Council—T'an Yen-k'ai, Hu Han-min, Ch'en Chao-ying, Shao Yuan-chung, Ch'en Li-fu, Chiao I-t'ang, and Chu P'ei-te—drew up a resolution in favor of government support for the proposed Institute of National Medicine.[6]

This opened a sharp cleavage within the Party and the

Government between these supporters of national medicine and progressive, Western-oriented elements favoring restriction and elimination of Chinese medicine. The former were strong in the higher echelons of the Party, especially as the Ch'en brothers tightened their hold on its organization, as well as in the legislative branch of the government. The latter's stronghold, particular after Wang Ching-wei became President of the Executive Yuan, was in the executive branch, notably the key ministries of Health and Education, whose leading members were mainly Western-trained. Throughout the 1930's these forces engaged in a prolonged tug of war over government policy toward Chinese medicine.

Licensing regulations remained a key area of this struggle. After beating back the Ministry of Health's threat in 1929, the partisans of Chinese medicine attempted to remove it entirely from the control of the unsympathetic health authorities. In 1933, twenty-nine members of the Central Political Council supported a resolution by Shih Ying, the Mayor of Nanking, which would entrust administration of "National Medicine Regulations" to the nongovernmental Institute for National Medicine.[7] This would legitimize the then legally ambiguous position of traditional practitioners, give the *Kuo-i kuan* quasi-official status, and delegate to the traditional medical world authority to supervise itself.

All this was highly objectionable to the modern medical profession and its supporters, who raised a storm of objections. Wang Ching-wei openly took their side in the issue. Speaking to the second national meeting of the amalgamated China Medical Association, he agreed that traditional medicine was an obstacle to medical progress: "Chinese medicine represents the old force in the medical world, and also is a sign of the Chinese people's conservative viewpoint."[8] He accordingly rejected the attempts to legalize and preserve this obstacle. Perhaps the most common argument against the proposed "National Medicine Regulations" was that they would mean an unwarranted delegation of government authority to an organization unfit to pass judgment on proper medical practice.[9] Some argued that they were illegal; others, like Ch'en Fang-chih, head of the National Health Administration's public health committee, argued on the more practical grounds that they were in direct opposition to the government's general policy of building a modern and scientific national health program.[10] Perhaps the decisive argument, however, was that they would be directly contrary to the National Government's efforts to build a modern unified administrative system for the whole country. If proper government administrative powers could be handed out to private organizations, "is this not the same as the former assorted Wuhan, Manchurian, Northwestern, Southern and Southwestern governments' attempts to extend the power of their own area." [11] Even more to the point, perhaps, was the reminder that Japan was, at that very moment, basing its claim to Manchuria on the allegation that China possessed no effective governmental administrative machinery.[12] Such arguments were apparently not without effect. Although the popularity of traditional medicine's cause with cultural conservatives was proved by the twenty-nine members of the Central Political Committee who supported the resolution, it failed of acceptance and was sent to the legislation drafting committee of the Legislative Yuan for further study. The "Chinese Medicine Regulations" which emerged on 15 December 1933 were not entirely pleasing to either side. The tendentious name, "national medicine," was changed to "Chinese medicine," and licensing authority was given to the Ministry of the Interior or relevant local organs, instead of the *Kuo-i kuan*.[13] The major objections to the original regulations had been met, but old-style doctors had also secured official legal recognition.

Such recognition was valuable, but so long as they remained under the control of the modern health authorities, the traditional doctors considered their position precarious. The Institute for National Medicine continued its agitation, and at the Fifth Kuomintang Party Congress in 1935 a resolution demanding "Equal treatment for Chinese and Western medicine" was passed.[14] This was apparently granted in the revised "Chinese Medicine Regulations" promulgated the next year. The National Health Administration attempted to prevent it from becoming a standing invitation for every sort of quack to get a government license by setting up a Chinese Medicine Committee to supervise the regulations.[15] This occasioned further complaints about discrimination against traditional doctors along with a continued demand that they be put on an equal status with Western-style doctors in one medical practice law. After prolonged and bitter debate in the Political Consultative Conference, on 22 September 1943 the National Government finally promulgated a single unified "Physicians' Law." Traditional doctors could qualify for a physician's license, carrying equal privileges as modern doctors, by meeting one of three criteria: receiving a diploma from a school of Chinese medicine; passing a government examination; having already practiced for five years with a "prominent reputation." [16]

Apart from the continued recognition of two types of medical practice, the modern medical profession found the five years' experience provision most objectionable, for in effect it allowed anyone who had practiced to continue doing so regardless of his qualifications. This was indeed a loophole in the attempt to impose standards on medical practice—even when recognizing two sets of standards, old-style and modern—but it was also a realistic recognition that the government was in no position to enforce any standards throughout the entire country. Just to get traditional doctors to register for licenses was in itself an advance. In fact, however, the vast majority remained unregistered and unlicensed.

GOVERNMENT SUPPORT FOR CHINESE MEDICINE

But if their political influence was able to secure legal status for Chinese medicine and frustrate the attempts of modern medical people to restrict its practice, what achievements could the modern supporters of Chinese medicine show in the institutional reform and scientification of the ancient medical tradition? As the more sensitive of them well knew, adaptation to modern institutional forms and appropriation of modern scientific methods (the much-discussed synthesis with Western medicine) was the only hope for the long-term survival of Chinese medicine. It was somewhat easier to borrow the organizational framework of Western medicine than to synthesize its contents with the indigenous system. In a sense, the organizations of traditional doctors formed to protest hostile government legislation were the first gropings toward a modern type of professional society. By the 1920's there had emerged a number of such societies, obviously patterned on the modern doctors' associations.[17] Many of these societies published journals (another innovation for Chinese medicine) and generally strove to bring some unity to the hitherto jealously individualistic traditional medicine practitioners. In short, with the threat and the example of organized modern medicine before them, the more progressive of them tried to build a modern type of Chinese medical profession. The Institute for National Medicine was the culmination of these efforts.

The larger and better financed of these societies also tried to copy other institutional features of Western medicine— schools, hospitals, research centers—in general trying to change the entire organizational basis of Chinese medicine.

For instance, Yen Hsi-shan's "Reform Society" in Taiyuan was supposed to include a school and attached hospital as an integral part of its research plans. The Institute for National Medicine, also primarily a research institute, had a similar provision in its constitution. In practice, the schools were probably the most significant institutional innovation, for they provided a means of attempting to standardize education in Chinese medicine. In cooperation with the new Chinese medicine societies and research centers, they hoped to bring together the disparate elements of the traditional medical knowledge, form a unified curriculum, and train new Chinese-style doctors of a definitely assured standard. Such standardization was obviously highly desirable in the competition with Western-style doctors, and in a modernizing society where universal standards were beginning to replace the old criteria of personal reputation and private connections.

By 1930 a visiting League of Nations medical expert, Professor Knud Faber, found fifteen schools for traditional medicine in China. These varied tremendously in size, curriculum, and number of modern scientific subjects included. The three he personally visited in Shanghai each had about 100 students and offered a five-year course—two years of theory and three years' clinical instruction in attached clinics or hospitals.[18] They also included in their curricula some modern physiology, anatomy, and chemistry. Faber was not very much impressed, however, by their facilities for modern medical instruction: "There were no laboratories or other equipment, no textbooks in use; a few anatomical charts were the only aids in teaching."[19] This was a major problem with such schools. The type of progressive Chinese medicine education incorporating the best of Western science, which they theorized about, was generally beyond the financial and technical means of the Chinese medicine societies. Most of the schools thus remained poorly equipped, poorly organized institutions, offering a type of instruction that differed little from the traditional methods. The worst of them were nothing more than quick-study diploma mills, offering the "graduate" supposed proof of his mastery of the esoteric medical arts, old and new, with which to impress a credulous public. Even the Institute for National Medicine, which was able to graduate several classes of about 100 institutionally trained doctors, still taught mainly traditional medicine by a mainly traditional doctor faculty.[20] Although probably the best and the longest-lived of such schools, it could scarcely emulate the impressive modern medical centers of twentieth-century China. There were obvious limitations to what these private organizations could do toward institutionally modernizing Chinese medicine; their chief hope lay in getting government support for these goals.

Thus, demands that Chinese medicine be included in the government school system became a regular feature of the traditional medicine groups' agitation. Before the founding of the National Government, the most serious effort to obtain recognition of this principle from the Peking warlord regimes came in 1925 at the fourth annual meeting of the Chinese Educational Improvement Society. There a resolution was put through the medical education section calling on the Ministry of Education to include Chinese medicine in the education system.[21] The formula was purely eclectic. Just as there now existed university departments of Chinese literature and of foreign literature, there should be similar equality between Chinese and Western medicine.[22] For this, special schools to teach Chinese medicine were proposed which would have a unified curriculum of improved Chinese medicine with a heavy dose of modern sciences thrown in. This would permit an enforcement of standards which could gradually eliminate the quacks and charlatans who, in the minds of Chinese medicine's more responsible supporters, were basically responsible for its bad reputation.

During the 1930's the Institute for National Medicine became the most forceful lobbyist for such plans. After rebuffs in the Kuomintang Central Political Council and the Legislative Yuan, their efforts were finally rewarded at the Fifth Kuomintang Party Congress in 1935. There, two resolutions calling for general "equality" between the two types of medicine—notably inclusion of Chinese medicine schools in the education system—won support from a broad range of Kuomintang notables, and were accepted.[23] Some of the other implications of this "equality" were official support for Chinese medicine hospitals and research centers and, above all, independence from the control of the modern medical personnel who directed the National Health Administration.

Despite the loosely worded expression of Party will, none of this happened. To begin with, the modern medical profession set up an outcry at the inclusion of such old, unscientific subjects in the government-approved medical curriculum. According to one critic, it was analagous to "reviving the old classics-chanting education and reviving the Ming-Ch'ing examination system." [24] The Ministry of Education simply did nothing to implement the resolution. Similarly, the National Health Administration (successor to the Ministry of Education) remained entirely in modern medical hands and entirely modern in its policies. The party dictatorship of the Kuomintang was obviously not the monolithic structure that succeeded it.

In fact, the closest the *Kuo-i kuan* group ever got to obtaining direct government support for its ideals came right on the eve of the Sino-Japanese War. In March 1937 Chiao I-t'ang made a plea for funds from the Shanghai business community on behalf of a National Medicine Academy (*Kuo-i yuan*) which would be a semiprivate government-sponsored research center and experimental hospital for the preservation and "scientification" of "national medicine." The government had agreed to put up part of the funds for this, but since it was "for the benefit of the people," it was only fitting that private citizens put up the rest.[25] In effect, the government was willing to give the project only partial support. Funds were allotted for the building and a site actually purchased in Nanking before the outbreak of war in August shelved all such plans.

For the rest, the National Government supported scientific research on native Chinese drugs, although on a modest scale, and with the work entirely in the hands of modern-trained people. This, of course, was perfectly acceptable to even the most militantly scientific modernist. In fact, the most common complaint from the modern medical profession was that not enough was being done in this regard.[26] The National Health Administration's three-year plan in 1930 allotted the modest sum of $24,000 a year for a Chinese Drugs Research Institute,[27] and its first national pharmacopoeia, published the same year, included over sixty traditional drugs.[28] For the most part, modern research on Chinese materia medica remained in private hands. But as another sign of official approval of the idea, in 1931 the Chinese and Japanese delegates to the League of Nation's Health Committee jointly proposed the establishment of a League commission of international experts to examine the medical properties of traditional Chinese drugs.[29] Despite some reservations expressed by General John Graham, Public Health Commissioner of the Indian Medical Service, the general sentiment of the committee was overwhelmingly in favor of this venture in scientific cooperation between East and West. With the provision that Indian medicine be included, the proposal was accepted, thereby conferring international scientific approbation on scientific research on Chinese drugs.

Apparently this amounted to nothing more than approbation, for the Commission never actually began work. It does, however, provide more evidence of the scientific respectability of this type of pure research on Chinese drugs, as distinct from the very controversial proposals to "scientificize" a "national medicine."

In sum, then, the concrete results of all the talk about modernizing Chinese medicine's institutional framework and scientificizing its contents were rather unimpressive. Of course the very acceptance of the idea of professional associations, schools, hospitals, and research centers—indeed the idea of cooperative scientific progress itself—marked a very significant cultural change. The traditional Chinese medicine world was not insensitive to the need for change in order to survive in a new world. But by themselves the old-style doctors lacked the resources and the know-how to effect a rapid transformation of traditional medical practices and organization. Their schools and hospitals remained embryonic, more symbolic of modernizing intent than quantitatively significant in changing the face of traditional medicine. The only hope for a real institutional breakthrough lay in persuading the government to put its power and prestige behind this program. And here, although the "national medicine" supporters made a good try, they failed.

As for the content of Chinese medicine, the proposed synthesis with modern science showed even fewer results. True, it became fairly common practice in many of the quasi-progressive dispensaries to give out modern drugs along with traditional herbals. But beyond such superficialities there was little real meeting of the two medical systems. The new Chinese doctors trained in the schools had some smattering of modern knowledge, but for the most part they learned the old techniques and the old theory. For the most part, despite all the talk of synthesis, the two medical worlds remained sharply divided and generally hostile to each other. Western medicine controlled the government's health machinery and served a small proportion of the urban population; Chinese medicine, generally unchanged by contact with modern science, remained the common source of medical relief for the overwhelming majority of the people.

The existence of these two medical systems and the larger context of the cultural clash between them, enormously complicated the government's task of medical modernization. The well-entrenched position of the traditional doctors in the old society, plus the bitterness of their feud with the modern medical profession, made the health authorities reluctant to use them in introducing elementary modern medical concepts to the vast population beyond the reach of China's small number of modern doctors. In 1930 Professor Faber advised the National Government against instituting short-term retraining courses on the pattern used to retrain old-style midwives: "I do not think the time is ripe for such an enterprise. The organization of such courses would be considered as an official authorization of the native doctors, which would do more harm than good." [30] Fear of strengthening the traditional medical world, which they were trying to replace with modern medicine, thus inhibited a practical alliance with it.

Similarly, the intensity of the cultural clash bedeviled the government's attempts to enforce medical standards. Establishing and maintaining standards of medical practice and medical training had been a common problem in Europe and America only slightly earlier.[31] For instance, in the United States the great era of medical diploma mills had come to an end only at the beginning of the twentieth century. In China it was possible to establish standards for modern medical schools. But applying them to traditional medicine schools and practitioners, who based their practice on an entirely different body of doctrine, was impossible. Any attempt to do so, or even to insist that the schools offered proper traditional instruction, inevitably raised a cry of threatening the "national essence." With powerful political elements ready to heed such a cry, the health authorities' hands were tied.

On the political level, the National Government's irresolution over what policy to adopt toward traditional medicine revealed the diversity of cultural opinion within the Kuomintang. This situation bears a striking similarity to that of the Indian nationalist movement, which also split over the issue of the country's traditional medicine—the more modern, Western-educated political leaders and scientific specialists favoring its abolition, while less modernized political figures (often more attuned to popular sentiments) fought for its preservation and development. As in China, the split has been generally between the executive organs of government and the legislature or party machinery. In both Congress India and Kuomintang China this has tended to create something of an impasse over the role traditional medicine should be given in the modernizing society.

MODERN INTELLECTUALS' CRITICISM OF KUOMINTANG POLICY

One effect of the resurgent cultural conservatism within the Kuomintang was to alienate many of the medical modernists who had seen its rise to power as the beginning of China's break with the old and the rapid adoption of the new and scientific. The Party's blocking of the 1929 public health conference resolution on abolishing traditional medicine was accordingly a severe blow to them. Throughout the thirties, again and again they appealed for a ruthlessly modernizing government to force science and modern medicine upon a backward and lethargic society. One medical writer, Hsiao Shu-hsuan, spelled out the necessary authoritarian political leadership to accomplish this.[32] Although most modern medicine advocates would not put it so baldly, Hsiao declared frankly that only a thoroughgoing dictatorship, dedicated to overriding all obstacles to progress, could enforce rapid modernization in China. In view of how the reform spirit of the May 4th period was being crushed by the combined weight of "several thousand years of tradition" and present reactionary warlord politicians, he could not doubt that only with full government support would the "morning breezes" of science be able to sweep away "the old culture's noxious vapors." He wholeheartedly endorsed Hu Shih's position on the need for complete cultural revolution, but, unlike Hu Shih, insisted that the political revolution was a precondition for—not a consequence of—this basic cultural change. In the crucial area of medicine and public health, "medicine must turn to politics," for "to sweep out the noxious filth of the old medicine and build new scientific medicine, the only hope is that it can be carried out under an autocratic leadership." [33]

Many others insisted that the Kuomintang's concept of one-party tutelage should entail responsibility for exactly this kind of scientific, as well as political, national construction.[34] Indeed, bringing a backward nation into the modern world was the entire rationale for the "Party State," and in medicine this meant sponsoring modern scientific medicine rather than tolerating preservation of the old, unscientific native tradition. To this end, medical modernizers could invoke the potent political symbol of Sun Yat-sun, for Sun's own medical training and concern with China's scientific progress appeared to place him unequivocally on their side. The brief furor over the use of traditional medicine at his death-bed reflected the Western medicine advocates' sense of ownership over the legacy of Sun Yat-sun.* Actually, their

* See above Chapter IV.

claim was not so completely unambiguous. Under the National Government, right-wing Kuomintang spokesmen frequently enlisted Sun's memory in the cause of preserving Chinese medicine. For example, Chiao I-t'ang cited Sun's speech on psychological reconstruction: "Western pharmacy had adopted many products from China, and Western-style doctors in China took their products from Western pharmacy. These doctors thus unashamedly took a long detour in following Westerners step by step. National spirit was lost. To say this is extremely painful." [35] Yü Yün-hsiu was quick to reply on behalf of the modern medical profession that this was quoted out of context, and that Sun was unmistakably an advocate of modern science, including modern medicine, in order to serve the nation.[36] This was undoubtedly true, but it is also true that Sun was susceptible to nationalistic claims for China's own culture. He was never a thoroughgoing cultural iconoclast of the May 4th model and, although he certainly did prefer modern medicine, it is not so certain that the appeal of a "scientificized national medicine" would have been repugnant to him. Here, as in so many areas, Sun was available to the claims of widely diverse factions.

The medical modernists, in any event, clearly felt he belonged on their side and that the Kuomintang should also be unequivocally in support of modern medicine. Its failure to take such a course was another source of disappointment with the government's performance, another area in which the Kuomintang lost the confidence of China's progressive, modern-educated intellectual elite. Yu Hsien, a prolific writer on medical affairs for the *Ta-kung pao,* commented bitterly on Ch'en Kuo-fu's activities on behalf of the disputed "National Medicine Regulations".[37]

When the central committee in general one day fusses about putting in order national medicine, and the next day shouts about scientificizing Chinese medicine, regarding this medicine question, which concerns the people's very survival, it is still unable to select any definite measures for scientification or scientific medicine, when it is blindly and irresolutely shilly-shallying—to what kind of a nation's hands have the Chinese people been abandoned?

Whether material circumstances would have permitted the National Government a better record in medical modernization regardless of Party sentiment, is highly debatable. It is more certain, however, that the frequent expression of these sentiments about "national medicine" at the higher levels of the Kuomintang helped to alienate those intellectuals to whom science and scientific medicine were touchstones of a government's progressive intent.

Part Three
Science, Communism,
and
"The People's Medical Heritage"

"No patriotic medical worker should reject the legacy of our own nation. There was the clamor under the old regime to eliminate Chinese medicine. This is . . . a reflection of the despicable psychology of the bourgeois class."—*Kuang-ming jih-pao* editorial, August 13, 1954.

VIII

THE COMMUNIST REHABILITATION

OF CHINESE MEDICINE

THE YEARS BEFORE 1949

Early Chinese Marxists, as we have seen, generally shared their generation's animus toward Chinese tradition, including traditional medicine. True, Ch'en Tu-hsiu's condemnation of native doctors in "Call to Youth" comes directly out of his veneration for "Mr. Science" during his pre-Marxist phase. But neither Ch'en nor his radical compatriots lost any of their faith in science in their progress toward Communism after 1919. Rather, this new political faith emphasized their total break with tradition in a period when Chinese medicine was still inextricably bound up with a dying, but not yet dead, traditional social and cultural order. Thus, although the Communists, concentrating on political revolution as the essential lever of change, were not in the forefront of the medical or certain other "cultural" controversies,[1] their sympathies undoubtedly were on the modernist side of the argument. In this area, Lu Hsün, as well as Ch'en Tu-hsiu, may be regarded as an authentic spokesman for at least the first generation of the revolutionary Left.

Even after the initial passion of the May 4th period, the context of conservative support for preserving a reformed Chinese, or "national," medicine would have made it strange indeed to find Communists on that side of the controversy. Chang Ping-lin, Yen Hsi-shan, and, by the thirties, Ch'en Kuo-fu—these make unlikely bedfellows for bona fide radicals, and it was perfectly natural in such circumstances that Marxists should have found themselves in general agreement with other modernists of quite different political persuasions.

Thus, during the furor over the establishment of the Institute for National Medicine, Yü Hsiu, a professed Marxist, although probably not a party member, wrote in *Ta-kung Pao* on "Dialectical Materialism and Medicine." [2] His intention was to apply this latest and most scientific mode of analysis—dialectical materialism—to the question of Chinese versus Western medicine. His conclusions, expressed in somewhat different terms, were strikingly similar to those of Western-oriented liberals. There was no Chinese medicine to be opposed to Western medicine, but only old and new medicine. Instead of trying to synthesize these two, it should be realized that "the world is one entity and the unfolding of human knowledge only has one road, that is, from the unscientific stage to modern science." In other words, Chinese medicine was just an earlier stage of universal medical progress, which now, according to the universal law of the dialectic, had to give way to a more advanced form. Medical progress, built on the new antithesis' (modern medicine) overcoming the old thesis (Chinese medicine), came out of this process. In that sense the traditional medicine of China inevitably contributed to the higher synthesis, but not through any consciously manipulated "mixture" of the two. Just as "socialist society is produced out of capitalist society," new medicine was to come out of the old by superseding it. According to both dialectical materialism and the non-Marxists' more general evolutionary views, science was universal and the same road to progress shared by all, East and West.

Yet if early Marxists had a clear philosophical and emotional bias toward modern medicine, Chinese Communists in actual control of a region could not afford to be overly fastidious about traditional medicine. Scattered public health materials from the Kiangsi Soviet show that, while major stress was put on modern medicine and basic public hygiene, the acute shortages of medical supplies forced some reliance on native herbals. An article in the journal *Red Hygiene* for June 1933 included the study and controlled use of traditional drugs as one of five suggested measures for coping with the National Government's increasingly effective blockade. It was freely acknowledged by the writer that these drugs were not scientific, but, he declared, "Under enemy blockade, in a situation of great difficulty regarding pharmaceuticals, we should all the more adopt Chinese drugs and process or screen them. This not only is appropriate to our present needs but perhaps we might discover something new." [3] This was hardly warm praise for the native medical tradition. Moreover, either due to his own training or to the term's less nationalistic associations, the author used the Japanese, *Han-yao* rather than the Chinese, *Chung-yao*. [4] The tenor of the article did, however, indicate a willingness to adapt to practical necessities and utilize native resources which was to become much stronger in the ensuing Yenan period as the Party lost its original urban, Westernized outlook in many cultural matters.

Of course, modern medicine continued to form the backbone of the bravely improvised military and civil medical system in the "guerrilla areas" during and after the Sino-Japanese War. Yet both visitors' reports and surviving army medical journals[5] show that traditional drugs played a prominent part in the "ingenious improvisations and tolerable substitutes"[6] which Japanese and Kuomintang blockade forced upon the Communists. Both the Eighth Route Army and the Yenan Drug Cooperative maintained factories to manufacture native-style drugs.[7] As a lead editorial in the first issue of the Eighth Route Army's health journal explained, these could serve as an important supplement to modern pharmaceuticals, for, besides helping to solve wartime shortages, scientific study and processing of traditional drugs "has important meaning as a measure of using one's own resources."[8] In the same issue, November 1939, the head of the Chinese drugs section explained in greater detail how "nationally produced pharmaceutical products" could play an important role in "fighting the war on to final victory."[9] To do this, however, it was necessary to "scientificize Chinese drugs" by subjecting them to careful study and analysis by scientifically trained experts. The type of program envisioned had little in common with *Kuo-i kuan*-type preservation of the "national essence," as his approving reference to Yü Yün-hsiu's ideas indicated. National products were to be reformed and used, but there was no hint of approval for a distinct "national medicine."

Subsequent, more theoretical, articles on China's medical future made it clear that within Communist medical circles there were still strong currents of distrust and disapproval of Chinese medicine. Western medicine was suspect on social and political, but not scientific, grounds. Hence, Yang Shao in 1940 proposed a threefold approach to "scientificize, sinicize, and popularize" medicine in China.[10] The old medicine, confined within the scope of a feudal society, had been unable to avoid a "mystical idealism" which vitiated any approach to science. But, if the content of Chinese medicine was rejected as feudal and unscientific, the context of Western medicine was unacceptable as capitalist and imperialist. The present task, then, was to build a "new democratic medicine" in China by taking the latest scientific developments from abroad and assimilating them to Chinese conditions, while also "using Western medicine's scientific basis to improve Chinese medicine and study Chinese drugs." [11] The concern was not that the new medicine be Chinese in character, but that it be suited to the needs of the new society. Unlike feudal or capitalist medicine, it was to serve the people— serve them scientifically.

Another medical writer at this time, T'an Chuang, also accepted medicine as a reflection of its social background, and rejected both "feudal" and "colonial" medicine in building a "new democratic medicine" along the lines of Mao's "New Democracy." [12] While strongly critical of the colonial nature of Western medicine in China (missionary in origins and still dominated by foreigners or the foreign-trained), he was vehemently opposed to Chinese medicine which he called *Ju-i,* "Confucian medicine." [13] As a reflection of feudal society, it had to be rejected for the sake of progress. "Confucian medicine" was, in fact, not a unified body of knowledge at all, but a miscellany of privately passed-down experience: "The so-called rich national essence, is just the collected garbage of several thousand years." [14] The theories, to him, were the empty fantasies of a feudal society, so he castigated modern Chinese who tried to find elements of dialectical materialism in them. This was, in T'an's opinion, a strange perversion of the latest and most modern scientific thought to defend archaic, outworn feudal medical theories: cyclical theories were not dialectical, *yin* and *yang* not materialism, the five elements not basic material elements, and their "mutual production and dissolution" not the unity of opposites.[15] He was willing to concede that Chinese medical experience should be studied by modern science, but it had not yet occurred to T'an, or to those like him in Communist medical circles, that there would be demands to reconcile elements of the feudal past with their commitment to modern, scientific Marxism. Chinese medicine, while a proper subject for scientific study and wartime use, was not conceded any place in the "new democratic," and ultimately socialist, medicine of the future.

There were no official Party pronouncements on the subject until late 1944 when Mao himself, addressing the Yenan Border Area Conference on Culture and Education, urged modern doctors to "unite with and help reform Chinese doctors and old-style veterinarians." [16] In recent years these remarks have been repeatedly cited as the foundation of the later policy of synthesizing Chinese and Western medicine. The speech itself, however, in the context in which it was given, indicates that at this time Chinese medicine was given something less than the equal status later accorded it. It begins: "Western medicine is even more scientific than Chinese medicine." But then Mao admonished Western-style doctors to increase their efforts to train more modern doctors and to reform the old-style practitioners in order to meet the pressing need for more medical personnel. For this he urged a united front of old and new, but with modern medicine apparently playing the predominant role. "To surrender to the old style is wrong; to abolish or discard also is wrong. Our responsibility is to unite those of the old style that can be used and to help, stimulate, and reform them." [17]

The emphasis seems clearly on organizing, improving, and using traditional doctors to meet the critical needs of the present. The unification appears to be close cooperation toward common public health goals, rather than the full and equal synthesis of the two medicines which was later proposed. This in itself marked a significant step in the gradually mellowing attitude toward at least certain elements of the traditional culture, medicine among them. Old medicine and old doctors were no longer enemies of progress to be uprooted and cast aside as the May 4th radicals would have done. They could be helped, used, and reformed on their way to gradual oblivion before the growth of scientific medicine. The next year, 1945, Mao wrote in "On Coalition Government" that "the proper attitude toward old-style cultural workers, old-style educational workers, and old-style doctors is to choose appropriate methods to educate them and cause them to obtain a new viewpoint and new methods for the service of the Chinese people." [18] Neither of these statements suggests that anything more than the temporary use or reform of Chinese medicine was intended. Traditional doctors were needed for the present; certain of their techniques, mainly herbals, could be adobted by modern medicine. But there is nothing, in word or deed, from these years to suggest that the medical future of China was seen as anything other than modern medicine.

CHINESE MEDICINE FOR UTILITY, 1949-1953

In one sense, ascension to national power in 1949 brought the Chinese Communists into a new medical world. From the makeshift hospitals and simple field stations of Yenan and the guerrilla areas they stepped into the latest scientific facilities of the major urban medical centers.[19] Qualitatively, this was very important in providing an advanced scientific nucleus for developing a national medical policy; quantitatively, the old problem of the guerrilla years remained—too few modern facilities and too few trained scientific personnel. China's 10,000 or so modern physicians were pitifully inadequate to cope with the medical needs of the country, especially its huge rural population.[20] On the other hand, there was the large number of traditional doctors, perhaps as many as 500,000,[21] and there was the experience of the Yenan years in making do with native resources. This had already in the Party's eyes taken much of the curse off the "feudal medicine" which had so enraged their intellectual forebears of the May 4th era. Of course, its unscientific basis made it still unacceptable as the proper medicine for the new China, but there were no longer any serious emotional or ideological obstacles to organizing and using the large force of traditional doctors wherever possible.

The government moved quickly to spell out its policy in this area. This was necessary to reassure the old-style doctors, whose previous political associations and general cultural outlook has been anything but revolutionary, that they too had a place in the new society if they cooperated with its goals. It also served to check modern-style doctors from any premature assault on "unscientific medicine." A conference on public health administration in October 1949 received the Party leadership's directive "to unite the entire country's Chinese doctors and also help Chinese doctors raise their level of techniques," [22] rather than seek their speedy elimination. From the very start, then, traditional medicine was defined as one part of the old society that could be reformed and used. With full confidence that scientific medicine ultimately would prevail, there was no compulsion felt to wage bitter combat against the old medicine. It would give way slowly, and in the meantime its practitioners were to be exposed to modern science and led by modern doctors down the inevitable "road to science." There was no need to emphasize that this, as against the plans of the "national medicine" group, was also the road to oblivion for Chinese medicine as a distinct entity.

The Communists and Chinese Medicine

In March 1950 a small conference of leading Peking traditional doctors was summoned to hear the Minister of Health, Li Te-ch'uan, and other government spokesmen explain what was expected of them.[23] They were told that the long years of suffering and neglect under the imperialists in Hong Kong, Taiwan, and pre-liberation China were at an end, and that traditional medicine was now free to unite and go forward to serve the people. Li Te-ch'uan stressed that Chinese medicine represented a very large force with close connections to the Chinese people. On the basis of this mass foundation (not, we should note, because of its special medical properties), she promised that the Ministry of Health would respect it. For their part, the old-style doctors would have to abandon conservative prejudices, accept new knowledge, study science, and cooperate with Western-style doctors in raising their technical level. To encourage these reforms it was announced that the former North China National Medicine Academy in Peking would be converted into the Chinese Medicine Improvement Academy. Clearly, traditional doctors were to be tolerated only to the extent that they went along with the new regime's goals; and those goals, medically or otherwise, were emphatically not traditional.

Speaking for his colleagues, the noted Peking traditional doctor, P'an Chao-p'eng, was eager to express willingness to follow these guidelines. To get Chinese medicine off the hook of its former associations, he explained how under the old society true reform had been impossible. Whatever sincere desire for progress Chinese doctors may have had, had been frustrated by the reactionary forces around them. Like so many others in the bad old days, they had been more sinned against than sinning. The *Kuo-i kuan,* for example, had been a selfish, private organization just for seeking individual fame. Only under the People's Government could Chinese medicine, at last, seek basic scientific reform in order better to serve the people. P'an became a leading spokesman for the traditional medical world, and to it, on the government's behalf. In a subsequent article in *Jen-min jih-pao* he repeated and stressed the need to unite under the government's benevolent leadership for the scientific reform of the native medical profession: "The Central People's Government is concerned with Chinese doctors, strives to lovingly protect, assist, and elevate them." [24] Common gratitude (and, he might have added, common prudence) required cooperation with its wishes.

These wishes were more fully enunciated to both the new- and old-style medical profession at the first National Health Conference in July 1950, where a number of dignitaries touched on the question of Chinese medicine. Kuo Mo-jo, who only five years before had been a vigorous critic, modified his stand considerably to meet his new responsibilities as an official cultural spokesman for the new government. He now stressed the importance both for Chinese medicine to "scientificize" and for the two medicines to unite: "Chinese medicine must learn from the scientific knowledge of Western medicine; Western medicine must study the popular and widespread spirit of Chinese medicine." [25] In other words, modern science remained the sole criterion for technical excellence, while Western-style doctors were urged to get down to the level of the masses as their traditional colleagues did. Chu Te was somewhat more positive about the usefulness of Chinese medicine itself, and even acknowledged some real value in its accumulated experience. The main task for the present was to develop this value with the aid of science. This responsibility he charged to both types of doctors, but the brunt of his remarks lay in convincing modern medical personnel that the old medicine could serve a useful purpose. Indeed, they had no alternative: in many villages there were no doctors of any kind, and the peasants were naturally superstitious. Under such circumstances over-fastidious bickering over scientific qualifications was stupid. "Everyone knows China's scientific doctors are too few . . . and drugs inadequate . . . not to examine these problems, and only say who is good and who is bad, cannot solve this problem." [26] The salient point was that Chinese medicine was needed and could be used, not that it represented any unique value to be cherished for itself. The Conference's final report made this clear, for in stressing unity and co-operation between the two medicines, there was no doubt who was expected to learn from whom: "In this cooperation Western medicine should assume the main responsibility in research on, and raising the level of, Chinese medicine." [27] Policy toward Chinese medicine could, therefore, be summed up in two words—unite and reform.

In practice, much more attention seems to have been given to the latter aspect—reform, or scientification. The conference itself proposed the institutional means of achieving that goal through "Chinese Medicine Improvement Schools" and "Chinese Medicine Research Centers." In the next few years, these Improvement Schools and smaller Improvement Classes—both directed at giving traditional doctors some fundamentals of modern science and hygiene—proved by far the more significant institutions, indicating that the authorities were more interested in Chinese doctors for their numbers than Chinese medicine for its virtues.

Short-term retraining classes for traditional doctors had been begun soon after "liberation," but the Ministry of Health did not issue comprehensive regulations on their systematic organization until the end of 1951.[28] Then it directed that the seventeen existing Improvement Schools be classified as formal educational institutions with a twelve-month course of studies, and that new ones be set up in existing large medical colleges or hospitals. The much more numerous Improvement Classes were, as "popular organs," permitted more variation at first, although the objective was to standardize them on a six-month program of part-time study. The curriculum, for both schools and classes, heavily emphasized basic modern medical sciences.[29] Even so, there was evidently some skepticism among public health authorities about the value of such a program, for it did not develop on a very rapid nationwide scale until after the Party began serious prodding in 1954.[30] At the same time, private schools and apprentice training for new traditional doctors were permitted, with the stipulation that "their curriculum should be in accordance with basic scientific and political knowledge and their standards approved by the central public health department."[31] In all of this, scientific reform of the old-style doctors had top priority.

Scientific research into Chinese medicine itself, on the other hand, was relatively neglected. The ambitious plans for a network of research centers drawn up at the First National Health Conference remained largely on paper, and the research that was done remained for the most part in the familiar channels of chemical analysis of native herbs in modern medical centers.[32] Except for a few experimental hospitals, whose main function was clinical, there do not appear to have been any large research centers exclusively for Chinese medicine.

The other declared objective, uniting Chinese and Western medicine, also turned out to be very different from the stress on complete synthesis which later appeared. During the early 1950's, it consisted more of uniting traditional doctors in the sense of organizing and controlling them than of any meaningful integration with modern medical practice. Such organizational work was essential to the regime's medical and social objectives, for breaking down the feudal basis of the highly private practice and jealously guarded secrets of traditional medicine was a *sine qua non* of its use by the new order. Therefore, an intensive campaign was waged to convince the old-style doctors to share their secrets and serve the people under socialism, while at the same time, along with all other professions, they were rapidly organized into a general union or association. This took the form of provincially based "Public Health Workers Associations," which soon united the overwhelming majority of traditional doctors into a common organization with modern medical personnel.[33] Apart from this, the two types of doctors had little contact. Traditional physicians did not yet belong to the prestigious Chinese Medical Association nor did they have any national organization of their own. The closest approach to this kind of professional association was locally established "Chinese Medicine Study Associations," whose main purpose was cooperation in seeking technical improvement. The pilot project for such associations was the "Peking Chinese Medicine Association," organized in May 1950 and within a year encompassing 861 Peking traditional doctors. It managed an Improvement School, sponsored research on acupuncture, ran a clinic for Chinese medicine, and published a journal.[34] Such organizations, although useful in preserving Chinese medicine, did little to unite it with Western medicine. The medical literature from these years further illustrates a continuing dichotomy between modern and traditional medical organizations, with the modern journals virtually ignoring Chinese medicine, which was left to survive in some fifteen separate journals published by various traditional medicine associations.

Similarly, in the vital area of transforming private medical practice into a more socialist form, very little actual integration of old- and new-style doctors took place. The institution chosen to effect this transition was the "United Clinic" or "United Hospital." Essentially, these were groups of several doctors brought out of individual practice to form joint clinics or, in a few cases where the facilities existed, a hospital. They were run on a cooperative basis, with fees pooled to meet operating expenses and pay salaries to the member physicians. Since most United Clinics were private, although government-supervised, they did not draw on state funds. Some, being joint public and private enterprises, did claim limited state assistance. But, in either case, traditional medicine's lack of costly scientific equipment made these clinics a relatively economical means of providing medical care of a kind familiar to the bulk of the population.

The first United Clinics had appeared as early as 1949 in Manchuria, but only in July 1951 did the Ministry of Health issue comprehensive directives to the local public health branches on their widespread organization.[35] After this, the number throughout the country grew rapidly to over 15,000 in 1952.[36] Although intended also to cover Western-style doctors, and ideally to combine both types, the much smaller number of modern doctors and the demand for them in various government medical organs meant that in fact the United Clinics were mainly used to organize the large number of traditional practitioners. Even there, the pace of changeover from private practice was not forced.[37] For some time United Clinics incorporated only a minority of the traditional doctors, and, of the clinics established, only a few combined Chinese and Western-style doctors.

The net impression from all this is that medical integration, while it was an approved slogan, had not gone very far, and that it aimed at giving Chinese medicine a very subordinate role in the national health plans. In the countryside, where trained physicians were in desperately short supply, the old-style doctors were used on a large scale,[38] but they were almost entirely excluded from the large urban hospitals and government medical institutions.[39] Moreover, where the government did set up hospitals or large clinics for traditional medicine (and there were very few in the early 1950's), they were exclusively for its separate practice, not integrated with modern medicine. There was no doubt that Chinese medicine had a place in the new China. The provisional regulations for Chinese doctors promulgated in May 1951 attested to this by granting licenses on very liberal terms. Even the controversial "five years' experience" criterion, which had aroused modernists' ire under the Kuomintang, was preserved. Of course it was updated by adding the phrase, "and have a considerable reputation among the masses." [40] Yet such tolerance only meant that traditional doctors would be kept for the present. It did not assure the future of Chinese medicine or give its practitioners a very secure long-term position.

The uncertainty of their position as remnants of the old society under a revolutionary government—though practical necessity and still tenuous identification with the popular culture preserved them from immediate peril—is apparent in many of the old-style doctors' statements in these years. Like P'an Chao-p'eng, almost all of them expressed gratitude for the Party's solicitude and eagerly tried to disclaim any damaging past associations. Thus, Wang I-men self-consciously opened a statement on medical reform with the assertion, "I am a Chinese doctor . . . but my medical thinking is not conservative; it is revolutionary." [41] Indeed, it was important to establish that their thinking was not conservative, medically or in any other way. Chao Yu-ch'ing is a good example of these efforts to complete the disassociation of Chinese medicine from its old social and political context.[42] He did this by stressing the popular origins of Chinese medicine— even the *Nei-ching* was a "product of the laboring people," but under feudal conditions this had to be disguised so that the knowledge could be preserved. In modern times the Kuomintang under Chiang had "used fine-sounding but empty methods to toy with Chinese medicine," [43] and only now was it free to develop in the socialist society. The new masters in Peking were not blind to the past connections of many traditional doctors, but it suited their purposes to ignore them. When K'ung Chung-hua, director of the Peking National Medical College, was purged, it was for corruption and venality, not for his political connections. Similarly, during the Three-Anti Movement criticism was leveled at corruption, inefficiency, and waste in the traditional medicine world, but it was spared serious ideological or political charges. [44]

Nevertheless, the old-style doctors had to tread a precarious path, for, if the Party showed them considerable tolerance, there was not yet any great effusion of warmth about their art, and, among the modern medical doctors who managed national health policy, there was considerable coolness and even a scarcely disguised contempt. The Party, while encouraging those modern doctors not to neglect the native medical resources, had done little to change their prejudice against Chinese medicine. For example, in these years, it was highly unusual for a Western-style doctor to study any aspect of traditional medicine, and when one did it was hailed as a rarity. [45] There was not, as yet, any official program for such work. The studying was all one way—Chinese doctors learning elements of Western medicine.

That is not to say that the modern doctors were free from suspicion or above criticism. The very name "Western medicine" (which, try as they would, modern Chinese doctors could not shake) held unpleasant social and political connotations. If the old-style doctors were suspect for their ties to traditional society, the large number of modern doctors, either foreign- or missionary-trained, were doubly suspect because of bourgeois or imperialist influences. Thus, they were subject to ideological criticism and thought reform from the very beginning of the People's Republic. But for the first few years this criticism was entirely social or political, unrelated to technical or scientific qualifications. The only place where it entered the technical aspect of medicine was in the insistence on the study of Pavlovian theories and "the advanced medical experience of the Soviet Union." This would turn doctors away from bourgeois influences, while supposedly keeping them in the main stream of modern medical progress. There was only the slightest suggestion that study of their own national medical legacy would have these desirable ideological and scientific benefits. For the most part, the Soviet example was the cure-all. Even in rationalizing their own native herbal medicine, Soviet experience in herbal research was cited as the correct guide.[46] Of the many sins attributed in these years to such bastions of Western medicine as the formerly American-run Peking Union Medical College, disrespect for Chinese medicine did not figure among them. At the height of the Three Anti-movement, the chief surgeon of Peking Union could enumerate all his shortcomings about neglecting the masses, caring only for personal reputation, cultural arrogance, and so forth, without once touching on traditional medicine.[47]

FROM FEUDAL MEDICINE TO THE MEDICAL LEGACY
OF THE MOTHERLAND

All of this changed rather abruptly in the latter part of 1954 with the mounting of a full-fledged campaign to exalt the value of traditional medicine and condemn the bourgeois elements in the Ministry of Health who had allegedly sabotaged Party policy toward it. Signs of growing official appreciation for Chinese medicine and dissatisfaction with the public health authorities had begun to appear almost a year earlier. In June 1953 the Southern-Central Department of Public Health summoned the first of a series of regional conferences of traditional doctors to clarify policy on Chinese medicine and accelerate its implementation.[48]

Nothing very new was said, but Party spokesmen did voice the first faint criticisms over certain public health cadres' erroneous attitude toward traditional medicine. These became stronger at subsequent conferences held throughout the country, especially after *Jen-min jih-pao* held a small, but well-publicized conference on Chinese medicine where certain elements in the Ministry of Health were accused of "slighting the medical legacy of the motherland."[49] In Szechuan, for example, a traditional doctor complained that the authorities' attitude toward them had been "use much, education slight."[50]

Although criticisms were fairly restrained, their mounting number suggested that a major policy shift was in the making. Other straws in the wind were the Chinese Medical Association's decision to set up a special liaison committee with traditional doctors (this, reportedly, at the direct suggestion of Mao himself) and a special seminar held on medical unification by the Committee on Culture and Education of the People's Political Consultative Conference. There, without openly criticizing Western medicine, the Minister of Health, Li Te-ch'uan, and other spokesmen suggested that work in promoting unification be intensified.[51] In December 1953 *Kuang-ming jih-pao,* in its usual role as a channel of official opinion to the intellectuals, bluntly told modern doctors that it was not the government's intention to promote simple "Westernization of native medicine."[52] But such warnings remained in the realm of administrative error until the summer of 1954 when another *Kuang-ming jih-pao* editorial, on August 14, attributed them to serious ideological shortcomings on the part of China's modern medical profession: "Long under the influence of the European and United States bourgeois class medicine, our medical education workers not only pay no respect to Chinese medicine but show the erroneous sectarian attitude of belittling and despising Chinese medicine." [53]

In the following months modern doctors had this lesson driven home in a series of conferences and meetings where their errors were repeatedly attacked and a fuller integration with traditional medicine urged on them. The most authoritative statement on what correct policy and attitude should be was given in a *Jen-min jih-pao* editorial on October 20. Party policy, of course, had always been correctly to esteem and develop the country's own medicine. Blame for past mistakes regarding traditional medicine was placed on those elements in the Ministry of Health who, "poisoned by bourgeois concepts, had despised the medical legacy of the motherland." [54] These ideological errors now had to be removed so that a real unification of the two medicines could take place, one that would produce a new and unique medical science well-suited to Chinese needs and a contribution to modern science in general. The key to such a meaningful synthesis lay in modern doctors' studying and developing this valuable "cultural legacy," and the key to *that* was ideological reform.

The flood gates were now open for a torrent of criticism and self-criticism directed toward such thought reform. Typical of this was the confession of Ni Pao-ch'un, Deputy Director of the Shanghai Second Municipal Hospital. He readily acknowledged having ignored and ridiculed traditional Chinese medicine, an "unscientific attitude" which he attributed to his education in American and British missionary schools and later in the United States. There he had become imbued with bourgeois and imperialist attitudes so that he neglected his own language and culture, coming to believe that only Western medicine had value. After liberation, he reported, his ideological consciousness had slowly been raised to the point where he was now beginning to grasp the significance of Party policy and appreciate the value of traditional medicine. In a tone of great humility, he acknowledged all these past errors and pledged his readiness to learn from traditional doctors, as "a small student to ask for their instruction." [55] Finally, since this was now seen as an ideological problem, Ni stressed the need for studying Marxism-Leninism, Dialectical Materialism, and "the advanced theory and experience of the Soviet Union." These may seem the very antithesis of the ancient herbals and acupuncture needles of Chinese medicine but, from 1954 on, the compatibility of traditional Chinese medicine concepts and theories with "the modern theories of the great Pavlov" was a common theme in medical writings.[56] More important for China's modern physicians, both became touchstones of ideological reliability.

The criticism and thought reform campaign among modern doctors did not focus on specific individuals until early 1955, when Wang Pin, former Director of Public Health in Manchuria and a veteran Party member, was singled out as a leading culprit. Most of the criticism of his ideological mistakes drew on a number of articles Wang had written in the journal *North-East Public Health* during 1950.[57] The worst of these mistakes was his contention that traditional Chinese medicine was "feudal medicine." [58] He based his opinion on the apparently sound Marxist premise, "a certain political-economic system produces a certain form of medicine." This had been a fairly common viewpoint in Communist medical writings before and during the Sino-Japanese War, but it now became rank heresy. The arguments used to refute it have ranged from analyses placing medicine, as a natural science, outside the social superstructure, to its classification as a "relatively independent social phenomenon," [59] or, increasingly, to emphasizing its position as part of the people's culture, not that of the feudal ruling class. All such interpretations have aimed at freeing Chinese medicine from the taint of the despised old society (just as the more articulate traditional doctors had been striving to do since 1949), and in all of them there rings louder and louder a note of cultural pride in "the medical legacy of the motherland."

As for the specific mistakes stemming from Wang's ideological errors, they were typical of the charges leveled against the public health authorities. He had refused to recognize the scientific value of traditional medicine, claiming that "only among the peasants can it psychologically have a certain comforting function." [60] His policy in Manchuria had been merely to use traditional doctors for rural work, while gradually eliminating and replacing them. And, finally, he had advocated preserving native herbals but abolishing native medicine. The source of all these errors was, of course, Western bourgeois influence and "an education entirely colonial in nature." Since such ideas and the influence of Wang Pin's thought were widespread among Western-style doctors, it was necessary to carry out a large-scale criticism movement. After the initial attacks on Wang in the February issue of *Public Health*,[61] the Ministry of Health ordered a nationwide campaign of mass meetings and articles to criticize him.[62]

Wang Pin did not remain the sole scapegoat, however; attention was soon directed to the highest echelons of the central Ministry of Health in Peking. There, Ho Ch'eng, the First Deputy Minister and probably the most important figure in the Ministry,[63] was blamed for the Ministry's mistake regarding traditional medicine. Although he had never publicly opposed Chinese medicine as had Wang Pin, Ho's earlier work and statements, both as Eighth Route Army Medical Director and later Deputy Minister, suggest that he fully shared the rather common modern medical viewpoint that the old medicine had little inherent value apart from temporary use. Now, exposed to full-scale criticism (unlike Wang Pin, who stubbornly clung to his opinions about Chinese medicine[64]), Ho fully recanted and acknowledged the Party's supremacy in medical matters.[65] After admitting to all the familiar charges about despising Chinese medicine, seeking to restrict and eliminate it, ignoring Party policy, and persecuting old-style doctors, he was specifically condemned in a resolution at the next National Public Health Conference and dropped from his key position in the Ministry.[66] His successor, Hsü Yün-pei, is strictly a Party functionary without any medical background.

The duration and intensity of the prolonged criticism movement over the issue of traditional medicine must be seen in the larger ideological context and in relation to the general problem of the Party and intellectuals. Writings at the time, in fact, specifically related the issue to the larger battle against bourgeois thought: "This is a deep ideological struggle between dialectical materialism and bourgeois idealism; especially at the present moment, when the entire country is opening up criticism of the Hu Shih school's bourgeois idealism, the criticism of these ideological errors of Wang Pin has an even greater significance." [67]

Of all the technical intelligentsia, modern medical personnel have presented some of the most difficult problems in thought reform. By virtue of their scarcity in the face of such huge public health problems, the need for their highly specialized skills has been extremely acute. Yet the modern Chinese medical profession's close ties with the West has made it ideologically suspect and, compounding these undesirable influences, has come the fact that modern doctors' highly specialized and urgently needed knowledge has gained them a certain professional immunity from close political control by the Party.[68] When someone like Ho Ch'eng, a veteran Party member with Soviet medical training, could clash with the Party over a question of medical policy, there was obviously something more involved than just bourgeois influences. The crucial issue posed here was political supervision versus technical expertise—Red versus expert. Thus, while much of the criticism was leveled against the "compradore prejudice" of worshipping everything Western and despising the indigenous,[69] the most serious charge lay in their "refuting the ability of the Party in the supervision of scientific and technical work."[70]

Since 1954 this concern has pervaded the question of Chinese medicine. In some ways the subordination of purely technical knowledge to larger ideological principles suggests interesting parallels to traditional Confucian society, where the medical technician was certainly deemed inferior to the bearer of that society's general culture or ideology. But there are crucial differences. The bearers of Confucian culture felt no great concern about controlling a technical intelligentsia. Doctors, engineers, scientists—these were no more than skilled artisans to a society which placed little value on rapid material change through the technological mastery of nature. To the Communists—although they too may have their own classics, Marxist instead of Confucian—such change is vital and so are the technical experts required to effect it. In medicine, the old literati could rest content that physicians would emulate their values and strive to attain the status of "Confucian doctor"; the new mandarinate cannot be so complacent. It must insist that its physicians, like its other technical specialists, be "Red doctors," for in the modern world of scientific expertise, they cannot be denied status as experts. It is up to the holders of the new ideological orthodoxy to make sure that this expertise does not undermine their own claims to preside over the new society and its values.

Traditional physicians have not really been part of this problem in Communist China; divorced from the old society which supported them, they have been entirely dependent on the new authorities for their continued existence. Thus, it has not been so imperative to concentrate on their thought reform. They have been urged to become more progressive through the study of science, and more public-spirited by sharing their medical secrets, but they have not been subjected to any intensive criticism or thought reform. On the contrary, since 1954, especially, they have usually been praised for both their medical skills and correct political attitude. The familiar picture of the white-bearded venerable native physician, portrayed in innumerable press releases, came in fact to symbolize the regime's loving care for and appreciation of the healthy, popular elements in the old culture. Typically he would, after years of neglect and suffering before 1949, have assumed a responsible post in the new China and be vigorously contributing to its construction.[71] As proof of traditional doctors' improved status, the large number granted membership in the People's Congresses or Political Consultative Conferences was frequently cited, without reference to the fact that this closely paralleled the situation under the Kuomintang. There was no campaign to criticize "feudal" influences in their thinking—not because these had suddenly disappeared, and not because traditional doctors were needed so much more urgently than modern doctors— but simply because they were not seen as a threat to the new order. The modern doctors, with their links to a surviving and powerful foe in Western imperialism and their specialist's claim to autonomy, could represent a threat.

Hence, they have been criticized, while the erstwhile "feudal" doctors have been praised. Moreover, since 1954 the old-style medicine itself has constituted an important part of the criticism and reform of the modern medical profession.

As important as these ideological implications might be, they were not the only interesting facet of the official rehabilitation of Chinese medicine. Another was the strong tone of cultural pride in China's own unique medical achievements which pervaded writing on the subject. The application of such phrases as "national cultural legacy" or "medical heritage of the motherland" (the title "national medicine" was too closely identified with the Kuomintang) expressed the new value given to it. Literature on Chinese medicine, both scholarly and popular, rapidly expanded. The sudden rise in the number of publications specifically on traditional medicine can be seen from the fact that they went from 7 per cent of total medical publications in 1953 to 27 per cent in 1955.[72] These were of all types: reprints of ancient medical classics, new treatises on various branches of Chinese medicine, pharmaceutical compendia, simplified explanations of traditional medical theory, popularized histories or stories of Chinese medicine and its most famous historical figures. Typical of the genre devoted to the glorification of the nation's medical accomplishments were such popularized accounts as *China's Ancient Medical Achievements* by Chu Yen and a short biography of Li Shih-chen, the famous Ming pharmacologist.[73] Both of these were devoted to exalting the Chinese people's "incomparable intelligence and creative efforts,"[74] as displayed in the field of medicine. The feature that distinguished these publications from earlier works of nationalist self-congratulation was the concentrated effort to identify these figures and their accomplishments with the popular tradition. In their own lifetimes the great historical figures of Chinese medicine may have aspired to the title "Confucian doctor," but in this generation great efforts have been made to de-Confucianize them.

For the broader public, unlikely to see even popularized medical pamphlets, the newspapers reported in great detail every new development in Chinese medicine while lavishly praising its merits. Notable among such accounts were the numerous claims to remarkable cures, covering a wide range of maladies from high blood pressure to dysentery. There was also obvious satisfaction taken in citing particular cases where Chinese medicine had effected cures when Western medicine was helpless.[75] Again, this was an old cultural nationalist theme, but it was now given the added twist of the people's indigenous methods over the foreign techniques of the bourgeois specialist. In any event, by the middle 1950's a large-scale drive to raise the image of traditional medicine was well under way.

So much is obvious. Much less obvious, however, is why the increased emphasis on traditional medicine came at this particular time. The ideological background has been explored and its relationship to the general tightening of thought control over the intellectuals noted. The chronological coincidence of the anti-Wang Pin campaign, starting in early 1955, with the public denunciation of his former superior in Manchuria, Kao Kang, is suggestive of a possible connection between the fall of the most openly Russian-oriented faction in the Party and the new emphasis on indigenous Chinese medicine. This, of course, is highly speculative since the charges against Wang Pin never linked him to the treasonous activities of the Kao-Jui clique. It should also be noted that the rehabilitation of Chinese medicine in 1954 had its general counterpart in other fields as diverse as architecture, painting, and theater, in all of which the immediately post-1949 vogue for crude Russian imitation began to subside in favor of a greater appreciation of indigenous Chinese forms.[76] The beginning of this movement toward the "Chinese in form, socialist in content," cultural policy, naturally suited the greater weight given to traditional medicine.

Finally, practical considerations cannot be ruled out, for administrative consolidation of the whole country may have sharpened realization of the enormity of the government's medical and health problems. Perhaps the unexpectedly high census returns of 1953 were an added factor in deciding that the large numbers of native physicians had to be given an even greater role in national medical work. Certainly there was now much greater emphasis on traditional medicine in practice as well as in theory. Earlier rural work was continued and expanded, with mobile medical teams and village clinics used to reach the more remote countryside.[77] Similarly, the number of United Clinics expanded from 22,000 at the end of 1954 to over 50,000 in 1957.[78] Much more significant for the future of traditional medicine, however, was the new stress on integration of large numbers of old-style doctors into modern medical facilities. Large modern hospitals now began to add Chinese-style doctors to their staffs or in many cases to open special departments for Chinese medicine. By 1956, government public health organs—national, provincial, and local—had incorporated 30,000 traditional doctors.[79] Moreover, as a sign that they no longer occupied a second-class position, the once exclusively modern Chinese Medical Association now invited their membership.

Apart from this greater integration into the main stream of Chinese medical development, facilities for the separate practice of traditional medicine were also greatly expanded. Some idea of how rapidly these developed can be gained by the admittedly exceptional example of Kwangtung, where, from one hospital exclusively for traditional medicine in 1955, there were twenty-two by 1957.[80] The entire country had 144 such hospitals and over 450 outpatient clinics by 1957.[81] Admittedly, many of them were rather small and the total not nearly proportionate to the number of Chinese-style doctors. Yet their construction was a concrete sign of the government's intention to expand rather than contract the practice of Chinese medicine. These well-financed, fully equipped hospitals also went far beyond anything the National Government, even with prodding from the national medicine group, had ever done in providing traditional medicine with modern institutional facilities.[82]

Research on traditional medicine also enjoyed considerable expansion. In late 1955 the Ministry of Health established a large and well-equipped Chinese Medicine Research Institute in Peking. Staffed with both types of doctors, it was intended to provide a guide for the national effort in traditional medicine research and education.[83] This research, it was repeatedly stressed, had to go beyond a mere analysis of the chemical properties of native pharmaceuticals. The entire body of traditional medical knowledge should be considered and investigated in such work, for "Chinese drugs (*chung-yao*) cannot be separated from Chinese medicine (*chung-i*)." [84] This thesis was directly contrary to the whole line of endeavor of many modern scientists, foreign and Chinese, who had tried to do just that—separate useful herbals from what they considered an antiquated and superstitious medical tradition. Now, although it was still recognized that modern science was essential to rationalizing the accumulated native medical wisdom, the process required full respect for Chinese medicine as a whole and the full participation of Chinese-style doctors. Earlier research, of the 1930's and before, was accordingly denounced as too mechanistic and superficial because, grounded as it was in the cultural prejudices of the bourgeois West, it had failed to give due attention to the totality of Chinese medicine. With the socialist terminology removed, such criticism fitted in remarkably well with that of earlier cultural conservatives. In both there lay a deep aversion to "Westernization," a common distrust for many of the values which "bourgeois intellectuals" had welcomed as the essence of modernity.

The People's Government has simultaneously striven to turn Chinese medicine toward self-improvement. Traditional doctors were brought into the Chinese Medicine Research Institute, and in the provinces they dominated various provincial research centers and research committees.[85] It is difficult to estimate the success of this effort to turn traditional doctors into the relatively new direction of research. Certainly they have produced a large volume of commentary, but exegesis had been a familiar practice.[86] Most of the new discoveries or improvements in native medicine seem to have come mainly from Western-style doctors. Two notable areas would be in the improved processing and refinement of native herbals at such places as the Academy of Sciences' pharmaceutical research laboratory,[87] or the work in electric acupuncture by a young Western-style doctor in Sian.[88]

Yet, probably the most important aspect of the revalorization of native medicine was neither in research work nor clinical practice, but rather in the field of medical education. From late 1954 the drive for modern doctors to study Chinese medicine as the key to integrating the two schools received practical impetus in the form of a Ministry of Health directive for all units to organize a thorough "study movement." [89] How thorough this was in fact is somewhat doubtful. Press reports give the impression of modern physicians everywhere being organized for criticism meetings and study classes. Apparently in the major medical centers this was the case,[90] but elsewhere study fluctuated widely in intensity and effectiveness.[91] By the spring of 1956 several important decisions were made on the role traditional medicine was to play in medical education. To begin with, the program of having trained modern physicians study Chinese medicine was expanded and systematized. Four hundred young high-level doctors were to be chosen for a program of full-time study at classes in six major cities.[92] After almost two years of theoretical and technical study under famous old-style physicians, plus a year's clinical experience, they were expected to be competent in both types of medicine—the living embodiment of the policy of uniting the two schools. In addition to this elite, another 5000 were to be organized into a three-year program of part-time classes at various medical institutions throughout the country. Combined with a decision that all medical schools should include courses in traditional medicine in their curricula by the fall of 1956, the net effect was to give considerable realization to the objective of having China's modern medical profession also receive a basic grounding in traditional medicine.

On the other side, the Improvement Schools for giving the traditional doctors some skill in modern medicine were continued, but the curriculum changed to reflect the greater respect accorded Chinese medicine. As the Wuhan school reported, "The School for Improvement of Chinese Medicine has determined that Chinese medicine shall be the foundation for the educational materials used to improve Chinese medicine and has corrected the past prejudice in favor of Westernizing educational methods."[93] This determination to preserve and continue Chinese medicine—not to let it disappear in a "Westernizing" process—can also be seen in the 1956 decision to train more Chinese-style doctors. For this purpose, four colleges of Chinese medicine were opened—in Peking, Shanghai, Canton, and Chengtu—each offering a five-year course. Numerous other colleges and shorter-term "Chinese Medicine Schools" soon followed, the latter training a lower-level doctor similar to the product of the three-year modern medical schools. By 1958 there were thirteen Chinese medical colleges and several hundred lower schools.[94]

Attempts to teach Chinese medicine in a regular classroom manner went back to the early Republic. The 1956 decision, however, marked the breakthrough of this idea into the regular educational system, thus giving the new schools a much firmer basis of support than the various earlier private organizations had ever been able to provide. After all the agitation for such a government policy from traditional medicine circles under the Republic (and a contemporary agitation of the same kind on Taiwan), there is some irony in Chinese medicine's finally entering the school system through the administrative fiat of a revolutionary government which was completely uninfluenced by the desires of traditional doctors and their culturally conservative supporters.

Still, even state support did not solve all the problems of transmitting the "artistic" skills of traditional medicine.[95] Traditionally, these had mainly been conveyed through the highly personalized and individualistic method of a teacher–disciple relationship. Such particularistic social relationships, and especially the private monopoly of knowledge entailed, could not meet with approval in the new society. Nevertheless, along with the schools for Chinese medicine, the Ministry of Health also announced plans to encourage continuation and expansion of the disciple system. Within the next seven years it was hoped there would be "several hundred thousand young Chinese doctors trained through apprenticeship" as an "important measure to inherit the medical legacy of the motherland."[96] A *Jen-min jih-pao* editorial explained that the disciple system must continue to be the main method of transmitting traditional medical knowledge, for even though it was a "handicraft method of teaching," with such knowledge still scattered and not yet systematized into a coherent body of literature, there was no alternative.[97] Attempts were made at standardizing and controlling the disciple method by incorporating disciples into part-time classes and having them register for two- or three-year periods of instruction under a particular doctor. But, essentially, the method was the same as that used to train Chinese doctors for millenia—a social anachronism, but an important part of new China's medical plans. By 1958 there were at least 50,000 of these disciples registered.[98]

The steps taken in medical education during 1956 are the most conclusive evidence that the People's Government took its pronouncements on the value of traditional medicine seriously. Scarce resources were to be devoted to training a new generation to carry on its practice, and an ideologically offensive teaching system tolerated so that this could be done. Chinese medicine was not to be allowed to die the natural death many had predicted for it as its old practitioners passed away. Moreover, modern doctors were expected to give the slogan of integrating the two medicines real substance by assimilating some of the traditional knowledge. For this, some high-quality medical personnel were withdrawn from practice to study it. Such a policy—and the time now devoted in regular medical education to traditional medicine—made no sense as a simple stopgap until new doctors were trained, or as merely a test of Party ideological supremacy.

By 1956 the main features of rehabilitating, reforming, and integrating traditional medicine were all in evidence. So were some of the problems inherent in such a policy. On the one hand, extravagant praise for Chinese medicine and criticism of past errors by public health authorities made it difficult to maintain standards among the old-style practitioners. Soon, even Chinese-style physicians were complaining about the prevalence of harmful quacks and the government's uncritical acceptance of them.[99] Yet the emphasis on quantity and use of popular skills made strict enforcement of standards difficult so long as the mass line prevailed over technical expertise.[100] Evidently official enthusiasm at times outran even Chinese doctors' own claims for their profession. A famous old doctor in Manchuria cautioned against raising public expectations by publishing isolated cures in the popular press before the basis of such cures was understood.[101] His was, however, a lone voice among the paeans of uncritical praise for China's old medicine.

More serious were problems arising from residual suspicion and misunderstanding between the two types of doctors. This was probably inevitable after the prolonged "battle" Chinese and Western medicine had fought since the beginning of the Republic. The Party's repeated exhortations to respect Chinese medicine and overcome a narrow professional viewpoint attest to continued difficulties in overcoming Western-style doctors' prejudices. Moreover, as the Hundred Flowers liberalization unfolded through 1956 and early 1957, it became apparent from the criticisms of both schools that all was not well in their forced marriage. Many Western-style doctors withdrew from Chinese medicine classes as soon as circumstances permitted, and others allegedly showed their lack of real interest by reading outside books in class and ignoring the lectures.[102] There were also complaints that many of the hospitals which had incorporated traditional doctors virtually ignored them or gave them only the hopeless cases.[103] Other traditional doctors complained of continued discrimination among the public health authorities, lack of real authority for native doctors in public health posts, slowness in implementing the planned expansion of Chinese medicine facilities, and superficiality of research work. They also, as early as 1957, cited defects in managing the production and distribution of native herbals, indicating that the drug crisis of 1960 and 1961 had roots deeper than just the agricultural failures of those years.[104] A few even hinted that the responsibility for many of these defects lay with the Party or Party cadres, and one, later denounced as a rightist, charged that "consistently the Party has not esteemed Chinese medicine, but rather wanted to eradicate it."[105] The Party, on its side, while generally praising Chinese doctors along with Chinese medicine, occasionally voiced mild criticism of the persistence of old ways.[106] In Shanghai the sudden 50 per cent rise of average wages in the United Clinics during 1956 and early 1957 was cited as evidence that "not enough attention has been paid to the development of socialist elements";[107] that is, the doctors were still interested in maximizing personal income.

Western-style doctors, who bore the brunt of most of the criticism over traditional medicine, appear to have been even more dissatisfied with the situation, but after several years of vigorous ideological criticism, more hesitant to voice their grievances. Still, at the height of the Hundred Flowers campaign, there were "rightists" such as Hsüeh Yü, Dean of Pharmacy at Peking Medical College, who claimed "The Ministry of Public Health has dragged pharmaceutics back to the eighteenth century."[108]

CHINESE MEDICINE IN THE GREAT LEAP—
MASS LINE AND "THE PEOPLE'S MEDICINE"

None of these criticisms or problems, however, caused the Party to modify its policy. Instead, with the general fervor of the Great Leap in late 1958, they pushed the practice of traditional medicine even further and intensified ideological criticism against remnants of bourgeois thought. Chang Chi-chun, the Deputy Director of the Party's Propaganda Bureau, bluntly warned a national conference of medical workers in November 1958 that the Chinese medicine question was an important aspect of the continuing struggle between the bourgeois and the proletarian roads in medical work. To stand neutral in this struggle, not to accept the Party's leadership regarding traditional medicine, was "an impermissibly mistaken attitude." [109] The need now was to strengthen Party leadership and follow the mass line.

In this general context the decision was taken greatly to expand the program for Western-style doctors studying Chinese medicine. In November 1958 a special Party investigating committee reported on the results of the first class of modern doctors studying Chinese medicine at the Peking Chinese Medicine Research Institute. [110] Initial difficulties stemming from their bourgeois prejudices against traditional medicine had reportedly been overcome in the course of the antirightist struggle, and through gradually accepting the Party's views on the subject, they had acquired real competence in both types of medicine. The report therefore recommended standardization of a two-year course on a national level in order to produce a core of experts in both medicines. "The objective is . . . a new type of doctor, versed in both Chinese and Western medicines, and one who has acquired Communist consciousness under the immediate leadership of Party committees." [111] In other words, a new type of doctor was wanted—not just Red and expert, but Red, *Chinese,* and expert.

The Central Committee accepted these recommendations and issued a directive that the original four classes be expanded by setting up more like them throughout the country. The total number of full-time students was to increase five-fold, from 400 to 2000. In addition, medical colleges added more compulsory courses on native medicine, [112] and spare-time study was intensified for active medical workers. Numerous articles on how to study Chinese medicine made clear how important it was, both for improving their medical skills and raising their ideological consciousness. The latter, of course, was the key to the whole problem.

"First (you) must fix the proper attitude for study: believe in the Party and listen to the Party. This is an ideological question and also is a question which must be settled first." [113]

Along with this insistence on correct ideology went the new emphasis on the mass line as the guiding principle for medical development. As an important *Kuang-ming jih-pao* editorial defined the issue, it was a bourgeois prejudice that "medicine is a scientific art, something for a small number of authorities." Rather, "it comes from the masses' experience and hence can undergo a movement developing the broadest mass participation and not just rely on those so-called authorities." [114] The note of disparagement for technical expertise in favor of the masses' initiative and proper political consciousness—the emphasis on Red over expert— was, of course, typical of the Great Leap period. [115] In the medical field it manifested itself in several ways—partly through the frantic drive to collect from among the people enormous numbers of herbals and secret remedies as the popular essence of the nation's medical wisdom, [116] partly through more fervid and more copious publicity for traditional medicine in general and its more popular features in particular. It was at this time that the greatest stress was put on identifying traditional medicine with the "popular, democratic culture" that Mao had spoken of in his "New Democracy." The kernel of truth to this identification lay, of course, in the Confucian literati's disesteem for such vulgar practical skills as medicine. Whether this should place traditional medicine in the genuine folk culture is rather dubious, but it has served well in giving it ideological respectability in the new society. During the Great Leap, the enthusiasm for simple homespun methods almost led to Chinese medicine's being classed as folk medicine. This would have fitted nicely into the denigration of bourgeois medical experts, but other psychological pressures inhibited such a seemingly natural development. Consistently, admirers of Chinese medicine, of whatever political coloring, have been on guard against any definition of China's native medical tradition that would dismiss it as a collection of isolated empirical remedies, and not a complete medical system. To define it now as folk medicine would do just that, vindicating those same bourgeois experts in their dismissal of Chinese medicine as simply research material for modern science. Chinese medicine would be nothing unique, just another folk medicine comparable to that of the African bushman or Australian aborigine.[117] For all the Communists' respect for other peoples and their culture, no Chinese nationalist—even a Communist nationalist—could accept this kind of egalitarianism for his own culture. The popular character of Chinese medicine had to be emphasized to free it from feudal associations and bourgeois corruption, but a complete identification with folk medicine was also impermissible.

Still, at the height of the Great Leap this identification was approached. Outright folk medicine, simple popular remedies, and unlettered rustic practitioners, were very much in vogue. Even the disappointment with the celebrated tadpole experiment in early 1958—almost half of the women swallowing them as a test of their effectiveness in contraception became pregnant[118]—failed to dampen enthusiasm for indigenous remedies. The press of this period is replete with stories of remarkable cures effected by simple methods, and of "popular experts" being invited into the major hospitals and medical schools.[119] All of this was, and was intended as, a clearly implied rebuke to the modern medical profession's scientific pretensions. When indigenous remedies from the common people were so frequently hailed as superior to the latest products of scientific medicine, doctors had little cause to assume that their training made them superior to the masses. After all, if an agronomist could learn from a peasant and an engineer from a coolie, so could a modern doctor learn from a village herbalist, or, better yet, from a simple peasant who had brought forth some ancient family remedy. Of course, the prestige of science was maintained, but the need for political direction was reaffirmed, and Western medicine's claims to exclusive possession of that value were challenged. Many of the didactic articles on Chinese medicine at this time belabored the theme that it too was really scientific in nature, and only bourgeois prejudice claimed that Western medicine had a monopoly on science. It is this aspect of stressing the popular mass character of traditional medicine against specialist pretentions that explains why it escaped the eclipse which befell most elements of traditional culture in the "more present, less past" socialist fervor of the Great Leap.[120]

IX

OLD MEDICINE IN THE NEW SOCIETY

In many ways the few months of late 1958 and early 1959 marked the flood tide of official promotion of Chinese medicine, for since then the publicity accorded it has gradually subsided both in volume and fervor. This can be seen in the popular press (where surgical advances have become the chief showpieces of China's socialist medicine) and also in the professional medical journals, where the spate of articles on traditional medicine during the Great Leap has greatly receded. Yet, just as many other abandoned excesses of the Great Leap have left permanent changes in Chinese society, from this period there dates a more effective and more comprehensive integration of the two kinds of doctors in common medical practice.

One of the most important organizational changes of 1958 was the replacement of the cooperative type "United Clinics" with commune-run "Public Health Centers." This not only marked a change to a more socialist form of medical practice, but it also fostered a much closer integration of the traditional practitioners with their modern counterparts. Despite official encouragement of combined-type United Clinics, in fact only a minority of them had incorporated both kinds of doctors. The Public Health Centers, on the other hand, forcibly brought the traditional doctors into the same practicing institution with what Western-style doctors were available. At first these were largely "secondary medical school graduates" who had been given an abbreviated three-year medical course. Nevertheless, it was an integration of traditional and modern doctors, even if the latter were not of the highest standard.[1]

Simultaneously, the best traditional doctors were absorbed into district and municipal hospitals where they worked mainly with fully trained modern medical college graduates. Moreover, the Party now put much greater pressure on the hospital authorities to give these traditional doctors responsible positions and adequate facilities to practice Chinese medicine. Not only were they given wards for acupuncture and herbal therapy, but they were also invited into the Western medical wards for joint consultation and treatment.[2] At the height of the Great Leap this emphasis on using Chinese medicine reportedly went as far as requiring modern doctors to write traditional prescriptions in their daily practice as proof of a correct attitude.[3] This has certainly ceased, but all evidence indicates that Chinese medicine continues to occupy a prominent place in major urban hospitals as well as in the much more numerous small rural clinics and hospitals.[4]

But if Chinese medicine has become a regular feature in the large hospitals, its most significant role probably remains in the rural health centers. There it has continued to provide the bulk of the medical care for the peasantry, while simultaneously absorbing some elements of modern medical practice. Although evidence is rather slim, there is some in-

dication of considerable cooperation in the day-to-day practice of the two kinds of doctors staffing these centers. Usually
this has meant that the younger and less dogmatic Chinese-
style doctors have been able to absorb some of the ideas and
techniques of modern medicine, whereas the modern doctors
could pick up from their traditional colleagues some useful
medical knowledge and even more useful knowledge of han-
dling rural patients.

Apart from this interchange of knowledge (which outside
observers might consider mainly valuable as on-the-job training for traditional doctors), the integration in the rural
health center has probably had useful side-effects. First, by
bringing modern medicine to the villages in close association
with familiar traditional practice, it has probably minimized
suspicion of and resistance to new medical practices. The culturally conservative peasant, who might tend to avoid a
foreign-style doctor, can easily go to the Chinese branch of
the health clinic where he may obtain some modern medicine
even from the Chinese-style doctor or, if his case merits it,
may be turned over to the Western-style doctor. As Robert
Worth has argued: "The rural health center rode into being
on the coattails of the familiar figure of the village boy turned
apprentice practitioner." [5] And, as students of medical anthropology are well aware, this smoothing of a major cultural
transition has great advantages.

Another advantage in the use of Chinese medicine has undoubtedly been its comfort function for the populace in a period of great physical and emotional strain. There is no question of the continued popularity of Chinese medicine. A
recent visitor to a rural commune near Canton found both
kinds of medicine in use, but the number of outpatients
waiting for traditional treatment outnumbered those waiting for modern medicine by a ratio of about three to one.
For rural areas, most of which have seen modern medicine

only in the last few years, this preference is not surprising. Yet even among urban populations, where dual facilities give a real choice between modern and traditional treatment, Western-style doctors who have left China testify that many people (not just the elderly) will choose traditional methods. Preservation of Chinese medicine has therefore been a popular policy. It has allowed the government to give the Chinese people a type of medical care to which they were well accustomed, while introducing more and more modern medicine. Perhaps not all of this traditional medicine has been the best possible twentieth-century therapy, and undoubtedly a May 4th type of radical intellectual would criticize the Communist government for preserving outworn medical superstitions. But for every therapeutic failure, traditional medical practice has probably reassured and comforted a number of patients suffering from lesser complaints.[6] This has not only eased the burden on overworked modern physicians; it has also, in a culturally familiar form, served to reduce the anxieties of a population going through an unprecedented social and cultural transformation. Here, the frequent assertions of acupuncture's effectiveness in treating a wide variety of nervous disorders seems especially significant. In this sense, one might posit that Chinese medicine has indeed smoothed the road to socialism.

It is an open question to what extent the Communist leadership has consciously sensed this added dividend of its policy toward traditional medicine. As suggested earlier, their commitment to the scientific value of Chinese medicine seems genuine. They are probably not, however, insensitive to its popularity among the masses; they are not, perhaps, entirely unaware of the social usefulness of traditional medicine's psychotherapeutic functions.

In any case, the government has shown deep concern for

preserving the human and material bases for Chinese medicine. After the critical shortages of traditional herbs attendant upon the serious agricultural dislocations of 1960–1961, a number of measures have been taken to stimulate their production. These include directives that the communes systematically grow herbs where possible and increase the economic incentives for the gathering of wild herbs.[7] The government is also trying to put production on a more scientific footing by growing important herbs, such as ginseng, on a plantation basis rather than depending on forest collection.[8] All this has apparently corrected the more acute shortages. In 1965, Szechuan province, the leading producer of medicinal herbs, reported that output had increased 17 per cent over the previous year.[9] A more reliable index, the price of herbs in Hong Kong, also reflects the end of the herb shortage.

Besides the supplies for traditional practice, the government has also continued to produce new practitioners. The Chinese medicine colleges have gradually been expanded in size and number until there are now twenty-one, with a total of over 10,000 students.[10] These offer a six-year course including basic elements of modern medicine.[11] There are also reportedly some 60,000 new Chinese doctors being trained by the apprentice system. This would mean that, despite the high age pattern of the traditional medical profession, its total strength is being fairly well maintained. Its proportionate strength in China's total medical picture has, of course, greatly declined with the enormous growth of modern medical personnel. Figures here are imprecise, but by 1966 China reportedly had approximately 200,000 fully trained modern physicians (five-year medical college graduates) plus over 330,000 "secondary medical school" graduates. This means that the relative weight of the old-style doctors is rapidly declining. As compared to over 95 per cent of China's medical practitioners in 1949, they now are no more than half, and perhaps less.

Yet they still seem to play an important, if increasingly less independent, role in China's medical world. The government continues to devote precious resources to building schools, hospitals, and research centers for their use. In recent years it has even extended its concern over preserving the medical heritage to traditional veterinary practice. Since the founding of a National Chinese Veterinary Medicine Research Center at Lanchow in 1958, research, publication, and practice have been encouraged. With the Lanchow center intended to sum up and rationalize this branch of Chinese medicine, attention has been called to maintaining its ranks through the disciple system.[12] Evidently all the inhabitants of China, human and animal, are to be assured the continued blessings of Chinese medicine.

All this activity in the field of traditional medicine shows that it still holds an honored position in the People's Republic. But it has more than just honor. Rewi Alley, the emigré New Zealander, wrote in a recent issue of *Eastern Horizon* how, on a sightseeing tour through historic sections of Honan, he visited the memorial temple at the grave of the great Han physician, Chang Chung-ching.[13] It had recently been renovated, and there, with a tablet of praise from Li Te-ch'uan over the door, sat Chang, as he had sat throughout the ages, flanked by other statues of Hua T'o, the great surgeon, and Sun Ssu-miao, author of a famous pulse treatise. All this, perhaps at first surprising to those who still think of Chinese Communists as nihilistic destroyers of everything old in China, is familiar enough in other areas. The temple to Confucius is also well kept, and the Sage, too, is not without honor.[14] But Chang Chung-ching and Chinese medicine in general have not, as have Confucius and his classics, been relegated to a position of honor in a dead past. They belong as much, or more, in the hospital as in the museum, and, while the latter is for respect to the dead, a hospital is for those who hope to live. The Confucian *Analects* is no longer relevant to modern Communist life (although it may be accepted as another monument to China historical greatness); Chang Chung-ching's *Treatise on Fevers* is in the curriculum of modern Chinese medical schools. For, to honor Chinese medicine in the present, it is not enough to pay tribute to its past glories—the bitterest May 4th iconoclasts might do that. It was its survival in a living present that infuriated them. The People's Republic has insisted that, purged of the old social contamination and joined with science, Chinese medicine must be a part of the present, living China. Its main monuments are hospitals and laboratories, not temples and museums.

CHINESE MEDICINE ABROAD

Apart from their internal use of Chinese medicine, the Chinese Communists have been gratified by any signs of foreign interest in China's medical tradition. Earlier supporters of indigenous medicine, although often very anti-Western, had been eager to seize on this as ammunition in their battle with modern Chinese and antitraditionalists. The Communists have been just as pleased with such flattery. Here, acupuncture, which despite its bizarre image for most Westerners has a considerable tradition in Europe, has been the principal showpiece for China's own medical accomplishments. Any foreign interest in the art, Communist or capitalist, has been noted with great satisfaction. The most spectacular manifestation of this attitude was reported by Dr. Donald Gould who, visiting China in 1958, saw at the Peking Acupuncture Institute a large world map with a gleaming acupuncture needle suspended over China. From it ribands radiated to every other country where acupuncture is practiced.[15] During the palmy days of the Sino-Soviet alliance, this was also a stock-in-trade for the cultural exchange between the two countries. In 1956 three Soviet women physicians carried out several months of well-publicized study of acupuncture in Peking. Afterward the Russians opened clinics and research centers for acupuncture in Moscow, Leningrad, and Gorki, and there was considerable discussion of the subject in Soviet medical literature. In the last few years, however, acupuncture has dropped from sight in this literature, apparently another casualty of the Sino-Soviet split.[16]

But if Russian interest has dwindled, the Chinese government still finds traditional medicine a useful item in its cultural diplomacy with other parts of the world. At least two prominent Asian neutralist leaders, Ne Win and Sukarno, have reportedly been treated by Chinese traditional doctors.[17] Acupuncturists have also been included in technical aid teams sent to Algeria, Yemen, and Indonesia.[18] More recently, China's newest friend in Asia, Pakistan, has been privileged to exchange visiting teams of traditional doctors with China. The indigenous medical traditions of the two countries are naturally very different, but it is still felt that the Chinese model might be relevant in developing "Eastern medicine." [19]

Even closer to home, the Democratic Republic of Vietnam has adopted an official policy toward native medicine (and this is mainly Chinese medicine with some local features) strikingly similar to Peking's in tone and content—so similar, in fact, that the strong influence of the Chinese example is unmistakable.[20] North Vietnam, however, has not followed to the extent of imitating the medical populism of the Great Leap period, and the impulse to glorify a national medical tradition is also complicated by the fact that traditional Chinese medical theory was superimposed on a native "Southern" school of simple herbalism. Thus the Hanoi government, in warning against harmful prejudices among medical workers, cautions not just against modern doctors belittling the traditional, but also against "the underestimation of Southern medications among many practitioners of traditional medicine. At bottom, such an attitude bears the mark of a national inferiority complex caused by the long years of foreign domination." [21] In their goal of creating "an original, scientific, national, and popular medicine," evidently a strong Chinese coloration is no more welcome than a Western one.

But there is one foreign audience which has been highly receptive to the emphasis on the Chineseness of Chinese medicine. That is the overseas Chinese communities which have been impressed by the Peking Government's loving care and patronage of distinctively Chinese culture. The Communist press in Hong Kong has given it extensive coverage, and in China there has been a consistent policy of welcoming back overseas Chinese-style doctors, with wide publicity for their delight of the new government's solicitude for the national medical heritage.[22] This has been embarrassing to the Kuomintang in its competition for overseas Chinese loyalties and in its claim to be the exclusive protector of Chinese tradition. On Taiwan, Communist policy toward traditional medicine has been studiously ignored, while the pro-Kuomintang press in Hong Kong has usually impugned the motives behind it by questioning the sincerity of the Communists' respect for national tradition. During the height of the Great Leap vogue for Chinese medicine, the *Hongkong shih-pao* was somewhat undecided as to what bad light could be thrown on Communist policy. The drive to collect herbals was described, "Kwangtung Communists Force Chinese Doctors to Give up Secret Prescriptions." [23] If this was abusing traditional doctors, the project of Western-style doctors studying Chinese medicine was also condemned: "Chinese Communists Force Western Doctors to Study Chinese Medicine; Throw Away the X-ray and Use the Acupuncture Needle." [24] Another pro-Kuomintang paper, the *T'ien-wen t'ai-pao,* took the more common position that Chinese medicine, the national tradition, was the real victim of Communist duplicity. "All this does not smack of the Chinese Communists' respecting Chinese medicine, but just the contrary, it is the Chinese Communists' use of Chinese medicine as a tool for their propaganda about 'respecting the peoples cultural heritage' and 'letting a hundred flowers bloom.'" [25] Conservative nationalists, no more than Chinese Communists, could admit any affinity with their political foes over this cultural question. This does not mean, however, that Communist medical policy has had no appeal to very unrevolutionary Chinese nationalists.

Yet there are significant differences from the attitude of simple Chinese nationalists. One of the added dimensions to Communist policy that has become apparent in recent years can be seen in the attention given to preserving and reviving the traditional medical system of the various minority peoples. Part of this has been simple investigation of their folk medicine for useful items "to enrich the medical legacy of the motherland." But wherever there has been a complete and coherent medical tradition, even where its literature is scanty, this tradition has been encouraged and cultivated in much the same manner as has the "Chinese medicine" of the Han people. Thus, Mongolian, Tibetan, and Uighur traditional medicine have all received marks of Party favor. Uighur medicine, which in recent centuries has mainly depended on surviving Persian and Arabic texts, has recently had several works published—in Uighur, not Chinese.[26] The government has also set up hospitals and clinics in seven Sinkiang cities for its practice. Mongolian and Tibetan medicines, in addition to research and practice, have had schools set up to train more doctors in their respective native traditions.[27] Obviously the appeal here is not simple integral nationalism. The Han people have a medical tradition which should be cherished and carefully developed. The other constituents of the Chinese nation also have their own traditions which should be treated similarly. No doubt this has some advantage in placating local cultural nationalisms among Uighurs, Mongols, and Tibetans (similar to official respect for their folk dances or national costumes), but it also speaks for a different attitude toward nationalism on the part of the predominantly Han leadership of the Chinese Communist Party. The common denominator for all these national traditions is respect for them as products of the people's wisdom—Uighurs, Mongols, Hans, Tibetans—but all "people" and all contributing, according to their own national genius, to the common weal of the Chinese nation. None of the earlier conservative nationalist supporters of traditional medicine saw it in this light. For them, "our Chinese medicine" was exclusively and ethnically Chinese.

ONE MEDICINE OR TWO?
THE PURSUIT OF THE HIGHER MEDICAL SYNTHESIS

But all of this—the greater cooperation between new and old-style doctors, the pride in displaying China's medical heritage at home and abroad, the approving nod toward the old medical systems of the non-Han peoples—does not tell us how successful the Chinese Communists' medical policy has been in terms of its self-professed goal of achieving a new medical system out of the fusion of Chinese and Western. Is the higher medical synthesis, China's anticipated contribution to world medicine, foreseeable?

In recent years there have been some instances of successfully combining medical techniques from the two traditions. This has come about from the integration of the two types of doctors and particularly from the Party's strong encouragement of "combined therapy." Usually this combined therapy—the practical application of medical synthesis —has been effected by modern physicians' including some elements of traditional technique in their practice. This reputedly has manifold advantages for the patient and for medical progress in China. At times, the effusive praise for this approach has sounded suspiciously like the old "mechanistic" criticism of Western medicine—Chinese medicine, of course, supplying the necessary "organic" corrective. For example, Tung Pin-k'un wrote of combined therapy at Peking Union Medical College: "This method of treatment lays stress on the human body as a whole; attention is paid both to the disease and the man, both to local areas and to the whole, both to medication and to development of the patient's conscious activity." [28]

Disregarding the fanfare, it appears that in some areas "combined therapy" has proved its merit through practical results. One notable achievement is in setting fractures with mobile willow twig splints, after determining the nature of the break through X-rays.[29] The Tientsin People's Hospital, which pioneered this adaptation of traditional bonesetting methods, has treated over 6,700 cases with better healing and faster recovery of function. A paper on this was read at the Twentieth International Surgical Conference in Rome, and it has apparently become the accepted method of setting broken limbs in China's best hospitals. Of course, the scope of "combined therapy" is not limited to broken bones. A recent survey of developments in internal medicine in the last five years spoke of its being applied to such "chronic diseases as aplastic anemia, late schistosomiasis, hypertensive diseases, chronic nephritis, ulcers, diabetes, and bronchial asthma." [30]

It is difficult for foreign observers to assess most of the claims made for such traditional, or combined, therapy.

Usually, noting the absence of closely controlled clinical testing, they have tended to be rather skeptical.[31] In the only area where some kind of statistical comparison with non-Chinese experience is possible, the Chinese claims of cures are somewhat higher. Seven sets of figures published for acupuncture practice in various parts of China in the period 1955–1959 give an average of 90 per cent cured or improved for a wide variety of diseases. This compares to claims of 81 per cent cured or improved for the French acupuncturist, Dr. Marries, and 78 per cent by Professor U. G. Bogralick of the Gorki Medical Institute.[32] Western medical authorities, however, might question the nature of all these cures.

Medical visitors to China usually have not found the top level of medical practice very different from that in the West. They have occasionally noted native medicine and have been impressed with some specific practices such as bone-setting, but seem to regard the system of medicine as very familiar. Proceedings of medical conferences and scholarly medical journals in the last few years also give the impression that traditional medicine has not greatly altered the character of modern medical development in China. Occasional papers on traditional techniques appear which are respectfully treated,[33] but they do not seem to affect in any vital way the principles of modern medicine; nor do they seem to be pointing toward a new medical system.

The several thousand modern doctors who have gone through two and a half years of intensive full-time study of native medicine (the second group graduated amid much fanfare in 1961) would seem the logical leaders to show the way toward the new system. This had clearly been the government's intention. However, although they are supposedly equipped to practice both medicines, there have been complaints that "some individuals, after studying Chinese medicine, abandoned Western medicine, seldom read Western medical books, and paid no attention to new developments in the modern science of medicine." [34] Dr. Felix Mann, on his recent visit to China, formed a similar impression from the doctors of this type whom he encountered. Evidently, for some of them at least, the Party has been too successful in breaking down their allegiance to Western medicine. The authorities have also faced other problems in integrating the two medicines which might be attributable to the rigor with which the policy had been pushed. After 1960 it was a common complaint that, despite the Party's explicit encouragement for a hundred flowers to bloom again in the medical world, Western-style doctors in particular were very hesitant to put forward any views about how to improve traditional medicine. It was noted that "the main reason seems to be lack of a clear demarcation line between political and academic questions." [35] The prolonged ideological criticism of traditional medicine has indeed made the separation of purely scientific questions rather difficult.

But the type of successful medical synthesis envisioned in China must overcome more than ideological or political problems. It is not enough to bring the two types of doctors together and have them learn to apply some of each other's techniques. The strong current of cultural pride demands more than that modern medicine, ecumenical in scope, simply absorb a few herbs or practical skills from China's past medical experience. Instead, Chinese medicine, rehabilitated from its "feudal" associations as a product of the Chinese people's genius, must contribute substantially to this synthesis: "to create a new school of medical and pharmaceutical science, in which our country will be unique." [36] The task is not merely to preserve China's medical wisdom. By itself that would be "national essence" conservatism. The cultural legacy in medicine must be inherited critically, improved with science, and developed into this unique and higher medical science, one which is both scientific and unmistakably Chinese.[37]

The ultimate stumbling-block to this synthesis so far has been the body of ancient and unique theoretical principles which form the foundation of traditional Chinese medicine. The Communists, no less than earlier cultural conservatives, have found it impossible to dispense with them and still retain respect for Chinese medicine as a medical system. Many earlier researchers had, of course, simply ignored them and turned to the techniques and products of Chinese medicine. Since 1954, however, this has been condemned as a superficial approach and a manifestation of bourgeois prejudice. As a *Jen-min jih-pao* editorial expressed it: "Chinese traditional medicine is a great science . . . It does not, as was imagined, consist merely of a body of unrelated experience. It is a unique theoretical system."[38]

Thus, there has been much discussion of Chinese medicine's theoretical foundations. In the summer of 1959 a national conference on acupuncture, held in Shanghai, discussed at great length the twelve meridians which supposedly form its physiological rationale, but with inconclusive results.[39] Since then, although there is not yet agreement even on their existence, a great deal of theorizing has been done on the relationship of these meridians to the central nervous system. The most spectacular theory so far has been advanced by a non-Chinese, Professor Kim Bong-han of Pyongyang University.[40] He has reportedly discovered, by means of measuring variations in electrical resistance on the skin, groupings of small oval cells corresponding closely to the traditional acupuncture points. Further, these are connected by clusters of thin tubular cells generally corresponding to the meridians of classical acupuncture theory. The official announcement of his discoveries was greeted with considerable fanfare in the Chinese press, *Jen-min jih-pao* devoting over two full pages to it.[41] Apparently it has not, however, revolutionized Chinese acupuncture in theory or practice. An article in *Hsin chien-she* (New Construction) for August 1965 summed up the main lines of acupuncture research in China without once referring to Professor Kim's "third system." [42] It concluded cautiously that scientific research, while proving that acupuncture could stimulate the nervous system and increase internal secretions, found it "still difficult to produce comparatively definitive conclusions." The meridians seem to remain an unsolved puzzle for China's modern scientific researchers.

Similarly, other central parts of Chinese medical theory remain unrationalized. There have been numerous attempts to explain away *yin-yang* and the five elements as merely symbolic in meaning. The trouble with this facile rationalization—now as in the 1930's—is that it only explains away, and itself explains nothing of why Chinese medicine works. More fashionable of late have been attempts to find dialectical processes in these theories.[43] This, of course, was vigorously condemned by some earlier Marxist medical writers, but it is now commonplace in Communist China. The argument would perhaps be more convincing if it did not convey the impression that the real aim is to establish the respectability of indigenous tradition by new criteria rather than to find a scientific explanation for the old medical theories. Since traditional Chinese cultural assumptions were first shaken by Western intrusions, there have been too many attempts to find democracy in Mencius, science in Taoist alchemy, and socialism in well field theories, for the hasty identification of *yin-yang* with Marx's dialectic to seem anything more than the latest effort to establish Chinese roots for what is manifestly new, and foreign, to China. Despite the best efforts of Party theorists and medical scientists, *yin-*

yang and five elements—Han dynasty anachronisms in the modern world—remain the most formidable stumbling-blocks to a full medical synthesis which would be both scientifically meaningful and psychologically acceptable.

Perhaps a growing realization of the difficulties in such synthesis partly explains the somewhat less enthusiastic attitude toward Chinese medicine since the Great Leap forward. It no longer appears at the center of publicity about China's socialist medicine, as was certainly the case in the middle and late 1950's. For a time Chinese medicine fitted reasonably well into the stress on ideology over technical expertise during the period of the Great Leap. Although much of the medical publicity in these years stressed socialist fervor, as in the much-heralded saving of a badly-burned worker's life,[44] the emphasis on improvisation and overcoming technical difficulties was eminently well-suited to stressing Chinese medicine.[45] The greater emphasis on technical skill and scientific achievement subsequent to the cooling off after the Great Leap has not been so conducive to exuberant claims about old herb doctors surpassing modern specialists. "Combined therapy," it should be remembered, is usually carried on by well-trained Western-style doctors. Similarly, the latest show pieces of China's socialist medicine have been surgical successes by young, Communist-trained surgeons, not the accomplishments of venerable herbalists or acupuncture specialists.[46]

Nor do ideological implications of Chinese medicine seem to be a current issue in maintaining the modern medical profession free from bourgeois contamination. As late as 1961, Hsü Yün-pei, the Deputy Minister for Health, warned that Western-style doctors had not overcome all their prejudices against Chinese medicine. "There are still a great number of persons who have stupid ideas, asserting that there is but one truth, and there can be one correct science only." [47] Since then little has been said on the subject; but neither have these doctors said anything in contravention of the established policy of respect for and uniting with traditional medicine.

This does not mean that medical experts, along with other intellectuals, are not still suspected of lingering bourgeois tendencies and pretensions to special status. By 1965 the socialist re-education campaign and struggle against revisionist tendencies seriously involved the medical world. Its major effect on medical organization has been to send teams of urban doctors from the large medical centers on periodic tours of duty in the countryside. [48] The motives were partly practical—to provide more medical care for the relatively neglected peasantry and to train rural health cadres on the spot. But political, or ideological, considerations were also prominent—"In these areas they can arrive at a deeper understanding of the rural situation and *undergo a more comprehensive education in class struggle*" [49] (emphasis mine). The preoccupation with bourgeois influences may seem somewhat strange, because the large majority of these doctors were trained entirely under Communism. Apparently the key to what it really means lies in the oft-repeated accusation of their being "alienated from the masses." In other words, they threaten to form a separate class of those who—in good old Mencian terms, but not in a Mencian fashion—work with their minds. The cure for this is to send them to the villages to mingle with those who work with their hands.

Simultaneously there has been a drive to train huge numbers of "basic-level health workers" for the countryside. In these related movements there has at times developed a tone reminiscent of the deprecation of technical expertise in favor of enthusiasm and socialist purpose that characterized the Great Leap Forward. Thus, a *Jen-min jih-pao* article in August asked rhetorically, "What school did Hua T'o enter? At which higher-learning medical institution did Li Shih-chen spend five, six, seven or eight years?" [50] It went on to ask the more pertinent question about training these basic-level cadres: "Why can't we allow them to study while working and to improve themselves through practice?" Yet, despite the renewed emphasis on quantity and correct ideology, Chinese medicine has been given a relatively small part in this latest attempt to overwhelm China's rural health problems with enthusiasm and to correct the modern doctor's unhealthy ideological tendencies with exposure to the masses. This can be seen in an authoritative article by the new Minister of Health, Ch'ien Hsin-chung, summing up the purposes of the "to the villages" campaign. [51] The integration of Chinese and Western medicine is referred to as one of the effective methods of raising the level of medical care in the countryside, but the major virtues of traditional methods in his discussion appears to be their low cost and availability. [52] They are not particularly praised for their superiority to modern medicine, as was the case in 1958. [53] It appears, then, that in calling upon the countryside once again to purify the contagion of urban bourgeois living, traditional medicine has been dropped to the role of a minor additive in the latest Maoist prescription.

Of course, it may be that China's modern doctors have been completely re-educated in their attitudes toward Chinese medicine. From interviews with doctors from Communist China in 1962 Robert Worth formed the opinion that the younger ones had come to accept it without serious reservations. [54] This is somewhat similar to my own impression from interviews done in 1964, but with some qualification. That is, though none of the doctors interviewed was hostile toward traditional medicine per se, and most expressed admiration for its effectiveness in certain circumstances, it was still an admiration tinged with a condescension—strange that these old things sometimes really work!—which betrayed no loss of confidence that they, as possessors of modern science, were the holders of China's medical future.

The recent trends described here are difficult to assess with any confidence. Basic policy has remained constant; the only changes are of tone or attitude. Yet, for this subject, such changes are significant. Thus it may be noteworthy that Chinese medicine has not figured prominently in the socialist education movement. Western doctors are still encouraged to study Chinese medicine, but this no longer appears to be central to their thought reform. In fact, during 1965 a rather ominous portent for Chinese medicine's high status appeared in an article in the journal, *New Physical Education*.[55] The article criticized only certain abuses in the traditional therapeutic breathing exercises of *ch'i-kung,* noting that there are still quacks able to capitalize on lingering superstitions about its magical properties and wonder working powers. This criticism in no way endangered Chinese medicine, but when the author denounced *ch'i-kung* for its "superstitious" teachings about tranquillity and harmony—"it is completely contrary to our active physical training . . . for the sake of making even greater contributions to socialist constructions"[56]—he touched on a sensitive spot. It was not just that *ch'i-kung* enthusiasts might close their eyes to seek inner harmony during production meetings; the danger lay in calling attention to the world of difference between socialist striving to conquer disease, imperialism, or natural difficulties and Chinese medicine's basic emphasis on restoring harmony as the principle for all cures.

To emphasize this aspect of traditional medicine—even to call attention to its most obvious manifestation in *ch'i-kung* therapy—arouses the possibility of serious ideological difficulties. There is no evidence that this will be allowed to happen, but the logical possibility is there. If Chinese medicine should be considered too tranquil and pacific for the construction of socialism, material for its indictment is still at hand. It should be noted that Chinese medicine no longer enjoys the protection afforded by an extreme shortage of modern doctors.

In spite of this, there is no real evidence that the present prestige and institutional position of Chinese medicine is in any way threatened, and the psychological and ideological pressures behind its rehabilitation still seem to be operative. If Chinese medicine is no longer quite the same issue in Communist China that it was in the mid-fifties, this is hardly surprising, for if this study shows anything, it is that attitudes toward Chinese medicine in the twentieth century have not been static. They have shifted with the rapid changes in China's physical and intellectual environment and may be expected to continue to shift in response to the changing forces which operate upon the minds of modern Chinese.

X

TAIWAN — REMEMBRANCE

OF THINGS PAST

Outside of Communist China there are perhaps thirty million Chinese among whom, from San Francisco to Rangoon, Chinese medicine continues to survive and flourish. But, although Chinese form a large majority of the population in places like Hong Kong and Singapore, it is only on Taiwan that a sovereign Chinese government deals with the problems of a totally Chinese society. Thus, only there has there been a genuine arena for the type of debate over the merits of Chinese medicine which formerly flourished in mainland China.[1] To some extent, overseas Chinese have joined in the controversy as it developed on Taiwan, but the stage has again been set under the auspices of the National Government. It should not be surprising, therefore, if the issues and arguments seem somewhat similar to those advanced earlier and, at the same time, very different from those in the People's Republic.

Taiwan, to begin with, had been without the legal practice of Chinese medicine for almost half a century, since the Japanese, in keeping with medical policy in their own country, had granted licenses only to modern-trained physicians. This does not mean that Chinese medicine vanished entirely from the island, for its practitioners maintained a surreptitious existence and the common herbal remedies remained in widespread use.[2] Still, lacking any legal status, it was greatly eclipsed by the efficient modern medical system built by the Japanese. By 1945 Taiwan had approximately 3000 modern-trained physicians as compared to only four or five times that number for all the rest of China.

After 1945 Chinese medicine returned with Chinese government, both in the form of traditional doctors from the mainland and native Taiwanese traditional doctors who now, under Chinese law, were entitled to full legal practice. Although it was reportedly popular with the poorer classes,[3] some educated Taiwanese were not very enthusiastic about the return of Chinese medicine. In 1946 the Association of Taiwanese University graduates sent an article to the Medical Supplement of *Ta-kung pao,* lamenting the spread of these unscientific, old-style practitioners.[4] They were held at least partly responsible for the breakdown of the Japanese-built public health system and the resulting appearance of epidemics on the island for the first time in forty years. According to the article, Taiwan (unlike mainland China) had enough modern doctors for its medical needs. Traditional doctors were therefore unnecessary and detrimental to existing public health standards.

The number of old-style doctors increased tremendously with the massive influx of mainland refugees in 1949.[5] Japanese-educated Taiwanese were not the only intellectuals who found this distressing. In February 1951 Chu Chia-lo, German-educated geologist, educator, and Kuomintang member from Chekiang, referred to the harmful influences of traditional medicine in a speech on medicine and public health to the Chinese United Nations Society. To him, it was stagnant and unprogressive—"stuck in a mystic stage." The recent inundation of Taiwan by these old-style doctors, after the province had acquired a good modern medical foundation, he described as "a very painful affair." [6] Judging from the bitterness of the replies from traditional doctors, he had touched a sensitive spot. In vitriolic language, they accused him of being unqualified to pass judgment on medical questions, underhanded in his schemes to destroy Chinese medicine, and heartless toward those traditional medical practitioners who had fled to Taiwan. Their final trump, however, was the assertion that, despite such slanders by Chinese who had lost all confidence in their own national traditions, the National Government, under the 1943 medical law, welcomed traditional doctors and gave them legal recognition as a "liberal profession."

Yet, for all their professions of gratitude to the National Government, the Chinese-style doctors evidently were not entirely sure of its favor, or pleased with its support. In the early 1950's organized Chinese medicine circles in Taiwan began to agitate for greater official recognition and some tangible assistance. This took the form of a series of petitions to the Legislative Yuan requesting that the government establish a school for traditional Chinese medicine. The initial request, a telegram from a private Chinese doctor, Hu Hsiao-ch'uan, argued the advantages of this most succinctly: "For the sake of preserving our national essence, preserving the peoples lives, regaining our lost cultural rights, and reviving the nation . . . the school should be established." [7] This conveyed the tone and meaning of much longer subsequent petitions from various traditional medicine organizations, mainly in Taiwan but also from Hong Kong. Significantly, there was a considerable native Taiwanese element among them. The President of the Taiwan Provincial Chinese Physicians' Association, for example, was a local Taiwanese Kuomintang member with a long record of resistance against the Japanese.

In all of these pleas and petitions there was only one really new argument introduced. That emerged from the Communist conquest of the mainland, which was portrayed as the final catastrophe to Chinese culture in general and Chinese medicine in particular. With the Communists allegedly completing the foreign-inspired persecution and destruction of traditional Chinese medicine, Taiwan was held up as the last bastion for this national cultural treasure. If it were lost there, for want of proper government attention, this vital part of the national essence would be lost forever.[8]

Yet, despite the marked similarity of this agitation to earlier political efforts by organized traditional medicine, its political influence within the Kuomintang was not what it had been in the 1930's. Ch'en Kuo-fu, Hu Han-min, Chiao I-t'ang— all these worthy protagonists—were no longer available to champion its cause. However, in the Legislative Yuan, the arena traditional medicine had chosen for its campaign to gain government support, there was a block of thirty Chinese-style doctors ready to lead the fight. Traditional doctors also claimed to have support in higher Kuomintang circles—they gave Ch'en Ch'eng lavish credit for their legislative successes—but this is rather dubious.[9] What is clear, is that Chinese medicine in Taiwan had formed a fairly powerful pressure group and that its appeal to national tradition (especially in an anti-Communist context) had a more or less receptive audience in broad areas of the Kuomintang and the government.

The Legislative Yuan referred the Chinese medicine school question to a special subcommittee on educational and administrative affairs for prolonged study. After two years this committee issued a report affirming the legal basis for such a school and recommending that it be established along with a research institute for traditional medicine. The latter reflected a widespread feeling that there should be more emphasis on research and the reform of Chinese medicine than the original petitions had suggested. This would presumably make the school proposal more acceptable on modern scientific grounds. During the Legislative Yuan debate on this dual proposal, opposition was much more restrained than the old Fu Ssu-nien-style rejection of anything tainted with old medicine. Wu Chih-hui, a Western-style woman doctor and Cantonese Kuomintang member, led attempts to defer any school for Chinese medicine until scientific research had determined its nature and value.[10] But prevailing sentiment clearly favored setting up both the research institute and the school simultaneously. An added factor in favor of such a demonstration of belief in the national medical tradition was the Communist treatment of Chinese medicine, for by 1956 it was apparent that they were not eradicating it as conservatives had expected. Several legislators noted that, despite the Communists' hostility to Chinese culture, they were preserving and encouraging Chinese medicine. It would therefore never do for the National Government, authentic protectors of what is Chinese, to fall behind the enemy in this regard.[11] The resolution, calling for the Executive Yuan to establish both a school and a research institute, passed overwhelmingly.

Such open official support for traditional medicine provoked a by now familiar reaction from the surviving May 4th-type liberals on Taiwan. The prominent Taipei journal, *Free China* (significantly a liberal emigré, not a native Taiwanese, organ) immediately attacked it as a harmful and retrogressive step. An unsigned editorial in the April 1956 issue called on the Executive Yuan to return the resolution for further consideration; to accept it would be a sign that the government lacked a true modernizing spirit.[12] In the next issue, the May 4th veteran, Mao Tzu-shui, wrote a short article agreeing that establishment of such a school was an outrage to modernity and science.[13] He reiterated, in good May 4th style, that since medicine was a part of science, a part particularly vital to human welfare, such factors as national origin or "national essence" were completely irrelevant. The school would obstruct scientific progress on Taiwan, and stand as a monument to the failure of modern, scientific principles in China.

These objections to the Legislative Yuan's resolutions were more fully developed in the September issue by a long article published under the pseudonym of Ju Pin.[14] The complaint, once again, was not against research on Chinese herbs, providing it was conducted by modern scientists. What was intolerable was that the government should allow old-style doctors to propagate their outworn scientific theories in an officially approved school. A school for Chinese medicine could only be useful if it adopted a completely scientific viewpoint, modern methods, and teaching materials. Echoing the old argument that "scientification" meant elimination of a separate "Chinese" medicine, he noted that there would then be no point in calling it a Chinese medicine school. As a modern note to these familiar arguments, he added that strengthening of the "national spirit" for the anti-Communist struggle was possible only through scientific methods, not by reviving archaic elements out of the past. A letter from a reader emphasized this point.[15] Nationalist China could not let national pride turn her toward traditionalism without giving the future to the Communists. In Taiwan a strong "school to restore the old" (*fu-ku p'ai*) was attempting to turn the nation away from the modern spirit of the May 4th period in the name of anti-Communism. Yet the essentials of that spirit—science and democracy—were still vital to the struggle for national survival against the new foe of Communism. The question of a school for Chinese medicine was to him, and others still imbued with the May 4th spirit, just part of this larger issue of which direction Nationalist China would take.

Most of the Taiwan press did not, however, see Chinese medicine, or the proposed school, in this light. The *Min-tsu wan-pao* greeted the resolution with an editorial acclaiming it as an end of government discrimination against Chinese medicine.[16] Of course, along with the other newspapers, it was for science and scientific research. But the editorial writer warned that present-day science was not omnipotent. There were still some things—the mysteries of religion, for instance—that it could not explain. Chinese medicine was another case in point. It had accumulated real value through its long experience, value which present limitations of scientific understanding should not obscure. In defense of this, the writer turned in familiar fashion to foreign authority for corroboration: "Foreign scholars thus highly esteem it, and yet we point to it as dregs to be spit out and discarded. What reason is there to this?"[17] Common sense and national pride both required that the government take Chinese medicine in hand, study and reform it to produce that "great new contribution" to the entire world which Chinese medicine advocates had been talking about for almost forty years. Some other Taipei dailies, while not quite so enthusiastic about Chinese medicine, also favored the resolution. The *Hsin-sheng pao* made a strong plea for ending the separation between the two kinds of medicine and the jealousy between their practitioners in the interest of creating a better combined medicine.[18] The *Kung-lun pao* was more enthusiastic about the need for genuine scientific research by scientifically trained personnel, but firmly supported the resolution.[19]

Much of educated public opinion, then, appears to have been mildly in favor of doing something for Chinese medicine. There was no strong partisanship, but, after all, so the underlying premise ran, it was a Chinese possession and it did have some genuine value. Respect for science and modernity did not, for the majority, preclude a limited acceptance of traditional medicine. In the realm of actual medical habits, a very limited sampling of National Taiwan University students in 1964 revealed that just over 50 per cent of them consulted both types of doctors, although only 4 per cent would use traditional medicine exclusively.[20] If this type of evidence has any value in substantiating the general impression from editorial comment, it suggests that adamant hostility was certainly not pervasive, even among the educated classes.

There were, of course, at the opposite extreme to the *Free China* group, the strong partisans of Chinese medicine, both within and outside the profession. Their animosity toward the liberal critics was perfectly understandable. The heart of their disagreement was most clearly explained by a group of Hong Kong traditional doctors who accused *Free China* of following the Hu Shih-inspired "May 4th spirit," the essence of which was defined as complete eradication of Chinese culture in favor of total Westernization.[21] An anonymous article in the Taipei journal, *Hsin-wen ping-lun,* although not written by a professional Chinese doctor, summed up the traditional medicine advocates' position very well. It, too, was disgusted with Chinese "who regard our own precious accumulated experience as dung, and only want to listen to things imported."[22] Chinese medicine, although "without a sign board 'science,' still amounts to the same thing as 'science' and naturally also is compatible with 'modernization.'"[23] In support of this assertion, it brought out all the old, familiar arguments: something that had survived so long must have real value, the precious experience collected, its complete organic approach to illness, and what Western medicine could learn from it. All these reasons were adduced in favor of speedy government establishment of the proposed school.

The proposal also drew considerable support from overseas Chinese. Articles and petitions urging the importance of such a measure came from Chinese medicine organizations and sympathizers in Japan, the United States, Macao, and, above all, Hong Kong.[24] Only in Hong Kong, however, was there anything approaching a debate over the issue in the local press, and its participants never actually questioned the propriety of establishing the school itself. Ting Wen-yuan, brother of the famous V. K. Ting, had in the *Free Man's Paper* expressed the opinion that the school and research center would have to use modern, scientific methods and probably modern personnel.[25] He was soon rebuked by those who took a much more positive view of the role Chinese medicine should play in its own reform and eventual synthesis with Western medicine.[26] The real fire, however, was directed at the *Free China* group for their alleged cultural apostasy in opposing the school. Again, among the traditional medicine advocates in Hong Kong, examples of foreign interest in Chinese medicine figured prominently in their case against native Chinese opponents.[27] In order to mobilize opinion against the views expressed in *Free China* and to exert influence on the National Government, Hong Kong's traditional doctors formed an ad hoc organization, expressly for the purpose of urging speedy adoption of the Legislative Yuan's resolution.[28]

In Taiwan, however, the proposal ran into serious trouble within the government, as well as among outside liberal intellectuals. It had been referred for implementation to the Ministry of Education, one of the organs in the government most open to Western, scientific influences, and with a long record of opposition to including Chinese medicine in the school system.* The Minister at that time, Chang Ch'i-yün, was certainly sensitive to the political significance of traditional culture (he has since founded the Institute for Chinese Culture while simultaneously serving as Commandant of the National War College), but he was also bound to respect pro-science sentiment among the intellectuals. On June 5, 1956, he convened a special meeting of twenty persons, with himself as chairman, for the purpose of initiating proceedings.[29] The composition of this select group was unsatisfactory to the traditional medical world because it included only five Chinese-style doctors. The decisions, reached at a stormy session, were even more unsatisfactory from their point of view. It was decided to give priority to research before training more traditional doctors. A modern research institute would be set up, and for this an eight-member preparatory committee was chosen. Only one of its members was a traditional doctor.

Clearly the entire emphasis of the measure was being shifted. From the initial requests to set up a school had come the Legislative Yuan's proposal for both school and research center. Now the research center was being put ahead of the school and responsibility for studying Chinese medicine was being given mainly to the modern medical profession. The traditional doctors reacted with expressions of outrage and betrayal. Two of their leading organizations retaliated with a joint ultimatum addressed to the Ministry of Education.[30] It set forth three basic demands: 1) immediate establishment of both the school and research institute; 2) equal status and representation for Chinese medicine on the Ministry of Education's Medical Education Committee; and 3) the school and research institute to be staffed from the traditional medicine profession. Unless these were

* See Chapter VII.

granted, they threatened to boycott the proposed institute and rouse opposition in Taiwan and abroad. It was a measure of the limitations on their political influence that these threats proved futile.

"The National Chinese Medicine and Drugs Research Center" that was finally established must have been a sore disappointment to their original hopes. Its director, Dr. Li Huan-ying, is a German-trained physician, and the center is entirely modern in its approach to research on Chinese medicine. Defining his objectives in the first issue of the center's journal, *Chung-kuo yi-ao,* Li studiously refrained from any talk of national essence or a separate medical identity.[31] The goal of scientific research into traditional medical lore and materials was to be the absorption of what was found useful into modern, universal medicine. This was beyond reproach by the strictest modernist's standards. Li, however, recognized the need to "preserve special characteristics of national medicine," [32] a concern which would not sit too well with the more adamant opponents of traditional culture. Furthermore, he affirmed the value of examining the vast corpus of traditional medical literature, as well as its materia medica. In his opinion, these ancient records contained in embryonic form many of the later theories of scientific medicine, psychosomatic illness and endocrinology being two notable examples.[33] All of this indicated a pride and faith in the value of traditional medicine that more iconoclastic modernists would not be likely to feel. It did not, however, make the institute a center for propagating Chinese medicine as the traditional practitioners would have wished.

The Center's actual research work to date lies mainly in the field of analyzing the medicinal properties and physiological functions of various traditional herbs. Despite a modern plant near Taipei, the scope of such research has been severely limited by lack of funds to purchase scientific equipment and maintain an adequate staff. So far, the government's general approval for scientific investigation of the national medical legacy has not produced financial support on anything like the scale given such work in Communist China. The National Government has many demands on much more limited resources, but any worthwhile results from the Center would seem to depend on more substantial support. It is somewhat ludicrous that all the debate and preparations for such an institute should end with its operating on a budget of U.S. $25,000 a year.[34]

The school for Chinese medicine has had an even sadder history. Eventually it was established in Taichung as a private institution, though with government approval. In 1962, however, the school's president, T'an Chin, a traditional doctor and member of the Legislative Yuan, was arrested for selling admission to the school as a means of evading military service.[35] Although he claimed he had been "jailed for preserving Chinese culture" and supporters of Chinese medicine, including the Roman Catholic bishop, Yü Pin,[36] rallied to his side, the scandal severely shook the school. It remains in existence, but has apparently been a disappointment to the traditional medicine world and a source of embarrassment to the Ministry of Education.[37] Reportedly, there have been serious difficulties in finding suitable teachers and teaching material for traditional medicine, and the present director is a modern doctor. The pressure to turn schools founded for propagating traditional medicine toward teaching modern medicine, largely because the students find it more economically rewarding, has also been noted in the Ayurvedic medicine schools in India. In Communist China the economic motive has been largely removed with the abolition of private practice, and, in addition, the central government has much stricter control over medical curricula and practice.

If traditional medicine has had little real success in securing an official institutional basis on Taiwan, it has remained very much a part of the common medical scene and so far has been able to resist any efforts to curtail its practice. The more than 1000 traditional doctors on the island have formed several organizations which, while not possessing anything resembling the high-level political connections of the *Kuo-i kuan,* in its heyday, still constitute a fairly effective pressure group. The most important of these organizations are by no means narrowly obscurantist, but, like the *Kuo-i kuan* before them, have accepted the necessity of basic scientific reform and synthesis with Western medicine. Hsi Fu-i, the secretary of the Taiwan Province Traditional Physicians' Association, for example, welcomed establishment of the Taichung school as an opportunity for effecting a genuine synthesis which would preserve the best of Chinese medicine.[38] The more research oriented Chinese Traditional Medicine and Pharmacy Society, founded in 1953, publishes a regular journal, *Reformed Chinese Medicine (Ke-hsin Chung-i).* Again, it should be understood that its idea of reform would not be acceptable to the modernists. The primary concern of all these organizations is to preserve China's unique medical tradition, both by research and by opposing any threats to its legal status.

During the last few years such a threat did arise largely at the instigation of the Taiwan Physicians' Association and its president, Dr. Wu Chi-fu. This organization, in contrast to the remnant of the once proud Chinese Medical Association in Taipei, is mainly composed of native Taiwanese and has its headquarters in Kaohsiung. Dr. Wu is himself a Japanese-trained ophthalmologist with scant respect for traditional medicine and its practitioners. In the September 1962 issue of *Wen-hsing* (after the closing down of *Free China,* probably the outstanding—certainly the most controversial—

intellectual journal in Taiwan) Wu Chi-fu opened a campaign to tighten the laws on medical practice. He took as his point of departure the recent cholera outbreak in Kaohsiung and the need it revealed for revised laws.[39] Part of the blame he attributed to the many quacks who were currently allowed to practice under the "five years' experience" provision for granting a physician's license.[40] Most of the "quacks," of course, were traditional practitioners, so any tightening of the law would affect traditional medicine the most.

Dr. Wu followed up with a much more exhaustive discussion of the problem in the November issue.[41] The present laws were to his mind hopelessly inadequate for the medical needs of a modern nation and urgently required legislative revision. In essence, what he wanted were regulations that would allow only modern-trained physicians to practice medicine, as had been the case under the Japanese. Of course, it was not prudent to make that comparison openly. On the worth of traditional medicine, Dr. Wu was prepared to concede it some value in isolated elements or techniques, but none as a system of medicine, and none for the popular practice of medicine. He drew an analogy with the discovery of an African paralysis poison which might be found useful as an anesthetic. This did not mean, however, that African tribal medicine should be preserved. The same was true for traditional Chinese medicine. It too was primitive medical knowledge, fit only to be absorbed and superseded by modern science. He had nothing but scorn for arguments about national essence or the claims of patriotism in medicine, which he likened to the charges of traitor by pre-war Japanese super-patriots, hurled at anyone who did not mouth their ultra-nationalistic slogans. Both were cases of irrational nationalism overcoming universal science and reason.

Much of Wu Chi-fu's indignation was directed not just at the old-style doctors who dragged down standards of medical practice, but also at the government for shirking its responsibility to control this harmful practice. The key was maintaining the high standards and prestige of a modern medical profession on Taiwan. It was his, and other Taiwanese physicians' opinion, that this could not be done so long as traditional medicine was allowed to flourish unchecked.[42] The government's alleged indifference to this situation seemed clearly an indifference to a basic social problem as well as to the scientific advice of its medical experts.

One is reminded here of the problems of the mainland scientists in their relations with political authority. There, however, political supervision and direction, rather than indifference, has been the main source of tension. The Taiwanese scientific elite might complain more of being ignored than of being browbeaten.

Since the appearance of his two articles, Wu and the Taiwan Physicians' Association have waged a steady campaign for revision of medical regulations. Most of the articles on this subject, by Wu Chi-fu and other doctors, have appeared in the Association's journal, *Taiwan Medical Society*. In general, they have stressed three specific improvements to raise the standard of medical practice in Taiwan, all of which would be detrimental to traditional doctors. First, the five-year experience rule should be eliminated. If a practitioner is unqualified, the fact that he has already been practicing medicine is no argument for giving him a license. Second, traditional and modern doctors should be differentiated in the regulations (as they were before 1937) so that old-style doctors could not use elements of modern science, such as X-ray machines, without understanding their principles. Third, the false and extravagant advertising of some traditional doctors should be banned for fraudulently misleading the public. Wu Chi-fu cited a flagrant example of this in a newspaper advertisement during the

Kaohsiung cholera outbreak which offered *yin-yang* as a cure—*yin* water from a well and *yang* water from the river.[43]

The Taiwanese Physicians' Association has not fought this campaign alone. Alongside Wu's second contribution to *Wen-hsing* appeared another article, "Reform 'Physicians' Law' and Abolish Chinese Medicine," written by a young intellectual, Li Ao.[44] The tone and position taken in this article were very similar to that expressed by cultural radicals since the May 4th movement. More significant, however, Li Ao, a young man in his twenties, was of that generation in spirit, not in years. For Li, who considers himself a follower of Hu Shih, the key issue was still basic cultural revolution, and attention to social and cultural problems, such as medicine, as the real task of intellectuals.[45] He condemned Chinese medicine in vitriolic terms worthy of Fu Ssu-nien at his best. According to his view, it was at the root of the present bad medical regulations and was also responsible for numerous social ills. After a historical resumé of medical regulations since the beginning of the Republic (and there was no mistaking which side of the Chinese-Western medicine controversy he took), Li Ao proposed to go beyond even the wishes of the modern physicians and abolish Chinese medicine altogether.

For him this was the clear duty of a progressive government—not to compromise with the "curse of tradition," but to root it out. Prefixing "national" to useless elements of the old culture, such as medicine, and then defending them as "national essence" could only impede the country's essential "modernization" (*hsien-tai hua*), without serving any useful purpose.[46] If public opinion was still backward and supported "national medicine," then the government had to override it, just as the United States Government was willing to override "public opinion" against racial integration.[47] To temporize and encourage such social evils only prolonged them. Yet he evidently had little confidence that the National Government would adopt such a militantly progressive stand, for he ended the article with excerpts from three turn-of-the-century works which praised Western over Chinese medicine. Li concluded: "Today, looking at these opinions of half a century ago, we should in shame ask: Where is our 'progress'?" [48] As a symbolic gesture of iconoclastic solidarity across the generations, Mao Tzu-shui commended *Wen-hsing* and Li Ao for breaking the silence over the continued harmful influences of traditional medicine.[49]

Organized traditional medicine and its supporters have naturally opposed any such legal changes. Li Ao's outspoken attack provoked some vigorous counterblasts denouncing him as a "traitor" after the manner of Wang Ching-wei (who also wanted to abolish Chinese medicine) and *Wen-hsing* as a "Red Magazine." [50] Traditional medicine advocates have also been able to take care of themselves on the political, as well as the polemical, front. Though unable to bend the government to their wishes, the Chinese medicine world still has a solid block in the Legislative Yuan capable of retarding any hostile measures. The legislature, while representing many shades of opinion, is also a fairly conservative body on any question concerning national tradition. Moreover, as shown in 1956, it is susceptible to the kind of "public opinion" which organized Chinese medicine can produce when its vital interests are threatened. In this regard, overseas Chinese opinion carries a great deal of weight, or at least Taiwanese opponents of traditional medicine give it that credit.[51] At any rate, when the Legislative Yuan did consider revising medical licensing regulations in 1963–1964, it refused to make any changes that would seriously hurt traditional medicine.[52] The obnoxious five-year regulation, for instance, remained unaltered.

The disgust and near despair of the anti-traditionalist liberals of *Wen-hsing* at the defeat of what they saw as a perfectly rational and urgently needed scientific reform was reflected in another article, by Lin Chen-k'e and even more forcefully in an "editorial report." The title of Lin's article, "Watching the Legislative Yuan Write Some 'Death Warrants,'" indicates their bitterness.[53] Lin claimed that he had written the piece, not in the hope that it would accomplish anything in the present hopeless milieu, but just for the "historical record." He did not dare wish for complete abolition of Chinese medicine as Li Ao had demanded. In the current political and cultural situation, one could only hope that "twenty or thirty words," a few harmful provisions, might be changed in the medical laws. The editorial was even less hopeful. Reviewing the futile campaign for legal revision, it roundly condemned both the hidebound legislature and the apathetic press and public opinion of Taiwan. To the *Wen-hsing* group here was another case of science and progress defeated by tradition and irrationality. Hence, the bitterness of their attack on the unsympathetic Legislative Yuan which, fossil of a past generation, still could condemn the new youth of China "to be buried alive with the dead." [54] This linking of the medical to other issues, plus the tone of passionate indignation, is, of course, reminiscent of earlier polemics back on the mainland.

In fact, viewing all these developments on Taiwan, one has the feeling of once again seeing a drama that was acted out some twenty or thirty years before. The agitation about schools for Chinese medicine, the plans for synthesis and reform, the passionate denunciations of corrupting the universality of science, the equally passionate counterblasts at Chinese who would abandon their national essence, the efforts to restrict traditional medical practice—the events, the issues, the arguments—all these had occurred before.

When *Wen-hsing* joined in the campaign to tighten medical regulations it ran, alongside the articles by Li Ao and Wu Chi, reprints of essays by Hu Shih and Fu Ssu-nien from the 1930's.[55] They were not just historical pieces. Fu Ssu-nien's arguments of 1934 were just as relevant to the issue in 1962 as those in Li Ao's contemporary article. Fu was still at the heart of a live issue, for the intellectual milieu had not shifted enough to make him irrelevant. Of course, this rerun, along with its familiarity, does seem to have a rather tired quality. The same battles are still being fought, and "still" implies (except for a zealous few like Li Ao) a certain weariness.

In Communist China, on the other hand, if the drama— how to adapt Chinese medicine to the dual demands of science and nationalism—is the same, the actors, stage, and stage directions have all changed. The People's Government imposes acceptance of the Chinese people's medicine with no tolerance for argument. But apart from the absence of a freedom to debate which is still permitted on Taiwan, larger changes in the entire social and cultural context of mainland China would, in any event, make much of the argument of the 1930's irrelevant there. That those arguments can be revived and those struggles re-enacted on Taiwan testifies both to the greater intellectual freedom there, and to the much slower pace of social and cultural change.

XI

CONCLUSION

MEDICINE AND INTELLECTUAL HISTORY

It should be abundantly clear by now that medicine is unique in the multifaceted ways in which it touches upon man and society. In following the Chinese medicine issue this book has glimpsed many of these facets—political, institutional, social—without being able to illuminate them fully. These are, to pursue Joseph Levenson's metaphor, hares started for others to catch. The present study has been more concerned with catching the intellectual issues aroused by the medical controversy, showing what it can reveal about intellectual history. Probably the most illuminating aspect has been the interaction of two of the dominant themes in modern Chinese thinking—the drive for national strength through modern science, and the concern that modernization not imply betrayal of national identity. The pervasive acceptance of science, at least as an abstract value, by almost everyone concerned in the controversy is yet another testimony to science's conquest of the mind of modern

China, if not of China's conquest of science.[1] As applied to medicine, this has a strong humanitarian aspect. Nevertheless, although it is difficult to disentangle humanitarian and sociopolitical motives in the arguments used, it appears that the major emphasis has been on the social or national goals of applying science to medicine rather than on more individual humanitarian benefits. With national survival at stake, it is hardly surprising that, even in medicine, science should be seen in terms of the broad drive for national "wealth and power." [2]

Why the concern for national identity, or cultural continuity, should have been manifested in medicine is less self-evident, but the motivations behind it should be clear by now. We might reiterate, however, that it has not been so much resistance to science itself as an attempt to find and assert elements of scientific value in China's own traditional culture. Most of the important proponents of Chinese medicine (or "national medicine") have felt both compulsions —toward science and toward Chinese culture—and have tried to reconcile them in some sort of syncretic formula. Much of this has been nonsense scientifically; some of it has been harmful medically—but all of it has been significant intellectually.

This has been apparent in tracing the development of the Chinese medicine debate over a span of almost seventy years as attitudes toward this particular subject were constantly shaped by the larger issues of the time. At the beginning, concern for national strength in a Social-Darwinist world prompted the first reformers to point out traditional medicine's inadequacies in public health. Then, in the May 4th period, the new radicals' bitter repudiation of everything associated with traditional medicine was an integral part of their complete rejection of traditional culture in favor of science and modernity. Similarly, the "national essence" defenders of Chinese medicine were defending it as part of the general struggle to save Chinese culture from total submergence in the flood of Western cultural importations. Their attempts to incorporate modern science into a reformed medicine, still recognizably Chinese, were typical of the modern dilemma over modernization and cultural continuity.

It has been noted how close the position of these modern cultural conservatives is to the official policy adopted by the Communist government since at least 1954. Neither have been diehard traditionalists trying to preserve Chinese medicine unchanged, yet both have criticized pro-Western "bourgeois" intellectuals who sought to eliminate it. There is something to be said here for the generalization that it is the Western-oriented "liberals"—proponents of democratic government, individual freedom, Western cultural forms—who are the real radicals in modern Chinese history. This has certainly been true in the Chinese medicine controversy. Yet it must also be noted that during the 1920's and 1930's the Marxists shared much of the liberals' animus toward traditional medicine. It was only when the old social and political associations of Chinese medicine had been effectively broken that it was safe to rehabilitate it as a legitimate part of the "people's national heritage." Only when there were no longer influential conservatives to uphold "national medicine" did the People's Government come forth as its protector. Without discounting practical considerations about medical shortages and public health problems, this suggests that the revival of cultural nationalism in Communist China has been facilitated by the elimination of earlier traditionalists and cultural nationalists. On Taiwan, it is still up to those conservative groups to combat the medical "Westernizers"; in Communist China the Party maintains a watchful vigil against such unpatriotic "bourgeois" prejudices.

INDIA AND CHINA: PARALLELS AND CONTRASTS

At the outset the broad similarity between traditional medicine in modern China and modern India was noted. Now, having covered the Chinese experience in detail, it is possible to point out how the Indian comparison can highlight some distinctive features of Chinese medicine in this century.

For the contemporary scene, the most striking contrast is the different sources of support for native medicine. In Communist China it comes from the political Left, from a revolutionary government; in India it comes generally from cultural and political conservatives—quite similar to the situation in China before 1949 and on Taiwan today. Another parallel between India and the Nationalist Government is in the indecision over official policy toward traditional medicine. Both Congress India and Kuomintang China made modern medicine the only government-approved and supported medical system, but both governments have come under strong pressure from the right wing of the ruling party to modify this policy in favor of at least partial support for indigenous medicine. Moreover, in both cases this political pressure has been effective in thwarting public health authorities oriented to modern medicine from imposing legal restrictions on traditional practices.

Hence, the general social and political alignment of the debate over traditional medicine is much closer between these two governments than between contemporary India and mainland China. Yet there are still some very striking differences between the situation in India and in Nationalist China. One is the much greater decentralization of efforts to revive and rehabilitate Indian medicine. Before and after independence, most of the official backing for Ayurveda has come from provincial governments, and this has varied widely. For example, there was a government school for Ayurveda in Madras as early as 1923, whereas the Bengal government has never granted its practitioners any of the legal privileges of modern physicians, much less supported them. The proponents of Chinese medicine, in contrast, even in the days of China's greatest political fragmentation, consistently directed their appeals to the central government. Except for Yen Hsi-shan's project in Taiyuan, efforts at rehabilitation of Chinese medicine on a regional basis were almost nonexistent. The controversy and reform proposals focused on the major intellectual centers of Shanghai and Peking; the expectation for effective government support was directed toward the national capital. In part, this may be attributable to a greater uniformity in traditional Chinese medicine's basic concepts and practices, despite certain regional differences arising from local climatic conditions and flora. More fundamental, I believe, was the heritage of Imperial China in focusing political and intellectual life on the capital.

There is also a more subtle, but perhaps even more important, difference in the tone and rhetoric of the debate. In both countries the main emphasis has been on progressive integration of the two medicines so that the benefits of modern science could be obtained without totally sacrificing the unique product of one's own culture. But in India the acceptance of "science" as an undisputed value (however imperfectly it may be understood in practice) seems far less universal. There is a much more widespread defiance of Western culture and Western medicine. This is most apparent in the flourishing "Pure Ayurveda" movement of the last ten years which has rejected any integration with Western medicine in favor of maintaining an uncontaminated Indian medicine. Such total rejection of Western science and medicine in China passed from serious intellectual dialogue almost forty years ago. Its survival in India—along with frequent assertions of spiritual superiority over Western materialism—illuminates how far the crux of the debate has shifted in China. There, under both Nationalist and Communist governments, the real issue has become the accommodation of traditional medicine to modern science, not its defense against science. Just as we have seen that in China the particular issues of the medical debate were not irrelevant to larger intellectual concerns, it seems that many of these key differences in the way a roughly similar battle over indigenous medical systems has been fought are not irrelevant to some of the larger differences between the modern histories of China and India.

CHINESE MEDICINE AND CHINA'S MEDICAL MODERNIZATION

Our main concern has been to relate Chinese medicine to the general pattern of China's modern history, especially her intellectual history. But it might also be useful to assess in a few paragraphs how, on the level of concrete achievements, the Chinese medicine question has affected China's medical modernization. There are several ways in which it appears to have been an impediment. First, and most obvious, it has enormously complicated the problem of establishing uniform standards in medicine. The problem of standardization has been universal in the century or so since scientific medicine began to establish a generally accepted superiority (at least in Western countries) over common folk medicine and various "unorthodox" systems. In the advanced industrialized nations, government-imposed legal restrictions, the codes of medical societies, and public education have all led to the establishment of uniform standards for medical education and practice. These have either excluded from practice those unqualified according to scientific medical criteria, or, in more permissive democratic societies, denied them the prestige and privileges of the regular medical profession.

In both Communist and Nationalist China, traditional physicians, without any scientific training, have the same legal rights and status as their modern counterparts. There are, then, two criteria for the status of physician—the one, scientific medical training, the other, mastery of the traditional medical lore. As we have seen, all attempts to make scientific medicine the sole standard have been frustrated by the proponents of Chinese medicine. It is as though the struggle between orthodox medicine and homeopathy in the United States had been complicated by the latter's appeal to cultural familiarity and patriotism in preserving a unique "national medicine" against a foreign importation. In China, the cultural dimension added to the struggle between scientific medicine and its competitors has made medical standardization much more difficult.

Secondly, the competing claims of traditional medicine on scarce material resources might also be cited as another factor retarding medical modernization. Hospitals, schools, and research centers built for traditional medicine could, according to its critics, have been better devoted to modern medicine. Effort and expenditure, government and private, have been directed away from vital scientific medicine and public health work.

Third, and last, there is the plausible argument that all this involved discussion about preserving the vital truths of the old medicine, plus the legal protection it has been given, has strengthened popular suspicion of newly introduced scientific medical techniques. The intellectuals, in worrying and theorizing about "national essence," have, according to this view, reinforced the innate resistance to cultural change among the illiterate masses instead of leading them to science and enlightenment.

There is some truth to all these charges, but their importance in influencing the actual course of medical modernization should not be exaggerated. No doubt, as the Chinese Medical Association frequently complained, support for traditional medicine has impeded the emergence of one unified and standardized medical profession in China. Yet it should be noted that the achievement of such medical standardization in other countries has come only with an economic and scientific base sufficient to support a qualitatively and quantitatively adequate modern medical establishment. With the possible exception of Taiwan, China has not achieved that base. And, without enough properly trained doctors, it is somewhat unrealistic to expect that universally high standards of medical practice could be enforced. Similarly, the diversion of resources from modern medicine to traditional medicine, even in Communist China, has probably been rather small. One advantage of Chinese medicine has been its relative cheapness, although its more devoted adherents would never admit that this was its main merit. There are no figures available as to what percentage of the national medical budget goes to traditional medicine, but an educated guess would be that since 1949 it has not been over 10–15 per cent in Communist China. Under other Chinese governments it has been infinitesimal.

In purely material terms, then, there is no evidence that the controversy over preserving Chinese medicine has significantly affected the drive toward medical modernization. The extent to which it reflects and reinforces popular medical conservatism is more open to conjecture. Again, however, I would point out that, under the direction of a strong central government, a policy of simultaneously pushing both traditional and modern medicine is not without advantages for introducing new medical and hygienic practices in close association with familiar, accepted forms. This has perhaps been not so much putting new wine into old bottles, as putting new antibiotics into the medicine cabinet along with the old snake oil. Hopefully, the patient will thereby get used to the new, and the old medicine itself (particularly its practitioners) will gradually change and improve. One may be legitimately skeptical about the will or capacity of earlier organizations like the Institute for National Medicine to do this, but the rural health centers of the People's Republic have evidently been fairly effective in introducing real change within a familiar context—in easing the cultural shock of medical modernization.[3]

All this may seem to minimize the importance of the Chinese medicine controversy in determining the course of medical developments in China. Modern medicine has steadily gained during the twentieth century despite all the furor over national essence, medical synthesis, and cultural continuity. This is perfectly true. Though these abstract cultural and intellectual factors have been far from irrelevant to actual medical developments, it would be misleading to consider them decisive. The prestige of science and the desire to build a strong, healthy nation have determined that the main thrust would be toward scientific medicine; concern with cultural continuity and vindication of a national tradition have modified the form this drive for modernization has taken. But, in the final analysis, the entire controversy over Chinese medicine has been more intellectually significant than medically important. By this I mean that it has been more revealing of many of the central pressures and compulsions in modern Chinese intellectual life than ultimately decisive in shaping modern China's medical history.

AN END OF "CHINESE MEDICINE?"

Finally, there arises the inevitable question of how long the anomalous situation of two distinct systems of medicine in China will prevail. It may have been possible in earlier times for two or more medical systems to coexist—witness Ayurveda and Unani in India—but this was never the case in China. More important, modern science exerts a profound pressure toward universal standardization which we still assume to be in the long run irresistible. Cautiously making a prognosis of the medical dichotomy in modern China, we first of all note that the main impulse has been toward ending it in a synthesis between Chinese and Western. The obstacles to such a synthesis have been formidable on both the technical and psychological level. Technically, or medically, the difficulties in reconciling the principles of traditional medicine with modern science have been discussed. It is the insistence that these principles must be validated by modern science that makes accommodation of the traditional practices to modern medical techniques and theory so difficult. If gradually this insistence is modified, as perhaps modern scientific achievements make it less necessary psychologically to find scientific value in China's cultural tradition, then an ultimate fusion of Chinese and Western medicines may be possible. That this new medicine will bear the mark of its Chinese origins seems not improbable; that it will be "new" in the sense of radically different from the general principles of world scientific medicine seems unlikely.

It should, however, be remembered that the final outcome of the clash between the two medical systems will be determined in the context of the larger pressures on the modern Chinese mind. It is not just a question of training enough scientific doctors, or determining what works and what does not in the native tradition. Such technical scientific factors are, of course, important. But so long as modern China has not worked out the problem of assimilating Western culture into a new cultural synthesis—both modern and still Chinese—nonscientific pressures are likely to complicate the problem of Chinese medicine. As with its origin and development, the ultimate solution of the controversy— the disappearance of the two systems and the end of a "Chinese" medicine—will be part of the resolution of the larger cultural problem.

Notes
Bibliography
Glossary

ABBREVIATIONS USED IN THE NOTES

SP:CK   *Shen pao, i-yao chou-k'an*
(Shen pao, weekly medical supplement)

TK:CK   *Ta kung pao, i-hsüeh chou k'an*
(Ta kung pao, weekly medical supplement)

JMJP   *Jen-min jih-pao* (People's daily)

KMJP   *Kuang-ming jih-pao*

SCMP   *Survey of the China Mainland Press*

ECMM   *Extracts* [later, *Selections*] *from China*

(SCMM)   *Mainland Magazines*
(Hong Kong: United States Consulate-General)

NOTES

INTRODUCTION: MEDICINE IN A CONTEXT OF CULTURAL CONFRONTATION

1. Chang Chün-mai, Ting Wen-chiang, *et al.*, K'e-hsüeh yü jen-shang kuan (Science and philosophy of life; Shanghai, 1923), p. 3.

2. These problems are mostly fully analyzed in Joseph R. Levenson, *Confucian China and Its Modern Fate: The Problem of Intellectual Continuity* (Berkeley and Los Angeles, 1958).

3. The recent literature in medical sociology reveals an increasing awareness of the cultural dimensions of medicine. See, for example, Steven Polgar, "Health Action in Cross-Cultural Perspective," in Howard E. Freeman, Sol Levine, and Leo G. Reeder, eds., *Handbook of Medical Sociology* (Englewood Cliffs, N.J., 1963) pp. 397–419.

4. The attempts to revive indigenous Indian medicine are discussed in Charles Leslie, "The Rhetoric of the Ayurvedic Revival in Modern India," *Royal Anthropological Institute, Proceedings*, No. 82: 72–73 (May 1963). There is also a wealth of information in the official Indian Government reports on the subject. *Report of the Committee on Indigenous Systems of Medicine* (Delhi, 1948) 2 vols. and *Report of the Committee to Assess and Evaluate the Present Status of the Ayurvedic System of Medicine* (Delhi, 1958).

5. There has, however, been some interest in reviving Greco-Arabic, or Unani, medicine in India and Pakistan. See, for example, Institute of History of Medicine and Medical Research, *Theories and Philosophies of Medicine* (Delhi, 1962).

6. The rash of recent English-language works on Chinese medicine does not seem likely to change this situation. Perhaps the most useful is Felix Mann, *Acupuncture: The Ancient Chinese Art of*

Healing (New York, 1962). Even here, however, many problems are left unsolved. Most other works, such as Heinrich Wallnöfer and Anna von Rottauscher, *Chinese Folk Medicine,* tr. Marion Palmedo (New York, 1965), Louis Moss, *Acupuncture and You* (New York, 1966), and Evan Shu, *The Developmental History of Medicine in China* (Seattle, 1963), may titillate Western readers but cast precious little light on the subject. Serious readers can only await with impatience the forthcoming volume on the biological sciences in Joseph Needham's monumental work, *Science and Civilization in China.*

CHAPTER I: THE TRADITIONAL MEDICAL SYSTEM

1. Confucius, for example, remarks in the Lun-Yu that "a person without perseverance, cannot [even] become a shaman doctor." Ch'en Pang-hsien, *Chung-kuo i-hsüeh shih* (A Medical history of China; Shanghai, 1937) pp. 7–10, gives numerous quotations from ancient texts showing the shamanistic origins of early Chinese medicine.

2. Arturo Castiglioni, *A History of Medicine,* tr. E. B. Krumbhaar, 2nd ed. (New York, 1958), Chaps. 3 and 4.

3. One particularly interesting study of this is George Way Harley, *Native African Medicine: With Special Reference to its Practice in the Mano Tribe of Liberia* (Cambridge, Mass., 1941), especially Chap. 7. Henry Sigerist comments, "Primitive therapy is a combination of empirico-rational, magical and, as we shall soon see, religious elements, which are interwoven inextricably, and while the motivation of a treatment may be primarily magical or religious, it may well be combined with methods that are used in scientific medicine today for totally different reasons." Henry E. Sigerist, *Primitive and Archaic Medicine,* vol. 1 of *A History of Medicine* (New York, 1951) p. 194. For more extended treatment see Erwin A. Ackerknecht, "Problems of Primitive Medicine," *Bulletin of the History of Medicine,* 11:503–521 (May 1942).

4. Bernhard J. Stern, *Society and Medical Progress* (Princeton, 1941), p. xi.

5. *Chou-li* (Rites of Chou) chüan 5.

6. Stern, pp. 5–6.

7. The *Nei-ching* belongs to that large group of important texts from this period whose exact date and authorship are unknown. The present text could be a Former, or even Later, Han product but parts of it may be of Chou authorship, or at least preserve an earlier oral tradition. The only available translation is Ilza Veith, *Huang Ti Nei Ching Su Wen: The Yellow Emperor's Classic of Internal Medicine* (Baltimore, 1949).

8. The extremely complex problem of early Chinese scientific

thought is best analyzed in Joseph Needham, *Science and Civilization in China* (Cambridge, England, 1956), vol. 2, Chap. 13.

9. Needham, II, 232–244.

10. There is a chart, "Table of Organs and Their Relationships" in K. Chimin Wong and Wu Lien-te, *A History of Chinese Medicine* (Tientsin, 1932), p. 11.

11. The *Nei-ching's* passages on circulation of the blood have become a source of considerable controversy in the twentieth century. Many proponents of Chinese medicine have seen in this an anticipation of Harvey's discovery almost 2,000 years later. Yet one has only to think of how Harvey arrived at his discovery—he *measured* the volume of blood passing through the heart in a given time and found this is to be far heavier than the weight of the entire body—to realize the difference between even a crude, early scientific approach and the fleeting intuitive glimpses, backed by no evidence, of the *Nei-ching*. The most that Wong and Wu, both modern-trained doctors, can say for it is, "The ancients made a very near guess at the facts." K. Chimin Wong and Wu Lien-te, p. 20. But it is all the difference between a guess and a scientifically proven fact.

12. The concept of man as the microcosm of the universe is common to several civilizations. The Zorastrian Bible contains a chapter "On the Human Body: An Image of the World," Cyril Elgood, *A Medical History of Persia and the Eastern Caliphate* (Cambridge, England, 1951), p. 20. Hindu medical thought also saw this cosmic parallel and stressed restoring harmony between the two. Henry R. Zimmer, *Hindu Medicine* (Baltimore, 1948), pp. 109–132. And, in Europe, Henry Sigerist says of Hippocratic medicine: "Thus it was possible to establish a direct relationship between the macrocosm of the universe and the microcosm of the organism and to link them up with the atmospheric changes due to the seasons." Sigerist, *A History of Medicine*, II, 322.

13. Needham, II, 203.

14. Needham, II, 338.

15. These drugs are listed and discussed in Ch'en Pang-hsien, *Chung-kuo i-hsüeh shih*, pp. 40–46.

16. K. Chimin Wong and Wu Lien-te, p. 77.

17. Its contents are described in Bernard E. Read, *Chinese Medicinal Plants From the Pen Ts'ao Kang Mu* (Peiping, 1936).

18. E. H. Hume, *The Chinese Way in Medicine* (Baltimore, 1940), p. 124.

19. Dr. Edward Hume recounts an instance of this in Changsha when both he and a traditional doctor made an identical diagnosis of kidney disease using entirely different methods, E. H. Hume, *Doctors East and Doctors West* (Baltimore, 1946), pp. 190–192.

20. In English, perhaps the best historical description is in K.

Chimin Wong and Wu Lien-te, pp. 39–47 and, for its actual application, Mann, pp. 77–92.

21. The English-speaking reader can do no better than to consult Felix Mann's book on acupuncture. Mann is a Cambridge-trained physician, so he is aware of the problems of reconciling the theory of acupuncture with modern scientific concepts. His book does not do this, for it is essentially an explanation of the Chinese concepts, but it nevertheless remains the most systematic account to date. Much briefer, but more lucid, is Nathan Sivin, "The Demise of Chinese Acupuncture—An Essay Review," to appear in the first issue of *Wen Lin*. In French, the writings of Georges Soulie De Morant are most important, especially *L'Acupuncture Chinoise* (Paris, 1957). One of many recent Chinese simplified introductions to the art is *Chen-chiu ju-men* (An introduction to acupuncture; Peking, 1964).

22. This principle is discussed in Ilza Veith, "Some Philosophical Concepts of Early Chinese Medicine," *Transactions of the Indian Institute of Culture,* No. 4 (December 1950), 15 pp.

23. Traditional Chinese medical thought does not make the sharp distinction between physical and mental illness which we find in the West. It can be seen how the concept of harmony and disequilibrium could blur such a distinction. However, popular thought, and even respectable medical treatises, often attributed some disorders which we consider physical as well as others we would call mental to ghosts, demons, and spirits. There is some discussion of this in Ilza Veith, "The Supernatural in Far Eastern Concepts of Mental Disease," *Bulletin of the History of Medicine,* 37.2:139–158 (March-April 1963).

24. William R. Morse, Dean of Medicine at West China Union University, described witnessing an itinerant, market place acupuncturist in Suifu, Szechwan. His filthy appearance, the bravado with which he drove needles deep into the skull, and his total disregard for any kind of sanitary procedure (he would clean the needles by wiping them on his boots) make a gruesome picture of popular traditional medicine. Morse, *Chinese Medicine* (New York, 1934), pp. 150–157.

25. Conversation with Dr. Wilder Penfield, Montreal Neurological Institute, March 10, 1966.

26. *Hsiao ching* (Classic of filial piety), Chap. 1.

27. The description is found in the Edwin Smith papyrus from approximately the sixteenth century B.C. Castiglioni, pp. 55–56.

28. In the case of Paré, surgeon to the French army, the relationship is immediate and direct. Many other examples, from the Homeric wars to the use of blood plasma in World War II, could be cited to support this thesis.

29. B. J. Stern analyzes this social prejudice and its effect on surgery in medieval Europe. He also examines the general aristocratic

prejudice against doctors as persons who work with their hands, in earlier Western culture, and the medical profession's attempt to overcome this bias through building scholastic, textual, medicine. Stern, Chaps. 1–3, *passim.*

30. Castiglioni, p. 99.

31. Lee T'ao, "Ten Celebrated Physicians and Their Temple," *Chinese Medical Journal,* 58.9:267–274 (September 1940).

32. *Chou-li,* chüan 5. This, at any rate, is the interpretation given it by Joseph Needham and Lu Gwei-djen, "China and the Origin of Examinations in Medicine," *Proceedings of the Royal Society of Medicine,* 56.2:63–70 (February 1963). Ch'en Pang-hsien, in the latest edition of his *A Medical History of China* (Shanghai, 1957), also refers to it as "the earliest health insurance organization" (p. 26).

33. Ilza Veith has translated both the relevant passages of the *Chou-li* and Wang An-shih's comments upon them from his *Chou-kuan hsin-i* (New meaning to the Offices of Chou) in an article, "Government Control of Medicine in Eleventh-Century China, *"Bulletin of the History of the Medicine,* 14.2:159–172 (July 1943). The quoted passage is translated on p. 168.

34. Needham and Lu Gwei-djen, "China and Origin of Examinations," p. 68.

35. System outlined by K. Chimin Wong and Wu Lien-te, p. 70, and in more detail, by Ch'en Pang-hsien (1957), pp. 171–175. Lu and Needham postulate that, via Baghdad, this provided inspiration for the first medical examinations in Europe at the famous Salerno school of the thirteenth century.

36. Jen Ying-ch'iu, *T'ung-su Chung-kuo i-hsüeh shih-hua* (A popular history of Chinese medicine; Chungking, 1957). It should, however, be noted that many of these benevolent institutions were connected with Buddhist charity and Buddhist temples (Ch'en Pang-hsien, 1957, p. 138). Also, apart from charitable dispensaries, the hospitals themselves were, like their premodern European counterparts, mainly repositories for those who were hopelessly unfit for society—lepers, blind, cripples—or where the very poor went to die. The social institution of the modern hospital, where trained medical care and complete medical facilities are available for therapeutic treatment, is as modern as the advances in scientific medicine (notably ascpsis and scientific medical technology) that made it possible. Before then, in China and elsewhere, they could be nothing more than death houses for the poor. B. J. Stern recounts how in eighteenth-century England, "it was customary to demand a sum for burial expenses on admission" (Stern, p. 101). In China hospitals were perhaps somewhat less prominent because of the stronger family organization to provide care for the ill and the popular horror of dying away from home.

37. K. Chimin Wong and Wu Lien-te, p. 93.

38. Both examples cited in K. Chimin Wong and Wu Lien-te, pp. 54–55.

39. Of the former type, an excellent example is the forty-volume compilation by the T'ang scholar Wang T'ao, *Wai-t'ai pi-yao* (Medical secrets of an official). Of the latter, examples are legion. Some idea of the popularity of such activity can be gained from the fact that up to the end of Ch'ing there were forty-nine commentaries on the *Nei-ching;* 115 commentaries, concordances, or editors of *Shang-han lun;* and over 100 commentaries on Wang Shu-ho's "Pulse Classic." K. Chimin Wong and Wu Lien-te, pp. 23, 33, and 40. There are Western parallels for this scholarly interest in medicine by gentlemen, but they are very few. Celsus' *De re Medica,* written by a Roman patrician of the first century A.D., probably is the most obvious.

40. There are many stories illustrating this. One of the most interesting tells of Hsü Shu-wei, a Sung scholar, who upon returning home after repeatedly failing the provincial examinations, had a dream in which a man in white told him to be a doctor. He studied medicine and became a very famous doctor, treating rich and poor alike *without fees.* At the next official examination he passed with honors. Lee T'ao, "Medical Ethics in Ancient China," *Chinese Medical Journal,* 61.2:124 (April-June 1943).

41. Evariste Regis Huc, *Christianity in China, Tartary and Thibet* (London, 1857), III, 209.

42. T'ang Hsien-tsu, *Mu-tan-t'ing* (The peony pavillion; Shanghai, 1934) scene 4, p. 11.

43. Quoted in K. Chimin Wong and Wu Lien-te, p. 55. Actually Sun Szu-mo was a courtier in the T'ang, not a *chin-shih,* and he enjoyed high social status. The quotation would appear to indicate a later opinion of professional medical men.

44. This appears in the crude jokes about doctors contained in the seventeenth-century collection of popular humor, *Hsiao-lin k̨uang-chi* (Broadly collected humor), chüan 2.

45. The practice is described, with sample prescriptions in K. Chimin Wong and Wu Lien-te, pp. 91–92.

46. From John Earle, *Micro-cosmographie or a piece of the world charactiz'd* (London, 1678); quoted in Stern, p. 23.

47. Lee T'ao, "Medical Ethics," p. 125.

48. Throughout medieval Europe physicians jealously clung to their trade secrets. By the seventeenth century the Chamberlen family's preservation of obstetrical forceps as their own secret was considered scandalous. With the formation of medical societies and modern hospitals, such practices were to be found only among special healers outside of the regular medical profession.

49. Apart from their medical writings, medical amateurs might, in times of epidemic, publicly post certain effective prescriptions. This

was as much an act of benevolence as donating goods or money for the public welfare, because the prescriptions were regarded as private property. Instance cited in Hsu, *Magic and Science in Yunnan*, p. 51.

50. Ch'en Tzu-ming in his *Wai-k'e ching-yao* (Essentials of external medicine) denounces as immoral the common practice of keeping secret effective remedies and even changing prescriptions when transmitting them so that the secret would not be shared. In *T'u-shu chi-ch'eng* (Illustrated encyclopedia), chüan 521, p. 17b.

51. Zimmer, p. 180.

52. Needham, II, 203.

53. By far the most exhaustive study of this period is Fan Shih, *Ming-chi hsi-yang ch'uan-ju chih i-hsüeh* (Entrance of Western medicine at the end of Ming; Shanghai, 1943), 4 vols.

54. The most recent account of Japan's quest for Western medical knowledge is John Z. Bowers, *Medical Education in Japan: From Chinese to Western Medicine* (New York, 1965), Chaps. 1–2. The Japanese samurai culture's interest in military surgery is usually cited as the most obvious reason for its very different reaction from the Chinese civil mandarins. Dr. Bowers has suggested that a much more pervasive hypochondria in Japanese society might be another factor in the greater Japanese curiosity about a new medical system.

CHAPTER II: INTRODUCTION AND GROWTH OF
MODERN MEDICINE IN CHINA, 1800–1949

1. There is a very considerable literature on medical missionaries and the missionary movement in general. Some of the most useful works are Kenneth Scott Latourette, *A History of Christian Missions in China* (New York, 1929); Harold Balme, *China and Modern Medicine* (London, 1921); Clara B. Whitmore, *An History of the Development of Western Medicine in China,* Ph.D. thesis (University of Southern California, 1934); and the relevant chapters of K. Chimin Wong and Wu Lien-te, *History of Chinese Medicine.*

2. Balme, p. 85.

3. Edward H. Hume, "Medical Education in China: A Survey and Forecast," in *Addresses and Papers, Dedication Ceremonies and Medical Conference, Peking Union Medical College* (Peking, 1922), p. 90.

4. K. Chimin Wong and Wu Lien-te, p. 368.

5. The careers of this remarkable group are briefly described in Whitmore, pp. 178–180. By the time reliable statistics are available on the total number of female physicians, they occupy about 10 per cent of the modern Chinese medical profession by the 1930's. Nei-cheng pu (Ministry of Interior) *Wei-sheng t'ung-chi* (Health statistics; 1939), p. 34.

6. A list of Dudgeon and other translators' works are given in K. Chimin Wong and Wu Lien-te, pp. 329–330.

7. Actually, the Imperial Maritime Customs series of "Customs Medical Reports," started in 1871, performed some of the functions of a scholarly journal. K. Chimin Wong and Wu Lien-te, p. 252.

8. The common division on a basis of Western medicine for external medicine and Chinese for internal medicine has been noted by several writers. See, for example, Hume, *Doctors East and Doctors West*, p. 6 and Wu Lien-te, *Plague Fighter: Autobiography of a Chinese Physician* (Cambridge, England, 1959), p. 568.

9. Dugald Christie, *Thirty Years in Moukden, 1883–1913* (London, 1914), p. 5.

10. The content and basis of this anti-missionary agitation is analyzed in Paul A. Cohen, *China and Christianity: The Missionary Movement and the Growth of Chinese Antiforeignism, 1860–1870* (Cambridge, Mass., 1963).

11. Robert Worth recounts the fairly typical experience of his grandfather in a small Yangtze valley town near the end of the nineteenth century. The mission hospital was regarded with great suspicion, and even was sacked by an antiforeign mob, before a timely amputation of the gangrenous leg of a scholar-official's son saved the boy's life and, through the publicity, gained general acceptance for the hospital. Robert M. Worth," Institution-Building in the People's Republic of China: The Rural Health Center," *East-West Center Review*, 1.3:19–34 (February 1965).

12. Quoted in K. Chimin Wong and Wu Lien-te, p. 146.

13. *Tseng Wen-cheng-kung shou-shu jih-chi (Diary of Tseng Kuo-fan)* Ts'e 38, 19th day, 3rd month, T'ung-chih 10 (May 8, 1871), quoted in Teng Ssu-yu and J. K. Fairbank, *China's Response to the West* (Cambridge, Mass., 1954), p. 63.

14. Teng Ssu-yu and Fairbank, p. 102.

15. William Lockhart, *The Medical Missionary in China* (London, 1861), pp. 23–24.

16. Ch'en Pang-hsien (1957), pp. 326–327.

17. K. Chimin Wong and Wu Lien-te, pp. 289–290.

18. Ch'en Pang-hsien (1937), pp. 229–230.

19. K. Chimin Wong and Wu Lien-te, p. 406.

20. The dramatic story of this epidemic, which aroused international concern but was mainly controlled by the efforts of modern Chinese doctors working through Chinese governmental machinery, is well told by its chief participant. Wu Lien-te, *Plague Fighter,* Chaps. 1–4. Its international political implications are brought out in Carl F. Nathan, "Plague Prevention and Politics in Manchuria, 1910–1931" (Cambridge, Mass., 1967).

21. Wu Lien-te, *Plague Fighter*, p. 49.

22. K. Chimin Wong and Wu Lien-te, pp. 436–438; Ch'en Pang-hsien (1937), pp. 309–310.

23. K. Chimin Wong and Wu Lien-te, pp. 499–500.

24. Wu Lien-te, *Plague Fighter*, pp. 460–462. Liang Ch'i-ch'ao was the finance minister of the Peking government that made this appropriation.

25. Balme estimates that in 1920 there were around 1500 modern doctors of whom perhaps 600 were foreigners, either missionaries or in private practice. Balme, p. 181. According to the Nanking Government's figures for 1930, even by then about half of the countries' 500 hospitals were missionary-run. Knud Faber, *Report on Medical Schools in China*, (Geneva: League of Nations, Health Organization, 1931), p. 9.

26. Whitmore, pp. 232–237.

27. The report leading to its establishment was published as *Medicine in China*, China Medical Commission of the Rockefeller Foundation, New York, 1914.

28. This argument is summed up in Balme, pp. 128–130.

29. Wu Lien-te, *Plague Fighter*, p. 300.

30. K. Chimin Wong and Wu Lien-te, p. 442.

31. By 1935, no fewer than 178 modern medical journals, many admittedly ephemeral, had appeared in China. Sung Ta-jen and Shen Ching-fan, "Ch'üan kuo i-yao ch'i-k'an tiao-ch'a chi" (Investigation of medical publications in China), *Chung-hsi i-yao* (Journal of the medical research society of China) 1.1:286 (1935).

32. It was estimated in 1929 that out of 4000 modern-style doctors in China, about 1000 had a good medical education either in China or abroad. League of Nations, Health Organization, *Proposals of the National Government of The Republic of China for Collaboration with the League of Nations on Health Matters* (Geneva, 1930), p. 25.

33. Its first eight presidents were educated at Yale, Cambridge, Pennsylvania, London, Harvard, and Edinburgh.

34. K. Chimin Wong and Wu Lien-te, p. 444.

35. Shryock, *The Development of Modern Medicine* (New York, 1947), Chap. 13.

36. Statistics compiled in a Peking ward by the Health Demonstration Station showed that even in large cities only a small percentage of the population obtained modern medical care. Of the first 1000 deaths investigated, 16 per cent of the victims had received some modern medical treatment, 48 per cent traditional treatment, and 36 per cent none of any kind. National Medical Association of China, *Medical Directory* (Shanghai, 1930), pp. 9–10.

37. League of Nations, *Proposals*, pp. 29–30.

38. The effects of the years 1924–27 on medical missionary operations are described and tabulated in Whitmore, pp. 200–207.

39. The institutional structure is described in K. Chimin Wong and Wu Lien-te, pp. 505-508.

40. C. C. Ch'en, *Scientific Medicine as Applied to Ting Hsien* (Nanking, 1933) and Sidney D. Gamble, *Ting Hsien: A North China Rural Community* (New York, 1954).

41. In 1932 the number of registered physicians was 2,919, 65 per cent of them resident in the three provinces of Kiangsu, Kwangtung and Chekiang. Nei-cheng pu (Ministry of the Interior) *Ch'uan-kuo teng-chi i-shih ming-lu* (National register of physicians; Nanking, 1933).

42. Faber, pp. 24–25.

43. Faber, pp. 19–20.

44. Nei-cheng pu (Ministry of the Interior) *Wei-sheng t'ung-chi,* p. 34. The figure of 9,098 is somewhat exaggerated for it includes every physician who registered in the years 1929–37 without any subtraction for those who had subsequently ceased practice.

45. Described in *China Handbook, 1937–1945,* pp. 490–493.

46. *Ibid.,* p. 493.

47. J. Heng Liu, "The Origin and Development of Public Health Service in China," in H. F. MacNair, ed., *Voices from Unoccupied China* (Chicago, 1944), pp. 41–42.

CHAPTER III: MEDICINE AND NATIONAL STRENGTH IN A SOCIAL-DARWINIST CONTEXT

1. *Kung-ch'e shang-shu chi* (Shanghai, 1895).

2. Liang Ch'i-ch'ao, "I-hsüeh shan-hui hsü (Discussing the medical philanthropy society), in *Yin-ping shih wen-chi (Collected writings from the ice-drinker's studio;* Shanghai, 1916), ts'se 23, p. 29.

3. Liang Ch'i-ch'ao, p. 28.

4. *Ibid.,* p. 30.

5. Mai Chung-hua, comp., *Huang-ch'ao ching-shih wen hsin pien (New supplement to the Huang-ch'ao ching-shih wen-pien;* Shanghai, 1901), Chüan 2, p. 26.

6. Laurence G. Thompson, *Ta T'ung Shu: The One World Philosophy of K'ang Yu-Wei* (London, 1958) p. 256; K'ang Yu-wei, *Ta T'ung Shu* (Shanghai, 1935), p. 428.

7. Thompson, p. 257.

8. K'ang Yu-wei, *Jih-pen shu-mu chih,* (Japanese Bibliography), Vol. 1 (n.d.), pp. 6 and 18.

9. *Ibid.,* p. 6.

10. Chang Po-chen, *Nan-hai K'ang Hsien-sheng chuan* (Biography of Mr. K'ang of Nan-hai; Peking, 1932), p. 7.

11. Personal conversations with a former student of K'ang Yu-wei in the 1920's. Taipei, May, 1964.

12. Liang Ch'i-ch'ao, p. 31. If the society's proposed journal ever appeared, I have found no reference to it. Probably it was stillborn along with many of the other reform ideas of 1898.

13. Personal correspondence with Professor Charles Leslie, Western Reserve University.

14. Compiler of the *Tung-hua lu,* among other works, and a bitter opponent of Liang Ch'i-ch'ao and the reform school in Hunan.

15. Ch'üan Han-sheng, "Ch'ing-mo hsi-yang i-hsüeh ch'uan-ju shih kuo-jen so ch'ih te t'ai-tu," (Chinese attitudes toward the entrance of Western medicine at the end of the Ch'ing), *Shih huo* (Food and goods) 3.12:45–47 (May 16, 1936).

16. *Ibid.,* pp. 45–46. It is interesting to note the similarity of their criticisms with the views reached by the Japanese doctors who, at the risk of their lives, had sought to learn Western medicine and anatomy from the Dutch at Nagasaki, almost 300 years earlier.

17. *Ibid.,* pp. 47–49.

18. Ting Fu-pao, *Chung-hsi i-fang hui t'ung* (Combining Chinese and Western drug prescriptions; Shanghai, 1910).

19. Ch'üan Han-sheng, "Ch'ing-mo hsi-yang i-hsüeh ch'uan-jih shih," p. 50.

20. *Ibid.,* pp. 50–53.

21. Notably his book *Chung-hsi hui-t'ung i-hsüeh ching ching-i,* (The essential points of combining Chinese and Western medical classics; Shanghai, 1908).

22. Ch'üan Han-sheng, "Ch'ing-mo hsi-yang i-hsüeh ch'uan-jih shih," p. 49.

23. Hai-hu, "I-hsüeh yü she-hui chih kuan-hsi," (The relationship between medicine and society), *Tung-fang tsa-chih (Eastern miscellany),* 2.4:7–10 (April 1905).

24. *Ibid.,* p. 8.

25. Ku Yin (pseud.), "Lun Chung-kuo ch'ien-t'u yü i-hsüeh chih kuan-hsi" (On the relationship between China's road forward and medicine"), *Tung-fang tsa-chih,* 2.6:107–114 (June 1905).

26. Ku Yin, p. 111.

27. Wo Wo-sheng (pseud.), "Lun kuo-chia i-hsüeh chih hsing-chih" (On the nature of state medicine), *Hsin-min ts'ung-pao* (New peoples miscellany) No. 60:63–67 (1905).

28. Hume, *Doctors East and Doctors West,* p. 112.

29. Quoted in Ch'en Pang-hsien, *Chung-kuo i-hsüeh shih,* rev. ed. (Taipei, 1956), p. 137b.

30. *Ibid.,* p. 137b.

Notes to Chapter IV

CHAPTER IV: MEDICINE AND CULTURAL ICONOCLASM —
THE MAY 4TH ERA

1. Ch'en Tu-hsiu, "Call to youth", *Hsin ch'ing nien* (New youth) 1.1:6 (Sept. 15, 1915), tr. in Teng and Fairbank, *China's Response to the West*, p. 245.

2. Lu Hsün, *Na-han* (War cry; reprinted Hong Kong, 1962), p. 2.

3. *Ibid.*, pp. 2–3.

4. *Ibid.*, p. 3.

5. T'ang Ssu (Lu Hsün), "Sui kan lu" (Random Thoughts), *Hsin ch'ing nien*, 5.4:405–409 (October 1918).

6. *Ibid.*, pp. 23–32. In *Selected Works of Lu Hsün*, Yang Hsien-i and Gladys Yang (Peking, 1956), I, 29–39.

7. *Ibid.*, I, 40–48.

8. Lu Hsün, "K'uang-jen jih-chi" (Diary of a madman), *Na-han*, p. 17.

9. Translated in *Selected Works of Lu Hsün*, I, 394–401.

10. Pa Chin, *Chia* (Family; Shanghai, 1937), pp. 425–432.

11. Lao She, "Grandma Takes Charge," tr. in C. C. Wang, *Contemporary Chinese Stories* (New York, 1944), pp. 47–59.

12. Yeh Shao-chun, "A Man Must Have a Son," in Jorgenson, *Contemporary Chinese Short Stories* (Shanghai, 1946), pp. 68–101.

13. T'ang Erh-ho, "Hsüeh fa-cheng te jen k'e-i pu tung hsieh i-hsüeh ma?" (Can those who study jurisprudence remain totally ignorant of medicine?) *Hsin chiao-yü* (New education), 2.3:299–300 (November 1919).

14. Niu Jung-sheng, "Chung-i yü Hsi-i" (Chinese medicine and Western medicine), *Hsien-tai p'ing lun* (Contemporary critic), 5.114:18–20 (Feb. 20, 1927).

15. *Ibid.*, p. 19.

16. *Ibid.*

17. *Ibid.*, p. 20.

18. Chang Tsung-liang, " 'Old Style' Versus 'Modern' Medicine in China: Which Can Do More for the Health and Progress of the Country, and Why?", *Medicine As a Life Work Campaign, First Prize English and Chinese Essays of the 1926 National Essay Contest* (Shanghai: Council on Health Education, 1926), p. 7.

19. *Ibid.*, p. 5.

20. *Ibid.*, p. 8.

21. The other prize winners were Chang Chih, student at Futan University in Shanghai; Liu Ming, student at Ch'eng-tu Provincial Girls' Normal School; and Chou Te-lin, student at Hsiang Ya Pharmacy Preparation School, Changsha.

22. Quoted in Chiang Shao-yüan, "Chung-kuo jen tui-yü hsi-yang

i-yao ho i-hsüeh te Fan-ying" (Chinese reaction to Western pharmaceuticals and medicine) *Kung-hsien* (Offerings) 4.3:23 (1928).

23. *Ibid.,* 3.9:16 (1928).

24. The most recent analysis of this famous debate is in D.W.Y. Kwok, *Scientism in Chinese Thought 1900–1950* (New Haven, 1965), Chap. 6.

25. The episode is described in Sun Wen, *Sun Chung-shan ch'üan chi* (Complete works of Sun Yat-sen; Shanghai, 1929), VI, 16–17.

26. Hou Tsung-lien, "Sun Chung-shan hsien-sheng chih chiu-chih Chung-i" (Mr. Sun Yat-sen's final treatment with Chinese medicine), *Min-kuo i-hsüeh tsa-chih* (Republic medical journal), 3.3:164 (March 1925). The argument over Sun Yat-sen's legacy would rage in medical circles for another twenty years with both modern and traditional medicine advocates laying claim to him. See below, Chapter IV.

27. Yang Chi-shih, "Hsi-i shih shen-mo?" (What is Western medicine?), *Min-kuo i-hsüeh tsa-chih,* 3.6:4 (June 1925).

28. *Ibid.,* p. 4.

29. *Ibid.,* p. 6.

30. One of his earliest articles on the subject was "Yü Yün-hsiu, "K'e-hsüeh te kuo ch'ang yao-wu yen-chiu chih ti-i pu" (First step in scientifically studying nationally produced drugs), *Hsüeh i,* Vol. 2, Nos. 4, 5 (July and August 1920).

31. Yü Feng-pin, "Pao-ts'un ku i-hsüeh chih shang-liang" (A discussion on preserving old medicine), *Chung-hua i-hsüeh tsa-chih* (National medical journal of China), 2.1:4–6 (1916).

32. Huang Sheng-pai, "Lun chiu-i lieh wei hsüeh-k'e chih miu-wang." ("On the fallacy of including old medicine in the curriculum"), *I-yao hsüeh,* (Medicine and pharmacology), 2.12:3 (December 1925).

33. *Ibid.,* p. 3.

34. Yü Yen, (Yü Yün-hsiu) "Chiu-i hsüeh-hsiao hsi-t'ung an po-i" (Rejection of old medicine in the school system), *Min-kuo i-hsüeh tsa-chih,* 4.3:4 (March 1926).

CHAPTER V: NATIONAL ESSENCE AND NATIONAL MEDICINE

1. These terms and ideas about traditionalism in modern China come from Levenson, *Confucian China,* vol. 1.

2. Quoted in Chiang Shao-yüan, "Tui-yü Hsi-i te fan-ying," *K'e-hsüeh yüeh-k'an* (Science monthly) 1.6:26 (July 1929).

3. *Ibid.,* p. 26.

4. Lu Ching-sui, "Chiao Chung-Hsi-i lun (Comparing Chinese and Western medicine), *Hua-kuo yüeh-k'an* (China monthly), vol. 1, no. 3 (November 1923).

5. *Ibid.,* pp. 2–3.

6. Hu Shih, *K'e-hsüeh yü jen-sheng kuan* (Science and philosophy of life; Shanghai, 1923), p. 3.

7. See Ch'üan Han-sheng, "Ch'ing-mo te 'Hsi-hsüeh yüan ch'u Chung-kuo' (Late Ch'ing theories on "the Chinese origins of Western learning"), *Ling-nan hsüeh-pao* (Lingnan University journal) 4.2:57–102 (June 1935).

8. Wang Jen-chün, *Ke-chih ku wei* (Traces of natural science from antiquity), in *Chih-hsüeh ts'ung-shu Ch'u-chi* (Preliminary collection on physics; Wuhan, 1897), ts'e 13–15.

9. Nieh Tsung-k'uan, "Chung-Hsi-i chih k'e-hsüeh kuan" (A scientific view of Chinese and Western medicine), *Hsien-tai kuo-i* (Contemporary national medicine) 1.1:17 (1931).

10. In 1890 Li wrote "If scholars could combine Chinese and Western theories so as to create a situation in which the essence was extremely refined, how could this be called a small improvement in medicine?" Introduction to Reverend S. Hunter, *Wan-kuo yao-fang* (Prescriptions of all countries: Shanghai, 1890).

11. *I-hsüeh tsa-chih* (Medical journal) 1.1:15 (July 1921).

12. "Hui chang Shan-hsi Yen tu-chün chien sheng chang ti-i ts'e k'ai hui yen-shuo" (The inaugural address of the society's president, Military Governor Yen Hsi-shan), *I-hsüeh tsa-chih* 1.1:11 (July 1921).

13. "Hui chang Yen Tu-chün chih Ting Chiang-ku hsien-sheng shu," (Letter from Military-Governor Yen to Mr. Ting Chung-she), *I-hsüeh tsa-chih,* Vol. 1, No. 1 (July 1921), p. 102.

14. *Ibid.,* p. 103.

15. See letters to Ting Fu-pao and Chang Li-chih, I-hsüeh tsa-chih, 1.1:102–107 (July 1921).

16. Chiang Shao-yüan "Chung Kuo-jen tui-yü Hsi yang i-yao ho i-hsüeh te Fan-ying," *K'e-hsüeh yüen-k'an,* 1.8:10–15.

17. Huang Sheng-pai, p. 5, fn. 2.

18. See "Chang T'ai-yen ching-sui i-shu", (The precious medical writings of Chang Ping-lin), *Chung-yang jih-pao,* (Central daily), Taipei, Dec. 2, 1961.

19. Chang Ping-lin, "Shang-han-lun t'an-lun pen t'i-tz'u (Discussion of the original text of the Shang-han lun, *Hua-Kuo yüeh-k'an,* 1.6:4 (February 1924).

20. Chang T'ai-yen, "Shang-han lun chiang tzu" (An introduction to the Shang-han lun), *Shanghai Kuo-I hsüeh-yüan yüan k'an,* (Bulletin of the Shanghai Academy of National Medicine), 1.1:4 (1929).

21. Hsü Heng-chih, "Pen yüan ch'uang pan yüan ch'i", (The purposes in founding this Academy), *Shanghai Kuo-i hsüeh-yüan yüan k'an,* 1.1:2 (1929).

22. *Ibid.,* pp. 1–2.

23. Resolution summarized in Wu Lien-te, *Plague Fighter*, p. 506 and *Chung-i-yao nien-chien* (Chinese medicine and pharmacy year-book; Hong Kong, 1957), p. 153.

24. *Chung-i-yao nien-chien*, pp. 150–154.

25. The constitution and organizational bylaws of the central and branch institutes were found quoted in full in the organ of an overseas branch in Java. *Chung-i hui-k'an* (Chinese medicine report) 1.1:21–24 (January 1938).

26. *Ibid.*, p. 23.

27. As in Ch'en Kuo-fu, "I-hsüeh te yu-wei chi Chung-i k'e-hsüeh te pi-yao" (The infancy of medicine and the need for the scientifica-tion of Chinese medicine) in *Ch'en Kuo-fu hsien-sheng ch'üan-chi* (Complete works of Mr. Ch'en Kuo-fu; Hong Kong, 1952), VI, 26.

28. *Ibid.*, VI, 26.

29. A good example of this view is presented in a traditional medi-cal journal in 1936: "Although their aim is the same, their methods definitely cannot be confused. The former is purely philosophic in its approach to curing and the latter applies scientific methods. I there-fore call the former medicine." Chou, "Chung-kuo K'e-hsüeh i chih fa-ta shih" (The development of China's scientific medicine), in *I-wen* (Medical writings), Vol. 1, No. 1 (1936).

30. " 'Ch'ien shou i' ching-kao Chung-i chieh t'ung tao" ('The humble receive benefits,' announcement to the Chinese medicine world) *Ch'i-shih jih-pao i-yao wei-sheng chuan-k'an* (World benefit-ting daily, medical supplement) 1.10:1 (October 1947).

31. Tseng Chüeh-sou, "Chung-i wu hsü k'e-hsüeh-hua" (Chinese medicine has no need of scientification), *Chung-hsi i-yao*, 2:100 (1936).

32. This is expressed particularly strongly in his article "Tang chin i-che te tse-jen" (The responsibility of today's medical personnel), *TK:CK*, No. 213 (Oct. 17, 1933).

33. Chang T'ai-yen, "Shang-han-lun chiang tz'u," p. 4.

34. Ch'en Kuo-fu, VI, 26.

35. Chiao I-t'ang, "Chung-kuo te i-hsüeh" (China's medicine) *Wen-hua chien-she* (Cultural construction) 1.1:161 (September 1934).

36. T'an Tse-chung, "Chung-i k'e-hsüeh kai-tsao chih t'u-ching" (The road to the scientific reform of Chinese medicine), *Ming-jih i-yao* (Tomorrow's medicine) 1.1:14 (1935).

37. Yen Tu-chiao, "Fei-chih Chung-i te shang-liang" (A discus-sion on abolishing Chinese medicine), *Hsin-wen pao* (The news). Reproduced in entirety in an unpublished article by Yang Ching-ch'un (Taichung, Taiwan, December 1962). No date given for the original newspaper article, but presumably it was 1929.

38. Yu Hung-jen, "T'an-t'an Chung-i," *Hua-nien* (Chinese year)

1.36:710 (December 1932).

39. Chang Meng-chung, "Chung-hsi i-hsüeh jung-hua lun" (On the fusion of Chinese and Western medicine) *Ta kung pao,* October 3, 1928. Significantly, he was a graduate of the Peiyang Medical Academy, not of the foreign-run medical schools.

40. Yen Tu-chiao, "Fei-chih Chung-i te shang-liang," *Hsin-wen pao* article, n.d.

41. Ching Hua, "Hua-pei kuo-i lun-chan shu-chi" (Record of the national medicine debate in North China), *Ming-jih i-yao* 1.1:5 (1935).

42. Quoted in Ch'en Chih-t'u, "Tu Chiao I-t'ang wei i-ting kuo-i t'iao li ching-kao kuo-jen chu yu k'an'" (Reaction to Chiao I-t'ang's "Report on deciding the national medicine regulations," *Ta kung pao, i-hsüeh chou k'an,* No. 208 (Sept. 12, 1933).

43. *Ibid.,* VI, 25.

44. *Ibid.,* VI, 8–9.

45. See, for example, a letter from a Chinese in Paris on French use of acupuncture. T'ien-min, "Chung-kuo tsui ku fa-ming chih chen-chiu hsüeh" (China's most ancient art of acupuncture and moxibustion), *K'e-hsüeh te Chung-kuo* (Scientific China) 2.1:4–5 (July 1933).

46. Chiao I-t'ang, p. 162.

47. "The Yellow Emperor," has, of course, been a figure of much more than medical significance, and his particular attachment to Chinese medicine serves rather nicely to relate that subject to the larger one of modern Chinese cultural particularism. In the twentieth century many traditionalists have used Huang-ti as a national ancestor—even, in some journals, dating from Huang-ti's birth. There is an interesting treatment of culture heroes, now only partly de-historicized, in Chang Chi-yun, *Chinese History of Fifty Centuries* tr. Chu Ti-lien (Taipei, 1962), I, 1–70. Despite (perhaps, in part, because of) the vigorous iconoclasm of Ku Chieh-kang and other "antiquity doubters," modern cultural conservatives have felt a deep compulsion to hold onto something of a real historical personality about these figures.

48. Chiao I-t'ang, p. 162.

CHAPTER VI: SCIENCE AND MODERNITY:
THE REJECTION OF "NATIONAL MEDICINE"

1. "Chung-kuo pen-wei te wen-hua chien-she hsüan-yen," *Wen-hua chien-she,* 1.4:1–5 (January 1935).

2. The general problem of cultural identity is treated moest exhaustively in Joseph R. Levenson, *Confucian China and Its Modern Fate:*

The Rejection of "National Medicine"

The Problem of Intellectual Continuity (Berkeley, California, 1958).

3. "Pen-wei hsüan-yen," p. 4.

4. *Hu Shih wen-ts'un* (Collected writings of Hu Shih; Taipei, 1960), IV, 537.

5. *Ibid.,* p. 539.

6. Li Mai-mai, "P'ing'Chung-kuo pen-wei te wen-hua chien-she hsüan-yen'" (Criticizing "Manifesto on Cultural Construction on a Chinese Basis"), *Wen-hua chien-she* 1.5:30 (February 1934).

7. Chiang Hui-ming, "Ts'un hu? Fei hu?" (Exist or perish?), *Chung-hua i-hsüeh tsa-chih,* 21.7:757 (July 1935).

8. Sung Ta-Jen, "Chien-she pen-wei te wen-hua yü Chung-kuo i-hsüeh wen-t'i," (Cultural construction on a Chinese basis and China's medical problems), *Chung-hsi i-yao,* 1.3: 241 (November 1935).

9. Sung Ta-jen, *Chung-hsi i-yao,* 1.1:42 (September 1935).

10. The popularity of the special medical supplement in the leading newspapers is an interesting sociological phenomenon in itself. *Ta kung pao* (Tientsin) seems to have been the first to inaugurate this as a regular feature, but by the early 1930's it was joined by *Shen pao* (Shanghai), *Chung-yang jih-pao* (Nanking) and *Ch'en pao* (Peiping) among others. They all carried articles on various aspects of medical treatment, individual health problems, and public hygiene—serving as an important channel for the dissemination of modern medical and hygienic concepts among the literate population. The popularity of these medical supplements and the number of medical advertisements appearing in twentieth-century Chinese newspapers and journals suggest a deep concern with individual health problems. This should be seen in light of the enormous number of apothecaries in traditional China, the popularity of the classic medical literature among the educated classes, and the deeply rooted Taoist concepts of personal hygiene and cultivation of life. The depth and cultural significance of the literate classes' concern with health problems could perhaps be illuminated by careful anthropological research.

11. Yu Hsien, "Yü Ch'en Kuo-fu Hsien-sheng lun hsin i-hsüeh" (A discussion of new medical science with Mr. Ch'en Kuo-fu), *TK: CK,* No. 198 (July 4, 1933).

12. Chou Shao, "Wei yu-chih ke-hsin chung-kuo i-yao che chin-i chung kao" (A further announcement for those who are determined to revolutionize China's medicine and pharmacy), *SP:CK,* No. 43, (Oct. 16, 1933).

13. Fu Ssu-nien, "So-wei Kuo-i," (So-called National medicine), *Tu-li p'ing-lun,* No. 25 (Aug. 26, 1934); in *Fu Meng-chen hsien-sheng chi* (Collected works of Fu Meng-chen; Taipei, 1952), 6:338.

14. "Wei tsai hsing 'Kuo-i' t'iao-li fu Chiao I-t'ang hsien-sheng" (A reply to Mr. Chiao I-t'ang on choosing the "National Medicine"

article), *Chung-yang jih-pao, i-hsüeh chou-k'an* (Central daily, weekly medical supplement), No. 7 (July 30, 1933).

15. P'ing, "Wo kuo i shih chih wei-chi" (Our country's medical crisis), *TK:CK,* No. 68 (Dec. 18, 1930).

16. Fan Ling-feng, "Yü Yang Kao-ju yen-t'ao Chung-kuo chiu yu i-hsüeh" (Delving into China's ancient medicine with Mr. Yang Kao-ju), *TK:CK,* No. 203 (Aug. 8, 1933).

17. "The question is not whether we can preserve the 'national essence,' but whether the 'national essence' can preserve us."

18. Yu Hsien, "Kuo-i kuan chih shang-liang" (Discussion of the Kuo-i kuan), *TK:CK,* No. 66 (Dec. 4, 1930).

19. "Kuo-nan yü Kuo-i" (National difficulties and national medicine), *TK:CK,* No. 127 (Feb. 17, 1932).

20. Chien Ch'ing, "Wo tui-yü Kuo-i kuan chih kan-hsiang" (My reaction to the Kuo-i kuan), *TK:CK,* No. 73 (Jan. 22, 1931).

21. Chou Shao, "Wei yu chih...," *SP:CK,* No. 16 (Oct. 16, 1933).

22. The reactionary plot theme, clearly articulated by Chou Tso-jen in the 1930's, was repeated under the National Government. See, for example, P'ing (pseud.), "Wo Kuo i-shih chih wei-chi" (Our country's medical crisis), *TK:CK* No. 68 (Dec. 18, 1930).

23. Yu Hsien, "Yü Ch'en Kuo-fu hsien-sheng lun 'k'e-hsüeh hua'" (Debating "scientification" with Mr. Ch'en Kuo-fu), *TK:CK,* No. 200 (July 18, 1933).

24. Fu Ssu-nien, 6:556.

25. Yu Hsien, "Hsieh tsai 'Hsi-i Chang Meng-chung te Chung-hsi i-hsüeh jung-hua lun' chih hou" (Written after Western doctor Chang Meng-chung's "Discussion of medical synthesis") *TK:CK,* No. 14 (Dec. 7, 1929).

26. Yu Hsien, "Wei 'Chung-hsi i-hsüeh jung-hua lun' chih Chang Meng-chung chih shu" (Letter for Mr. Chang Meng-chung's "Chinese and Western medicine synthesis") *TK:CK,* No. 18 (Jan. 4, 1930).

27. See Yü Yün-hsiu's rejoinder to Chiao I-tang, *SP:CK,* No. 39 (Sep. 18, 1933).

28. P'an Leng-feng, "Yü Yang Kao-ju yen-chiu Chung-kuo chiu yu i-hsüeh" (Studying China's ancient medicine with Yang Kao-ju) *TK:CK,* No. 203, (Aug. 8, 1933).

29. Yu Hsien, "Hua T'o yuan-lai shih shen-hua" (Hua T'o originally was a religious myth), *TK:CK,* No. 69 (Dec. 25, 1930). The original article appeared in *Ch'ing-hua hsüeh-pao,* Vol. 6, No. 1.

30. An Jan (pseud.), "Su-wen chih hsüeh-shuo" (The theory of the Su-wen), *TK:CK,* No. 113 (Oct. 28, 1931).

31. Chiang Shao-yüan, "Hsi-i Chang Meng-chung te 'Chung-hsi i-hsüeh jung-hua lun,'" (The essay on fusing Chinese and Western

medicine by Dr. Chang Meng-chung) *TK:CK,* No. 14 (Nov. 30, 1929).

32. This is clearly expressed in an article by Chi Ch'i-lu "T'an i" (Discussing medicine), *SP:CK,* Nos. 82 and 83 (July 23 and 30, 1934).

33. Chou Shao, "Wei yu chih...," *SP:CK,* No. 16 (Oct. 16, 1933).

34. Shih (psued.), "K'e-hsüeh yü shih-ch'uan" (Science and the authority of the teacher), *Chung-hsi i-yao,* 1.2:157–161 (Oct. 1935).

35. Shih, p. 161. It is interesting to note that the Chinese Communists, who certainly have been dedicated to destroying the old mentality, have in recent years revived the disciple system for teaching Chinese medicine.

36. Fu Ssu-nien, p. 546.

37. Yü Yün-hsiu, "Pu k'e fu ... fu k'e chin" ("Cannot but ... cannot completely"), *TK:CK,* Nos. 17-18 (Dec. 28, 1929, and Jan. 4, 1930).

38. Notably by C. P. Snow, as in his *The Two Cultures and a Second Look* (Cambridge, Mass., 1964).

39. Fu Ssu-nien, pp. 537–541.

40. Ssu-nien, "Tsai lun So-wei Kuo-i," (again discussing so-called national medicine), in *Fu meng-chen hsien-sheng chi,* p. 546.

41. Personal conservations with Dr. Ting Chung-ying, San Francisco, Jan. 19, 1963 and Wang Yün-wu, Taipei, May 1964.

42. Hu Shih, "The Doctor, The Missionary, and the Scientist," *National Medical Journal of China,* 17.4–5:667 (August-October 1931).

43. Hu Shih, *"Jen yü i-hsüeh* te Chung-i-pen hsü (An introduction to the Chinese translation of *Man and Medicine),* reprinted in *Wen-hsing* (Literary star), No. 61:17–18 (November 1962).

44. For example, Lo Chia-lun, undoubtedly one of the militant modernists of the May 4th era, never wrote on Chinese medicine, but in personal conversation he told the writer that since childhood he had "not touched one drop of Chinese medicine," personal interview, Taipei, 1964. On the other side, P'u Ju, the eminent Manchu scholar and traditional style painter is reported, when dying of cancer, to have said among his last words, "I do not want Western medicine."

45. The entire case is most fully described by the traditional doctor Ch'en Ts'un-jen in his book *Chin chin yu wei t'an,* (Assorted conversational tidbits; Hong Kong, 1957) pp. 88–93. It is also referred to by Chiao I-t'ang, among others. Mao Tzu-shui, a personal friend of Hu Shih at that time, and certainly no admirer of Chinese medicine, confirmed the essentials of the story in personal conversation with the writer. Taipei, 1964.

46. The inscription is quoted by Ch'en Ts'un-jen (p. 93), who supposedly later saw the painting in Lu Chung-an's studio.

47. *Sun Chung-shan ch'uan chi* (Complete works of Sun Yat-sen; Shanghai, 1933), pp. 16–17.

48. P'an Leng-feng, "Yü Yang Kao-ju...," *TK:CK*, No. 203 (Aug. 8, 1933).

49. S. C. Wu, "Chinese Medicine," *Chinese Recorder*, 56.11:733–741 (Nov. 9, 1925).

50. Chao Yü-huang, "Sheng yao hsüeh yu Chung-kuo li-tai pen-tsao yen-ke chih kuan-hsi" (The relationship between herbology and the evolution of China's historical pharmacopoeia), *SP:CK*, Nos. 45 and 46 (Oct. 30 and Nov. 7, 1935).

51. Chao Yü-huang, "Shuo Chung-yao," (On Chinese drugs), *Chung-yang yen-chiu yüan yüan-wu yueh-pao* (Monthly bulletin of Academia Sinica) 2.1:95–98 (July 1930).

52. As shown in his book, co-authored by K. Chimin Wong, *History of Chinese Medicine*.

53. Wu Lien-te, "Chung-kuo i-hsüeh chih fu-hsing," (Renaissance of China's medicine), *K'e-hsüeh* (Science) 20.4:261 (April 1936).

54. For example, the medical editor in the *Ta kung pao, Medical Supplement,* commenting on such proposals, agreed that such work should be done, but thought that little of value would be found. Editor's note to P'an Chao-p'ang, "Tu wan ping heng i-hsüeh chou k'an chi erh tien kan-hsiang" (Two points in reaction to reading the Ping Heng Medical Weekly), *TK:CK*, No. 59 (Oct. 16, 1930).

55. Yü Yün-hsiu, "Huang han i-hsüeh p'i-p'ing (Criticism of Chinese medicine), *TK:CK*, No. 78 (Feb. 26, 1931).

56. Yü Yün-hsiu, "K'e-hsüeh te kuo-ch'ang yao-wu, yen-chin chih ti-i pu" (First step in scientifically studying nationally produced drugs) *Hseh-i*, .v2, no. 4 & 5, n.p. (July-August 1920).

57. "Ts'ung 'Ma-huang ching' lien-hsiang tao wo kuo te i-yao-chieh" (From "Ma Huang," reflections on our country's medical and pharmacy world), *TK:CK*, No. 36 (May 10, 1930).

58. *Ibid.*

59. A number of opinions on the desirability of this research and the government's responsibility to foster it were collected in "Yen-chiu Kuo-ch'ang yao i-chien an lu" (Record of opinions on the research of nationally produced drugs), *TK:CK*, Nos. 45–47 (July 10, 17, and 24, 1930).

60. Yu Hsien, "Yu Chu Shen-yu hsien-sheng lun 'Chung' 'Hsi' i" (Discussing "Chinese" and "Western" medicine with Mr. Chu Shen-yu) *TK:CK*, No. 201 (July 25, 1933).

61. Chao Yü-huang, "Shuo Chung-yao" pp. 95–98.

62. Mei Ju-ao, "Hsi-i yü Chung-yao" (Western medicine and

Chinese drugs), *Ching-shih* (Statesman) 1.1:73–75 (January 1937).

63. Chou Pang-hou," Pu k'e wu-shih chih Kuo-ch'ang yao ts'ai" (Unignorable nationally produced pharmaceutical materials), *Chung-hsi i-yao*, 1.3:245 (November 1935).

64. Feng Yu-lan, "Lun Chung-hsi i-yao" (On Chinese and Western medicine and drugs), *Hsing-ch'i p'ing-lun* (Weekly review) 21:3–5 (Apr. 25, 1941).

65. Mao Yün, "Shih tang-pu tai-piao hsün ssu" (Address by civic party representative), *Chung-hsi i-yao* 1.1:17–18 (September 1935).

66. See James Eckman, "Anglo-American Hostility in American Medical Literature of the Nineteenth Century," *Bulletin of the History of Medicine*, 9.1:31–71 (January 1941).

67. Sung Kuo-pin, "Lun Chung-kuo chu-t'i chih i-yao chien-she" (On China's concrete medical construction), *SP:CK*, No. 163 (Feb. 25, 1936).

68. Huang Wen, *San-min-chu-i yü i-hsüeh* (San-min-chu-i and medicine; Chungking, 1943), especially section on "National medicine and national drugs."

69. Kao Te-ming, "Hsin Chung-hua i-hsüeh yün-tung te li-lun yü shih-chien" (New China's medical movement in theory and practice), *Hsin Chung-hua* (New China) 2.3:63–72 (September 1944).

70. "Chung-i k'e-hsüeh-hua lun-chan t'e chi" (A special compilation on the debate over scientification of Chinese medicine), *Chung-hsi i-yao*, 2:96 (1936).

71. Their messages to the new journal can be found on the first pages of its first and second issues. *Hsin Chung-hua i-yao yüeh-k'an* (New China medical monthly; March and April 1945).

72. Liu Tuan-cheng, "Chung-hsi i-hsüeh chih i t'ung te shih" (The differences and similarities, advantages and disadvantages of Chinese and Western medicine), *Hsin Chung-hua i-yao yüeh-k'an* 1.5–6:27–30 (July 25, 1945).

73. Kuo Mo-jo, "Chung-i k'e-hsüeh-hua te i-i" (Proposal for the scientification of Chinese medicine), *Hsin-hua jih-pao* (New China daily; Oct. 2, 1944).

74. *Ibid.*

75. Within ten years such a view would become bourgeois heresy in Communist China, but by that time Kuo had trimmed his sails accordingly.

76. *Ibid.*

77. Wang Te-ch'uan, "Tu Kuo Mo-jo hsien-sheng Chung-i k'e hsüeh-hua i-i" (Ideas from reading Mr. Kuo Mo-jo on the scientification of Chinese medicine), *Hsin-Chung-hua i-yao yüeh-k'an*, 1.1:34–35 (February 1945); and Ch'eng Jung-liang, "Chien Kuo Mo-jo hsien-sheng" (To Mr. Kuo Mo-jo), *Hsin Chung-hua i-yao yüeh-k'an*, 1.2–3:23–24 (April 1945.)

78. Ch'eng Jung-liang, p. 23.

79. Yen Kung-ch'en, "Tu 'Shen-shu kuan-yü Chung-i k'e-hsüeh-hua te wen-t'i hou' " (After reading "Shen Shu on Chinese Medicine's Scientification"), *Hsin Chung-hua i-yao yüeh k'an*, 1.5–6:20–24 (July 1945).

80. *Ibid.*, p. 22.

CHAPTER VII: GOVERNMENT AND CHINESE MEDICINE — TENSIONS WITHIN THE KUOMINTANG

1. *National Medical Journal of China*, 6.1:10 (March 1920).

2. "Message to the Medical Conference from the Minister of Education," *National Medical Journal of China*, 6.1:56 (March 1920).

3. "I-shih chan-hsing t'iao-li", *Chung-hua Min-kuo i-shih tsung-lan* (Medical handbook of the Chinese Republic; Tokyo, 1935), pp. 30–32.

4. *Chung-i-yao nien-chien*, pp. 153–154.

5. "Hsi-i t'iao-li" (Western doctors' regulations) *Chung-hua Min-kuo i-shih tsung-lan*, pp. 29–30.

6. *Chung-i-yao nien-chien*, p. 139.

7. "Shanghai-shih i-shih kung-hui wei po-kuo-i t'iao-li . . ." (Shanghai physicians' association petition for rejecting national medicine regulations) *I-yao p'ing-lun* (Medicine and drugs review) 5.6:53–54 (Oct. 15, 1933).

8. Wang Ching-wei, "Hsing-cheng-yüan Wang Yüan-chang tui i-hsüeh chieh chih hsi-wang," (The hopes of Executive Yuan President Wang for the medical world), *Chung-hua i-hsüeh tsa-chih*, 20.4:454 (April 1934).

9. A number of these protests from individuals and medical societies can be found in *I-yao p'ing-lun*, Vol. 5, No. 6 (October 1933).

10. Ch'en Fang-chih, "Chung-hsi-i wen-t'i chih shang-liang" (Discussion of the Chinese and Western medicine question) *SP:CK*, Nos. 39 and 40 (Sept. 18 and 25, 1933).

11. Wang Chih-chang, "Kuo-i kuan yü fen-k'e cheng ch'uan-wu i pieh tsu cheng-fu" (The desire of the Institute for National Medicine to split government administrative authority), *SP:CK*, No. 33 (Aug. 17, 1933).

12. "Shanghai shih i-shih. . . ," pp. 53–54.

13. Text in *I-yao p'ing-lun*, 6.1:3 (January 1934).

14. *Chung-i-yao nien-chien*, p. 154.

15. Hollington K. Tong, ed., *China Handbook, 1937–1945* (New York, 1947), p. 501. More fully described in *TK:CK*, No. 399 (June 5, 1937).

16. "I-shih Fa" (Physicians' law), *Chung-hua i-hsüeh tsa-chih* (December 1943).

Tensions within the Kuomintang

17. In 1930 a visiting League of Nations expert, Professor Knud Faber, was told that there were fifteen schools for traditional medicine in existence, plus "about 570 medical organizations for the purpose of encouraging the study of Chinese medicine." Faber, p. 12. It should be remembered that many of these must have been very small.

18. *Ibid.*, pp. 35–36.

19. *Ibid.*, p. 36.

20. Curriculum and Faculty given in *Kuo-i k̲uan i-wu jen-yuan hsü-lien pan, ti-ssu pi-yeh t-ung hsüeh lu* (Institute for National Medicine, medical personnel training class list of fourth graduating class; Chungking, 1944).

21. Text in *Hsin chiao-yü,* 11.2:296–308 (Sept. 1925).

22. *Ibid.,* p. 307.

23. Text in *Chung-i hui-k̲'an,* pp. 184–187. Among the Central Political Council members supporting these resolutions were Ch'en Kuo-fu, Ch'en Li-fu, Sun Fo, Feng Yü-hsiang, Yü Yu-jen, Ho Ch'eng-chun, Li Tsung-hung and, of course, Chiao I-t'ang.

24. Hua Hsin-jen, "Chung-i chiao-yü, ju-ho K'e-i lieh-ju hsüeh-hsiao ssu-t'ung chung?" (How could Chinese medicine be included in the education system?) *TK:CK,* No. 399 (June 5, 1937).

25. *Shen pao* (Mar. 24, 1937), p. 10.

26. As in Chao Yü-huang, "Shuo Chung-yao," pp. 95–98, or a compilation of opinions "Yen-chin Kuo-ch'ang yao i-chien hui-lu" (Compendium of opinions on studying native drugs), *TK:CK,* Nos. 45, 47 (July 10, 24, 1930).

27. "Note by Dr. J. Heng Liu on the Three-Year Plan for the Chinese National Health Service," *League of Nations, Health Organization. Minutes of 17th Session, May 4–8, 1931* (Geneva, 1931), Annex 5, p. 92.

28. Bernard E. Read, "Chinese Pharmacopeia," *The China Medical Journal,* 44.6:519–526 (June 1930).

29. League of Nations, *Minutes May 4–8, 1931,* pp. 15–17.

30. Faber, p. 33.

31. Abraham Flexner, *Medical Education: A Comparative Study* (New York, 1925).

32. Hsiao Shu-hsüan, "Tu-ts'ai cheng-chih yü i-hsüeh chien-she" (Autocractic government and medical construction), *Chung-hsi i-yao* 1.1:62–65 (September 1935).

33. Hsiao Shu-hsüan, p. 65. It is one of the ironies of modern Chinese history that, when China finally got the type of ruthlessly modern autocratic leadership envisioned here, it regarded the old medicine as something very different from "noxious filth." See Chapters VIII and IX below.

34. This idea, for instance, is clearly enunciated in an open letter by the Republic Medical Society of Peking in *TK:CK,* No. 83 (Apr. 2, 1931).

35. Quoted in Yü Yün-hsiu, "Chiao I-t'ang wei ts'ai-hsing kuo-i t'iao-li kao kuo-jen shu chih shang-liang" (Discussion of Chiao I-t'ang's letter on behalf of the National medicine article), *SP:CK*, No. 39 (Sept. 18, 1933).

36. *Ibid.*

37. Yu Hsien, "Yü Ch'en Kuo-fu hsien-sheng lun hsin i-hsüeh" (Discussion of new medicine with Mr. Ch'en Kuo-fu), *TK:CK*, No. 198 (July 4, 1933).

CHAPTER VIII: THE COMMUNIST REHABILITATION
OF CHINESE MEDICINE

1. Chow Tse-tsung draws what, from the evidence of the medical controversy, seems to be a valid distinction between the emphasis given to "cultural revolution" as a precondition to successful political change by the Western-oriented, liberal intellectuals of the Hu Shih type, and the Marxists' priority to political revolution, with all else following. *The May Fourth Movement* (Cambridge, Mass., 1960), Chap. IX.

2. Yü Hsiu, "Pien-cheng wei-wu-lun yü i-hsüeh" (Dialectical materialism and medicine), *TK:CK*, No. 60 (Oct. 12, 1932).

3. "Wo-men mu-ch'ien te chin-chi jen-wu" (Our present urgent responsibility), *Hung sze wei-sheng* (Red hygiene), 2:5 (June 1933). Ch'en Ch'eng collection, Microfilm, Hoover Institute.

4. Similarly, the only article found that was exclusively concerned with traditional medicine was a translation from a Japanese text. Apparently China's own traditional medicine experts were considered too involved in the struggle to preserve Chinese medicine. The Japanese represented a more impartial, scientific attitude. "Lin-ch'uang ying-yung han-fang i-hsüeh chieh-shuo," (An explanation of the clinical use of Chinese medical prescriptions), *Hung-sze wei-sheng,* 3:37–42 (Oct. 24, 1933).

5. From this period issues of the Eighth Route Army's journal *Kuo-fang wei-sheng (National defense hygiene),* 1939–1942, and the New Fourth Route Army's, *Hua-chung i-wu tsa-chih* (Central China medical personnel's journal), 1946, have been located.

6. Harrison Forman, *Report from Red China* (New York, 1945), p. 50.

7. As a note of contemporary interest, according to Wilfred Burchett's report, the Vietcong are using a very similar policy. He quotes a French-trained Vietcong pharmacologist concerning their ability to produce 70 per cent of their medicine in extremely primitive conditions. "This has been possible because we made a careful study of traditional oriental medicine and based ourselves on the great wealth of our forest products." Wilfred G. Burchett, *Vietnam, Inside Story of the Guerrilla War* (New York, 1965), p. 77.

8. Shao Cheng-yang, "Wo-men te ch'i wang nu-li te fang-hsiang" (The direction toward which we labor), *Kuo-fang wei-sheng,* 1.1:2 (November 1939).

9. Chun Kuei-t'ien, "Tsemme-yang li-yung chung-yao" ("How to use Chinese drugs"), *Kuo-fang wei-sheng,* 1.1:45 (November 1939).

10. Yang Shao, "T'an i-hsüeh k'e-hsüeh-hua, Chung-kuo-hua, yü chung-hua" ("Discussing medicines' scientification, sinicization, and popularization"), *Kuo-fang wei-sheng,* 1.2:40–44 (March 1940).

11. *Ibid.,* p. 44.

12. T'an Chuang, "Tui-yü Chung-kuo mu-ch'ien i-hsüeh te shang-t'ao" (Discussion of China's present medicine), *Kuo-fang wei-sheng,* 2.3–4:7–16 (December 1941).

13. *Ibid.,* p. 9.

14. *Ibid.,* p. 10.

15. *Ibid.,* p. 12.

16. Original in Yenan *Chieh-fang jih-pao* (Oct. 31, 1944), reprinted in Yeh Ching-ch'iu, ed., *Chung-i te hsüeh-hsi tzu-liao* (Materials for the study of Chinese medicine; Shanghai, 1950), p. 1. There is a textual problem here as the text does not correspond to that in Mao Tse-tung, *Hsüan-chi* (Selected works; Peking, 1955), III, 1010. The meaning is close, however, and I here translate the 1950 version.

17. *Ibid.,* p. 1.

18. Mao Tse-tung, *Hsüan-chi* (Selected works; Peking, 1960), III, 1083–1094.

19. The most notable of these was the Rockefeller-financed Peking Union Medical College. Its administrative director at that time, Miss Mary Ferguson, has recounted the awe with which the first Communist medical cadres to enter Peking observed the hospital's modern equipment and techniques. Conversation with writer, New York, July 1963.

20. William Y. Chen uses the figure 12,000, "Medicine and Public Health," in Sidney Gould, ed., *Sciences in Communist China* (Washington, 1961), p. 384. There are, however, slightly higher estimates during the postwar years ranging up to 20,000 in "Lun Chung-i went'i" (On the Chinese Medicine Question), *Ta kung pao* (Nov. 26, 1946), p. 10. The Vice-Minister of Public Health, in 1950, referred to 20,000 Western-style doctors. Ho Ch'eng, "Chung-hsi i t'uan-chieh yü Chung-i te chin-hsiu wen-t'i), (Uniting Chinese and Western doctors and the question of Chinese medicine's improvement), *JMJP* (June 13, 1950).

21. The lack of established qualifications for recognition as a Chinese-style doctor makes estimates of their total number very difficult. For the year 1955, after the government had defined medical qualifications, the national total of Chinese-style doctors was given at 486,700. *Jen-min shou-tse* (People's handbook; 1957), p. 608. If one

includes every kind of old-style healer and drug peddler, the total would be much higher. Faber had been told by a Chinese medicine association in 1930 that there were 1,200,000 practitioners and 7,000,-000 druggists. Faber, p. 8.

22. Cited in Ho Ch'eng, "Chung Hsi i t'uan-chieh yü Chung-i te Chin-hsiu Wen-t'i" ("The question of uniting Chinese and Western medicine and the improvement of Chinese medicine"), *JMJP* (June 13, 1950).

23. *JMJP* (Mar. 6, 1950).

24. P'an Chao-p'eng, "Chung-i-yao tsou shang k'e hsüeh te tao-lu" ("Chinese medicine must take the road to science"), *JMJP* (July 25, 1950).

25. "Kuo Mo-jo fu-tsung-li te chiang-hua" (Speech of Vice-director Kuo Mo-jo), in Yeh Ching-ch'iu, pp. 6–10.

26. "Chu tu-chu . . . te chiang hua" ("Speech of Vice-chairman Chu . . ."), in Yeh Ching-ch'iu, p. 205.

27. "Ti-i ts'eng ch'uan-kuo wei-sheng hui i tsung-chieh pao-kao" (Concluding report of first national health conference), in Yeh Ching-ch'iu, p. 26.

28. Text of these, dated Dec. 27, 1951, is printed in *JMJP,* Jan. 2, 1952.

29. A breakdown of the class hours shows that the schools provided 288 hours on basic medical sciences, 123 hours on traditional medical practices, 72 hours on politics, and the remaining 381 hours on various areas of clinical application, apparently mainly according to Western medicine. The classes had 116 hours on basic medical sciences, 18 hours on social science, and the remaining 184 hours on clinical application. From tables in *Pei-ching chung-i* (Peking Chinese medicine), Vol. 1, No. 3 (June 1952).

30. Scattered provincial figures suggest that well under 25 per cent of the traditional physicians had taken such courses by late 1954.

31. Li Te-ch'uan, "Kuan-yü ch'uan-kuo wei-sheng Hui-i te pao kao" (Report to the national health conference), in *Chung-i chin-hsiu tsu-chih kuan-li hsüan-chi* (Selection of the organization and management of improving Chinese medicine; Peking, 1953), p. 11.

32. One indication of the type of Western-medicine-oriented research going on was the Peoples' Publishing House's publication of a book by Yü Yün-hsiu, ed., *Ku-tai chi-ping ming hou su i* (Explanation of ancient disease categories; Peking, 1953). The book was written in 1947, but not published until six years later.

33. In this it resembled the Soviet "Medical Workers' Union" *(Medsantrud),* except that Chinese unions were originally organized on a provincial basis. Strikingly different, however, was the continuation and control of a modern physicians' professional organization,

The Communists and Chinese Medicine

"The Chinese Medical Association," in contrast to the Bolsheviks' abolition of all such professional medical associations.

34. *Pei-ching Chung-i*, 1.2:53 (July 1951).

35. Text in *Pei-ching Chung-i*, 1.2:2 (July 1951).

36. Ku Hsing-yuan, et al., "Survey of Combined Practice (Chinese, Native and Western Medicine) Clinics" *(History of medicine and organization of health services, I-hsüeh-shih yü pao-chien tsa-chih* Vol. 2, No. 3 (Mar. 25, 1958); tr. in *Joint Publications Research Service*, No. 1480.

37. The writer has talked with a traditional doctor who was able to resist pressures to give up his private practice in Canton until the Great Leap Forward of late 1958. Interview, Macao, August 1964.

38. Traditional doctors were used extensively in the various mass public health drives, such as that accompanying the Korean War bacteriological warfare scare. A detailed description of their activities in Hopei and Kiangsi may be found in *KMJP* (May 23, 1954).

39. Afterwards, the then Deputy Minister of Public Health, Ho Ch'eng, acknowledged in his self-criticism that "Chinese doctors could not legally join hospital," translated in "Examination of the Mistaken Thinking in Health Work," *Union Research Service*, 3.20:283 (June 8, 1956).

40. Text of regulations reprinted in *Ta kung pao* (May 22, 1951).

41. Wang I-men, "Cheng-tun Chung-kuo i hsüeh te chien-i" ("Opinions on reforming China's medicine"), *JMJP* (Nov. 3, 1951).

42. Chao Yu-ch'ing, "Hsin Chung-kuo te Chung-i yao chi-chi wu-chuang ssu-hsiang ts'ai neng tsou hsiang k'e-hsüeh-kua," (New China's Chinese-style doctors must arm themselves ideologically to be able to move toward scientification"), *Pei-ching Chung-i*, 1.3:11–14 (June 1952), pp. 11–14.

43. *Ibid.*, p. 13.

44. "Pei-ching Chung-i chieh san-fan yun-tung chieh-shao" (Brief introduction to the Three-Anti Movement in the Peking Chinese medicine world), *Pei-ching Chung-i*, 1.3:6–7 (June 1952).

45. Yang Chien-te, "Wo Tseme-yang tzu hsüeh chen-chiu liao-fa," (How I studied acupuncture on my own), *KMJP* (Dec. 17, 1952).

46. See report on Seminar of the Chinese Pharmacy Association, *KMJP* (Nov. 3, 1953).

47. Teng Chia-tung, "Wo-men yao p'i-p'an kuo-ch'ü 'hsieh-ho te i-ch'ieh" (We must criticize everything about the Peking Union Medical College in the past), *I-yao hsüeh*, 5.1:3–4 (January 1952), pp. 3–4.

48. "Chung-nan wei-sheng-chu chao-kai ti-i ts'e chung-i tai-piao hui-i" (Southern-Central department of public health convenes first Chinese medicine congress), *KMJP* (June 23, 1953).

49. "Cheng-ch'üeh te tui-tai Chung-kuo i-hsüeh i-ch'ang" (Correct

attitude toward China's medical legacy), *JMJP* (Aug. 26, 1953).

50. Reported in *KMJP*, Mar. 28, 1954.

51. "Chao k'ai ti-erh ts'e chung-hsi i-hsüeh hsiao liu tso-t'an-hui," (Second seminar on Chinese and Western medicine communication convened), *KMJP* (Mar. 5, 1954).

52. "Organize and Bring Forth the Strength of Native Medicine," *JMJP* (Dec. 2, 1953); in *SCMP*, No. 711: 23–26.

53. "Endeavor to Carry Out the Spirit of the National Higher Education Conference," *KMJP* (Aug. 13, 1954); in *SCMP*, No. 885:11.

54. "Kuan-ch'e tui-tai Chung-i te cheng-ch'üeh cheng-ts'e," (Implement the correct policy regarding Chinese medicine), *JMJP* (Oct. 20, 1954).

55. Ni Pao-ch'ün, "Nu-li hsüeh-hsi Chung-i i-hsüeh . . ." (Strive to study Chinese medicine), *Chieh-fang jih-pao* (Oct. 13, 1954).

56. As in Ch'engtu, *Kung-shang tao-pao*, (work and commerce paper; Nov. 10, 1954).

57. Unfortunately these issues appear to be unavailable outside of China, so we have to rely on reports of the content of these articles.

58. Quoted from *Tung-pei wei-sheng*, Vol. 5, No. 9 (1950) in "Pi-hsü p'i-p'an ch'ing-shih . . . Chung-i . . ." ("We must criticize slighting of Chinese medicine . . ."), *KMJP*, editorial (Mar. 27, 1955).

59. Ch'eng Chih-fan, "Criticize Wang Pin's Erroneous Concept of Despising Traditional Medicine; Correctly Accept the Medical Legacy of the Motherland," *K'e-hsüeh t'ung pao* (Scientific report), No. 6 (1955); in *SCMP* (supplement), No. 1094:1–6.

60. Quoted in *KMJP* (Mar. 27, 1955).

61. Some of these articles are translated in *SCMP*, No. 1031:36–38.

62. The early stages of the "Anti-Wang Pin Campaign" are summarized in "Tui-yü Wang Pin ch'i-shih Chung-i te tz'e-ch'ang chieh-chi ssu-hsiang chan-k'ai p'i-p'an," (Developing criticism of Wang Pin's bourgeois thought in despising Chinese medicine), *Nan-Fang jih-pao* (May 19, 1955).

63. According to an informant who worked in the Ministry of Public Health in these years, the Minister, Li Te-ch'uan, is largely a figurehead appointed because of her husband, Feng Yü-hsiang, and her own leftist activities before 1949. Ho Ch'eng, who had been with the Red Army Medical units since Kiangsi days, was the real power in the Ministry until his downfall over the question of traditional medicine. Interview, Hong Kong, July 1964.

64. The informant from the Ministry of Public Health was present at mass criticism meetings where Wang refused to acknowledge any error. Furthermore, he expressed dissatisfaction at being reassigned to Sinkiang and subsequently went through labor reform. In the Hun-

dred Flowers period he revealed himself as an unreconstructed rightist and has been excluded from any important position. Interview, Hong Kong, July 1964.

65. Text of his self-criticism *JMJP* (Nov. 19, 1955), in *Union Research Service*, 3.20:280–285.

66. The resolution is translated in *SCMP*, No. 1234:9–10. However, because of his self-criticism, Ho has since been made president of the Army Medical College, a respectable, but powerless position. Interview, Hong Kong, July 1964.

67. Li Yuan-hu, "Chi-chi ts'an-chia p'i-p'an wei-sheng pu-men cheng te tz'e-chieh-chi wei-hsin chu-i ssu-hsiang te tao-cheng" (Actively join the struggle to criticize the bourgeois idealistic thought of elements in the Ministry of Public Health), *Nan-Fang jih-pao* (Apr. 20, 1955).

68. Interviews with medical refugees reveal that a relative freedom from tight political control is one of the most attractive features of medicine as a profession in China. See Marie Sieh, "Medicine in China," *Current Scene,* Vol. 3, Nos. 5 and 6 (Oct. 15 and Nov. 1, 1964).

69. As in an important *Hsüeh-hsi* article: "There has prevailed a trend of blindly worshipping Western culture among the bourgeois class and intellectuals who tend to belittle and even negate the cultural legacy of their own country." Li P'ei-san, "Take a Correct Attitude toward the Medical Legacy of the Motherland," *Hsüeh-hsi* (Study), No. 10 (Oct. 2, 1955); in *ECMM,* No. 15, p. 1.

70. Jen Hsiao-feng, "Criticize Comrade Ho Ch'eng's Error in His Policy toward Chinese Medicine, "in *Union Research Service,* 3.20: 287–298 (June 8, 1956).

71. See Peking, *Kung-jen jih-pao* (Worker's daily; Aug. 10, 1955) where there is discussed an eighty-six year old traditional physician who is now a representative to the National People's Congress.

72. Statistics compiled in *Chinese Publishing Statistics, 1949–1959* (Ann Arbor, 1960).

73. Chu Yen, *Chung-kuo ku-tai i-hsüeh ch'eng-chiu* (China's ancient medical accomplishments; Peking, 1955); and Chang Hui-chen, *Li Shih-chen; Great Pharmacologist of Ancient China* (Peking, 1955).

74. Chu Yen, *Chung-kuo ku-tai i-hsüeh ch'eng-chiu,* p. 52.

75. As in, "In Some Cases Chinese Medical Surpasses Western," *JMJP* (Dec. 20, 1955); in *SCMP,* No. 1234:6.

76. Official attitudes toward China's cultural tradition in the specific fields of archaeology, architecture, theater, and medicine are discussed in Andre Travert, "The Attitude of the Communist Party Towards China's Cultural Legacy," in E. F. Szczeparik, ed., *Symposium on Economic and Social Problems of the Far East* (Hong Kong, 1962),

pp. 353–368. My own unpublished work on painting and theater substantiates this impression.

77. A typical use of these "roving teams" was reported for Nanhai Hsien near Canton where 460 Chinese-style doctors were organized "to deeply penetrate each village to serve the peasants." Each subdistrict (ch'ü) organizd three or four such teams. Hong Kong, *Ta kung pao* (Nov. 17, 1954).

78. Figures from *JMJP,* Sept. 23, 1955, and Sept. 12, 1957 respectively.

79. *JMJP* (Sept. 12, 1957).

80. Hong Kong, *Wen-hui pao* (Jan. 9, 1959).

81. *JMJP* (Sept. 12, 1957).

82. Such a hospital in Fukien is described in "In a New Style Chinese Medicine Hospital," Chung-kuo hsin wen (China news agency), (Sept. 29, 1961).

83. Described in "Fa-chan tsu-kuo i-yao i-ch'ang" (Develop the medical legacy of the Motherland), *JMJP* (Dec. 20, 1955).

84. *Tsingtao jih-pao* (Tsing tao daily; Dec. 12, 1954).

85. Most provinces seem to have set up at least one committee to stimulate and coordinate research in traditional medicine. See, for example, "Provincial Chinese Medicine Research Center Established," *Shensi jih-pao* (Shensi daily; Sept. 12, 1956) and "Kwangtung Chinese Medicine and Drugs Research Committee Meets," *Nan-fang jih-pao* (Southern daily; Apr. 30, 1956).

86. In Shanghai, for instance, there was established an institute to do nothing but textual research in the ancient medical literature. See *KMJP* (July 18, 1956).

87. There is a summary of such work in "Present Status and Future of China's Research in Pharmacology," *Sheng-li ko-hsüeh chin-chan* (Progress in Physiology), 1.1:23–30 (March 1957); in *Joint Publications Research Service,* No. DL 1134.

88. *Kung-jen jih-pao* (May 2, 1956).

89. Text in *KMJP* (Dec. 28, 1954).

90. The informant from the central Ministry of Public Health reported that such was compulsory for all, even nonmedical personnel, and was quite intensive. Interview, Hong Kong, July 1964.

91. This impression is supported by extensive interviews with doctors who have practiced in China by a project under the direction of Professors Ezra Vogel and John Pelzel of Harvard.

92. *KMJP* (May 9, 1956).

93. "Wei kuan-ch'e tang te Chung-i cheng-ts'e erh nu-li" (Strive to implement the party's Chinese medicine policy), *Ch'ang-chiang jih-pao* (Yangtze daily, Wuhan; Oct. 3, 1955).

94. Ling Yang, "Integrating Chinese and Western Medicine" *Peking Review,* 1.51:23 (Dec. 23, 1958).

95. The adjective is used advisedly, despite its incongruous ring to Western ears, so accustomed to hearing of medicine described only in scientific terms. Dr. Felix Mann uses the phrase "artistic appreciation" to convey the quality of Chinese pulse diagnosis. Mann, p. 91. The eminent herbalist, Ting Chung-ying, in personal conversation with the author, also referred to Chinese medicine as being an art, not a science. It may not be so inimical to systematic classroom instruction as Zen (certainly all the efforts to rationalize and systematize Chinese medicine have been based on the assumption that it can be so taught), but there is something of the same elusive quality to it. Dr. Ting summed up the quandry of instruction by quoting Lao-tzu, "*Chih-che pu shuo, shuo-che pu chih*"—"those who know do not speak, those who speak do not know."

96. *KMJP* (May 9, 1956).

97. "Chi-chi pei-yang Chung-i . . ." ("Actively train Chinese doctors . . ."), *JMJP* (May 27, 1956).

98. Figures here are very unsatisfactory, perhaps due to inconsistencies in registering disciples. The *Chinese Medical Journal* gives 52,000 for 1958. (*Chinese Medical Journal,* December 1959, p. 490). Others are considerably higher."

99. Hsin Shao-chou, "Chung-i chung te pu p'ing-teng cheng-lun" (Unequal contending in Chinese medicine), *Hei-lung-chiang jih-pao* (Heilungchiang daily; June 8, 1957).

100. Apart from the difficulty of testing traditional medical qualifications, the official approval of "local specialists" gave a free reign to many dubious practices. "A practitioner is qualified if he has only one special skill . . . if his skill is actually proved and trusted by the people." Jen Hsiao-feng, "Criticize Comrade Ho Ch'eng's Error in His Policy toward Chinese medicine," in *Union Research Service,* 3.20:287–298 (June 8, 1956). The "people," then, rather than medical authorities actually became the judge of his qualifications.

101. *Shen-yang jih-pao* (Shenyang daily; May 4, 1957).

102. Speech by Chinese doctor to Kwangtung Administrative Council. Reported in *Nan-Fang jih pao* (May 10, 1957). In their defense, it was occasionally recognized that the old doctors' lectures were often totally incomprehensible to men trained in modern science. "Most of the Western medical personnel who had enrolled to study traditional medicine withdrew because of their inability to comprehend the theories and their reluctance to accept the abstract and unscientific theories." *KMJP* (May 20, 1957). Usually, however, and especially during the Great Leap period, such behavior was attributed solely to ideological defects.

103. Chao T'i-chien, "The Phenomena of Still Despising Chinese Medicine," Shanghai, *Wen-hui pao* (May 23, 1957).

104. Shanghai, *Wen-hui pao* (Jan. 22, 1957).

105. Quoted in *JMJP* (Sept. 12, 1957).

106. Peking traditional doctors, for instance, were accused of cling-ing to their own secrets and retaining capitalist profit-making ambi-tions until convinced of their errors through Party-led criticism meet-ings. *Pei-ching jih-pao* (May 22, 1958).

107. Ku Hsing-yuan et al.

108. *JMJP* (July 31, 1957).

109. "Hsi-i hsüeh-hsi Chung-i chüeh wu chung-chien te ti-ch'ang" (In Western doctors studying Chinese medicine there is no middle ground). Shanghai, *Wen-hui pao* (Nov. 28, 1958).

110. "Report from the Party Group of the Ministry of Health Con-cerning Study of Traditional Medicine by Doctors of Western Medi-cine" *NCNA* (Nov. 19, 1958); in *SCMP*, No. 1903:12–15.

111. *Ibid.*, p. 15.

112. The Sun Yat-sen Medical College in Canton, for example, now required 108 hours of Chinese medicine courses in each of the first two years and 48 hours for each of the last two. Shanghai, *Wen-hui pao* (Dec. 15, 1958).

113. *Kung-jen jih-pao* (Dec. 25, 1958).

114. "Chung-i kung-tso yeh pi-hsü tsou ch'ün-cheng lu-hsien" (Work on Chinese medicine also must follow the mass line); *KMJP* (Nov. 24, 1958).

115. Richard D. Baum, in his article, " 'Red and Expert': The Polit-ico-Ideological Foundations of China's Great Leap Forward." *Asian Survey*, 4.9:1049–1057 (September 1964), notes that "emphasis on human will" over technical factors or material conditions plus height-ened politico-ideological consciousness were the two main features of the Great Leap mentality. The former is obvious in the exaltation of popular medical wisdom over scientific methods; the latter in stric-tures on wholeheartedly accepting Party leadership.

116. *JMJP* (Dec. 14, 1958).

117. In recent years many valuable new drugs have been discovered in the botanicals used by primitive peoples. A lively and interesting account of the modern pharmaceutical industry's search for such prod-ucts is Margaret B. Krieg's *Green Medicine* (New York, 1964).

118. "Test of Chekiang Research Institute of Chinese Medicine Proves that Tadpoles are Useless for Contraceptive Purposes," *JMJP* (Apr. 14, 1958); in *SCMP*, No. 1759:17.

119. Hong Kong, *Ta kung pao* (Jan. 30, 1959), reported a typical case of a rural Kwangtung snake bite expert joining the staff of Sun Yat-sen Hospital in Canton.

120. André Travert, in his discussion of traditional medicine, seems to miss this crucial point about its social and ideological ramifications. "What is most astonishing in the case of ancient Chinese medical sci-

ence is that it did not suffer, as did other branches of cultural activity, from the reversal to the 'more present, less past' line which occurred in 1958 with the launching of the Great Leap Forward." Travert, p. 364.

CHAPTER IX: OLD MEDICINE IN THE NEW SOCIETY

1. Some of the most useful information on these developments has been obtained from interviews with medical personnel who have left China (see Chapter VIII, n. 91). Also Robert M. Worth, "Institution-Building in the People's Republic of China: The Rural Health Center," *East-West Center Review*, 1.3:19–34 (February 1965).

2. Information from a senior doctor at largest Shanghai thoracic hospital, July 1, 1964.

3. *Ibid*. See also *Kuang-chou jih-pao* (Canton daily; Jan. 11, 1959).

4. Evidence for the major urban centers is copious. For a Canadian doctor's observations, see Wilder Penfield, "Oriental Renaissance in Education and Medicine," *Science*, No. 141:1156 (Sept. 20, 1963). Doctors from places as diverse as Nanking, Hangchow, Shanghai, and Kwangtung reported Chinese medicine departments in their hospitals. On the rural scene, see "Modern Medical Care Comes to Country Folk," *NCNA* (Apr. 12, 1962); in *SCMP*, No. 2727:20–21. This describes a hospital in rural Kueichou. One difference between cities and countryside in integrating the two kinds of doctors is that the latter was hard-pressed to get modern-trained doctors for its small hospitals and clinics, whereas the large hospitals had always had a fully modern medical staff to which they now added traditional doctors and departments for traditional medicine.

5. Worth, p. 31.

6. Ezra Vogel has pointed out the role Chinese medicine can play as a substitute for technical psychiatric care. "Regardless of the strictly physical benefits that may derive from traditional Chinese medicine, there is no question but that the continuance of an indigenous medical practice has had important secondary benefits in treating the less serious psychiatric disorders of a functional nature," Jan Cerny, "Chinese Psychiatry," *International Journal of Psychiatry*, 1.2:229–238 (April 1965) Discussion by Ezra Vogel, *ibid*., p. 240.

7. *JMJP* (Feb. 23, 1961).

8. Mi Ching-sen, "Ginseng, China's Famous Medicinal Root," *China Reconstructs*, 13.5:43–44 (May 1964).

9. "Good Harvest of Medicinal Herbs in S-W China Province," *NCNA* (July 15, 1965); in *SCMP*, No. 3500:9.

10. "Facts About Chinese Medicine," *NCNA* (Jan. 29, 1966); in *SCMP*, No. 3629:23.

Notes to Chapter IX

11. "Pei-yang tsu-kuo i-hsüeh te chieh pan jen" (Cultivate successors to the medicine of the motherland), *KMJP* (Mar. 25, 1963).

12. "Thirty Centuries of China's Veterinary Medicine Summarized," *NCNA*, No. 2950 (June 4, 1963); in *SCMP*, No. 2950:18 and "Future Shortage of Chinese Traditional Veterinarians Feared," *Nan-fang jih-pao* (May 18, 1962); in *SCMP*, No. 2766:6–8.

13. Rewi Alley, "Around Nanyang in Honan," *Eastern Horizon*, 4.2:24 (February 1965).

14. See Joseph R. Levenson, "The Place of Confucius in Communist China," *China Quarterly*, 12:1–18 (October-December 1962).

15. Donald Gould, "Galen in China," *The Lancet* (Sept. 20, 1958), p. 633.

16. This conclusion is based on a survey of the Soviet medical world's weekly *Medizinia Rabotnik* (Medical worker; 1961–1965).

17. *Yang-ch'eng wan-pao* (Canton evening news paper; Apr. 16, 1963).

18. *Chinese Medical Journal* (new series), 10:334 (May 1963) and 11:342 (May 1964) and, most recently, "Yemen jen tsan 'Tung-fang shen-hsien'" (Yemenese approve 'Miracle workers from the East'), Hong Kong, *Wen-hui-pao* (Mar. 31, 1966).

19. "Indigenous Medicine," *Pakistan Times* (Feb. 24, 1966); in *The Asian Student* (Mar. 5, 1966).

20. Policy and achievements are summarized by the Director of the Hanoi Institute of Traditional Medicine, Nguyen Van Huong, "Renovation of Traditional Medicine," *Vietnamese Studies*, 6:22–35 (1965).

21. *Ibid.*, pp. 29–30.

22. A good example is the story of an overseas Chinese traditional doctor from Vietnam who has become director of the Amoy hospital for Chinese medicine, Ch'en Yen-lung "Practicing Medicine in the Great Motherland," *Chung-kuo hsin-wen* (China news; Dec. 28, 1959).

23. *Hong Kong shih pao* (Hong Kong times; Nov. 18, 1958).

24. *Hong Kong shih pao* (Mar. 27, 1959).

25. *T'ien-wen-t'ai pao* (Observatory post; Dec. 12, 1958).

26. "New Publications on West China National Minority's Medical Science", *NCNA* (Oct. 12, 1963); in *SCMP*, No. 3081:13.

27. "First Graduates of Traditional Mongolian Medicine in China," *NCNA* (Nov. 10, 1963); in *SCMP*, No. 3101:20. Mongolian medicine seems to be quantitatively by far the most developed of the three. In 1963 there were reported 26,000 practitioners, with 2,000 of them in public health organs and hospitals. The school for Tibetan medicine is conducted in the Dalai Lama's former institute for medicine and astronomy. "Study of Traditional Tibetan Medicine in Lhasa," *NCNA* (May 9, 1962); in *SCMP*, No. 2739:23.

28. Tung Ping-k'un, "Face of *CUMC* Changed with the Combination of Traditional and Western Schools of Medicine," *KMJP* (Mar. 24, 1961); in *Current Background*, No. 662:5 (Oct. 3, 1961).

29. The method is fully described in Fang Hsien-chih *et al.*, "The Integration of Modern and Traditional Chinese Medicine in the Treatment of Fractures," *Chinese Medical Journal*, 82.8:493–504 (August 1963), and 83.7:411–421 (July 1964). This was the only area of traditional medicine which notably impressed Dr. Penfield on his visit to China. Penfield, p. 1156. With regard to the claims that this is a great triumph for Chinese medicine and for Party policy, it should be noted that Dr. John Loucks, former Chief Surgeon at Peking Union, attributes the success mainly to Dr. Fang's modern anatomical knowledge—knowledge which the traditional bone-setters did not possess.

30. "China's Achievements in Internal Medicine during the Past Five Years," *Chung-hua nei-k'e tsa-chih* (Chinese journal of internal medicine) 12.10:42; in *Joint Publications Research Service*, No. 30251.

31. As in E. Leong Way, "Pharmacology," in Sidney H. Gould, ed., *Sciences in Communist China* (Washington, 1961), p. 376.

32. Figures cited in Mann, pp. 157–165.

33. As at "Chinese Conference on Ophthalmology," *NCNA* (Dec. 26, 1965); in *SCMP*, No. 3608:20 where one paper presented "an effective treatment of cataracts by a new method which combines modern medicine and traditional medicine."

34. Chang Chih-nan, *et al.*, "Chinese Medicine is Good and Western Medicine is Also Good, but a Combination of the Two is Better," *KMJP* (Mar. 24, 1961); in *Current Background*, No. 662:9.

35. Huang Chia-szu, "Medical Science Marches Forward under the Guidance of the Hundred Flower Policy," *KMJP* (Mar. 16, 1961); in *Current Background*, No. 662:3.

36. Li Te-ch'uan speech to National Peoples' Congress, April 4, 1960; in *SCMP*, No. 2237:20.

37. There is an important article on the general problem of "creatively inheriting" the national culture. Wu Chiang, "Wen-hua i-ch'ang te hsueh-hsi ho p'i-p'an wen-t'i" (The problem of studying and criticizing the cultural legacy), *Hung-ch'i* (Red flag) No. 6:18–23 (Mar. 16, 1961).

38. *JMJP*, (Nov. 20, 1958).

39. Reported in detail in, Shanghai, *Wen-hui pao* (Aug. 15, 1959).

40. The official report appeared in *JMJP* (Dec. 14, 1963). It is summarized in Mann, pp. 172–174, and discussed by Han Su-yin, "Acupuncture—the Scientific Evidence," *Eastern Horizon*, 3.4:8–17.

41. A front page editorial was captioned "Wei Ch'ao-hsien k'e-hsüeh yen-chiu te cho-yüeh ch'eng-chiu huan-hu" (Hailing the profound accomplishment of Korean scientific research), *JMJP* (Dec. 14, 1963).

42. Chang Tien-hua, "Tsu-kuo i-hsüeh te pao-kuei i-ch'an-chen-chih" ("The precious legacy of the medicine of the motherland—acupuncture") *Hsin chien-she* (New construction) 7:72–77 (August 1965).

43. As in Wan Hua, "Chung-i chen-chung te pien-cheng-fa ssu-hsiang" (Dialectical-materialist thought in Chinese medicine diagnosis), *KMJP* (May 5, 1961).

44. Described in Pa Chin, *A Battle for Life* (Peking, 1959).

45. The strong subjective stress in all of this—determination can perform miracles—was clearly expressed by Teng Ying-ch'ao; "If our thought and viewpoint are correct, and if we use our subjective initiative, we can still overcome disease although our circumstances and medical facilities are not very satisfactory." "Overcome Disease with Revolutionary Spirit," *Jen-min jih-pao* (Sept. 18, 1960; in *SCMP*, No. 2353:19.

46. The literature on rejoining severed limbs is now quite sizable. One of the first cases is lauded in "Peking Papers Hail Success in Restoring Severed Hand," *NCNA* (Aug. 6, 1963); in *SCMP*, No. 3037: 13.

47. "Chinese Health Minister Reviews Achievements in Medical Work," *JMJP* (Feb. 7, 1961); in *SCMP*, No. 2440:15–16.

48. The campaign is analyzed, and criticized, in "Medicine to the Villages", *China News Analysis*, No. 602 (Mar. 4, 1966).

49. "A Revolutionary Measure for Health Work", *JMJP* (Feb. 26, 1965); in *SCMP*, No. 3418:16.

50. "Train Medical Workers by Using Revolutionary Methods," *JMJP* (Aug. 13, 1965); in *SCMP*, No. 3526:15.

51. Ch'ien Hsin-chung, "Wei-sheng Kung-tso hsiang nung-ts'un ta chin chün te hsü-mo" (Preface to a great advance in medical workers going to the countryside) Hung-ch'i 13.23:1–9 (Dec. 6, 1965).

52. *Ibid.*, pp. 20–22.

53. An interesting parallel is a *Red Flag* article praising a commune meteorologist for using native folk experience on weather forecasting when modern scientific instruments were not available. It does not claim that changes in the croaking of frogs is a more reliable indication of changing atmospheric pressure than a barometer, but the ingenuity and preservance in overcoming material difficulties (i.e., the lack of even a single barometer in the commune) is what is really praised. Something of the same spirit seems to infuse much of the recent writings on using acupuncture where surgical facilities are lacking, or in using herbals where antibiotics are not available. Tuan Ch'un-tso, "Make Use of 'On Practice' to Sum up Folk Experience in Weather Forecast," *Hung-ch'i* (Feb. 11, 1966); in *SCMM*, No. 514; 36–46.

54. Worth, p. 28.

55. Chiao Lu-ping, "Pu hsü chia-chieh ch'i-kung ming-i san shih Feng-chien mi-hsin tu-su" (Do not permit usurpation of the name *Ch'i-kung* to disseminate feudal superstitious poison), *Hsin t'i yü,* 3.25–26 (New physical education) 3:25–26 (March 1965).

56. *Ibid.,* p. 25.

CHAPTER X: TAIWAN — REMEMBRANCE OF THINGS PAST

1. The same attitudes may well exist in overseas Chinese communities. For example, the prominent Hong Kong educator Vermier Ch'iu urged inclusion of a "College of Chinese Medicine" in the new Chinese University because "Chinese medicine is an indispensable part of Chinese culture." Vermier Y. Ch'iu, "The Chinese University," *Hong Kong Standard* (Dec. 6, 1963). There has not, however, been the same type of full-fledged debate.

2. Some Taiwanese came to China to study traditional medicine. A few even went to traditional medicine schools in Japan. They were not, of course, recognized as accredited doctors by the Japanese Government.

3. Conversation with Dr. Wu Chi-fu, President of the Taiwan Physicians' Association, in Kaohsiung, June 6, 1964.

4. "Lun chung-i wen-t'i," (On the Chinese medicine question), *TK:CK,* No. 21 (Nov. 26, 1946).

5. According to the Taiwan Provincial Chinese Physicians' Association, there were over 1000 traditional doctors on Taiwan by the early 1950's. This figure probably does not give an accurate impression of the total strength of traditional medicine, for it does not include the much more numerous traditional druggists. "Taiwan sheng chung-i shih kung-hui chien-i shu" (Petition of the Taiwan Provincial Chinese Physicians' Association), in *Chung-i-yao nien-chien,* p. 8. The yearbook lists the names of 1089 traditional doctors in Taiwan.

6. "Chung-i yü hsi-i chih cheng" (The struggle between Chinese and Western medicine), *Chung-kuo hsin-wen* (Mar. 27, 1951).

7. Text of telegram in *Chung-i-yao nien-chien,* p. 7.

8. *Chung-i-yao nien-chien,* p. 8.

9. Frontispiece of *Chung-i-yao nien chien.* If Ch'en Ch'eng was an active supporter of traditional medicine, in the sense of Ch'en Kuo-fu, it is strange that he has apparently written nothing on the subject.

10. The complete text of the debate is printed in *Chung-i-yao nien-chien,* pp. 13–40.

11. See, for example, speech of Wang Han-sheng in *Chung-i-yao nien-chien,* pp. 19–20.

12. "Pu neng chieh-shou te 'shou-she chung-i hsüeh-hsiao' an," (The unacceptable proposal 'To establish a school of Chinese medicine'), *Tzu-yu Chung-kuo* (Free China), 14.8:4 (Apr. 16, 1956).

13. Mao Tzu-shui, "Lun Li-fa Yuan t'ung-kuo 'Shou-she chung-i hsüeh-hsiao' " (On the Legislative Yuan's passing the 'Resolution to establish a school of Chinese medicine' "), *Tzu-yu Chung-kuo*, (Free China) 14.9:283–284 (May 1, 1956).

14. Ju Pin, (pseud.), "Lun 'Shou-she chung-i hsüeh-hsiao' an," (On the resolution 'To establish a school of Chinese medicine'), *Tzu-yu Chung-kuo*, 15.5:10–20 (Sept. 1, 1956).

15. Lung Yüan-ming, "Yu 'Chung-i hsüeh-hsiao' hsiang-ch'i," (Reflecting on the 'Chinese Medicine School'), *Tzu-yu Chung-kuo*, 4.10:336 (May 16, 1956).

16. "Chung-i yü hsi-i chan-cheng," (The struggle between Chinese and Western medicine), *Min-tsu wan-pao* (National evening paper; Apr. 20, 1956).

17. *Ibid.*

18. *Hsin-sheng pao* (Mar. 27, 1956).

19. *Kung lun pao* (Mar. 28, 1956).

20. A questionnaire was circulated among a selected sample of 100 National Taiwan University students. Of the 71 who replied, 51 per cent consulted both types of doctors, and 4 per cent only Chinese-style doctors. For their parents' medical preferences the percentages were 51, 30, and 4 per cent respectively, with 15 per cent unknown. To the question whether Chinese or Western medicine is better 55 per cent chose Western medicine, only 4 per cent Chinese medicine, with 41 per cent undecided. A similar questionnaire was given to students at the JTAC language school in May, 1964. These were mainly technical intelligentsia preparing for advanced training abroad. The results for 47 replies are tabulated and compared with the other sample below.

	JTAC School	National Taiwan U.
	%	%
Use both kinds of medicine	40	51
Use only Western medicine	60	45
Use only Chinese medicine	0	4
Generally speaking, Western medicine is better	70	55
Generally speaking, Chinese medicine is better	0	4
Chinese medicine has some points superior to Western medicine	58	48[a]
Synthesis of the two is possible	67	78[a]

[a] Many failed to answer this question so it should not be assumed that all others held a contrary opinion.

21. Hong Kong-Kowloon Chinese Doctors' Association for Restor-

ing National Glory, "Yu chung-hsi yao tao chung-hsi wen-hua te cheng-chih" (From Chinese and Western drugs to the struggle over the Chinese and Western culture question), in *Chung-i yao nien-chien* pp. 70–73. The subtitle of this statement read "Criticizing Hu Shih for *Free China's* Opposition to the Chinese Medicine School Question."

22. "Shei wei chung i pu k'e hsüeh? Ch'ing k'an chung-i hsin p'ing-chia" (Who says Chinese medicine is not scientific? Look at its new value), *Hsin-wen p'ing lun (The news review),* No. 90:7 (July 1956).

23. *Ibid.*

24. A number of these are reproduced in *Chung i-yao nien-chien* pp. 1–138 *passim.* The arguments are too repetitious to bear individual treatment. In total they attest to the widespread organization of traditional medicine in overseas Chinese communities and the persistence of the type of thinking behind the "national medicine" movement of the 1930's. In places, such as San Francisco, branches of the Kuo-i kuan still survived. See *Chung-i-yao nien-chien* p. 138.

25. Ting Wen-yuan, "Chung-i yao yen-chiu chi-kou wen-t'i" (The question of a Chinese medicine research institute), *Tzu-yu jen san-jih k'an* (Free men's tri-daily; Mar. 31, 1956).

26. One of several articles would be: Wu Hsien-tzu, "Chung-hsi i-yao wen-t'i" (The question of Chinese and Western medicine and drugs), *Tzu-yu jen san jih k'an* (Apr. 18, 1956).

27. As in Yang Jih-chao, "Chung-kuo tsai kuo-chi shang te ti-wei," (China's international position), *Chung-kuo i-yao fu-yü* (The revival of Chinese medicine; Taipei, 1957).

28. "Chung-i yao chieh lien-ho t'an-hui yung-hu Taiwan tang-chu shou-she chung-i hsüeh-hsiao" (Chinese medicine world unites in a meeting to uphold the Taiwan authorities in establishing a Chinese medicine School), *Hong Kong ke jih pao* (Hong Kong daily; May 18, 1956).

29. An account of this meeting from the traditional doctor's viewpoint was carried in *Hsin-wen p'ing-lun,* 90:8–9 (July 1956).

30. Chinese Traditional Physicians' Association and Chinese Traditional Medicine and Pharmacy Society, "Chin-chi ch'i-shih" (Urgent notice), *Chung-yang jih-pao* (June 7, 1956).

31. *Chung-kuo i-yao* (China's medicine and drugs), 1.1:1–4 (January 1959).

32. *Ibid.,* p. 3.

33. These examples were given in personal conversation with Dr. Li at the Center in Hsin Tien on the outskirts of Taipei, June 1, 1964. It is impossible for one without a very considerable knowledge of both modern medicine and the ancient medical writings to pass judgment

on the truth of such assertions. They have a suspiciously familiar ring to one who has observed a search for native precedents for modern values ever since K'ang Yu-wei, but this in itself does not invalidate Dr. Li's claims. It should be noted that he is not making them with the motive of preserving traditional medicine, as was sometimes the case. There is an article making such claims for modern sex hormone theory in traditional writings on menstruation. Ho Cho-liang, "Ts-ung k'e-hsüeh kuan-tien k'an chung-kuo ku-tai i-hsüeh" (Looking at China's ancient medicine from a scientific viewpoint), *Chung-kuo i-yao*, 2.2:14 (March 1960).

34. Chang Ch'i-yün, who maintains an interest in developing traditional medicine on Taiwan, suggested that substantial research might be financed partly through American drug firms. Personal conversation, Yangmingshan, Taiwan, May 20, 1964. Considering the funds available for such research in the United States and the proven efficacy of some Chinese herbal products (e.g., ephedrine) the proposal is not without merit. Still, it is a rather strange commentary on the status of China's "national medicine" when its development is left to the whims of foreign financial backing.

35. The case is reported in *Min-tsu wan-pao* (Aug. 10, 1962).

36. Bishop Yü was quoted as saying "To open a new world for our China's medicine we have to sacrifice several people." *Min-tsu wan-pao* (Aug. 10, 1962).

37. The writer was strongly discouraged from visiting the school when he applied for permission at the Ministry of Education in 1964. The Research Center, on the other hand, was pointed to with pride.

38. Hsi Fu-i, "Chung-kuo i-hsüeh-yüan ch'eng-li yu kan" (Reactions to the establishment of the Chinese Medicine and Pharmacy Academy), *Chung-kuo i-yao*, 1.1:5–6 (January 1959).

39. Wu Chi-fu, "Ts'ung huo-luan t'an tao 'pien-fa'" (From a discussion of cholera to 'legal reform'), *Wen-hsing*, 59:3–6 (September 1962).

40. The 1943 law is still in force. It, of course, retained that provision while granting traditional doctors full legal equality in medical practice. Discussed in Chapter 7.

41. Wu Chi-fu, "T'ou-shih Taiwan i-chieh te 'ta tsa yüan'" (A peek into the Taiwan medical world's 'assorted grab bag'), *Wen-hsing*, 61:4–8 (November 1962).

42. In private conversation several physicians have complained that there has been a retrogression in medical standards since the Japanese were expelled.

43. Wu Chi-fu, "Ts'ung huo-luan," p. 5. Apparently quite unscientific medical advertisements are a common feature in Taiwan newspapers. *Chung-yang jih-pao*, the official government paper, ran one

by Dr. Hsi Fu-i, President of the Taiwan Province Traditional Physicians' Association, which offered a money-back guarantee that he could insure delivery of a male child. Apparently his method was at least 50 per cent effective.

44. Li Ao, "Hsiu-kai 'I-shih fa' yü fei-ch'ih Chung-i" (Reforming the 'physician's law' and abolishing Chinese medicine), *Wen-hsing,* No. 61:9–15 (November 1962).

45. *Ibid.,* p. 12. Also personal conversation with the writer, June 9, 1964, Taipei. In Li's opinion, too many young intellectuals in Taiwan seek a political career or go into an academic ivory tower, giving insufficient attention to fundamental social reform and cultural modernization. This, of course, reflects Hu Shih's influence. It also should be noted that for a young radical in Taiwan, cultural revolution is the only channel open for his energies. Li Ao has established something of a reputation as the *enfant terrible* of Taipei for his bitter and outspoken attacks on the status quo and the apathy of most intellectuals there.

46. *Ibid.,* p. 12.

47. *Ibid.,* p. 12.

48. *Ibid.,* p. 15.

49. Mao Tzu-shui, "Wen-hsing tsa-chih liu chou-nien chu-tz'u" (Commemoration of Wen-hsing magazine's sixth anniversary), *Wen-hsing,* No. 73:11 (November 1963).

50. Private letter by Ch'en Yu-heng, dated March 25, 1963.

51. Personal conversation with Dr. Wu Chi-fu, June 6, 1964. The legislators' isolation from their home constituencies, plus the keen competition with Communist China for the loyalty of overseas Chinese, probably does make the National Government very sensitive to any organized pressure group among the overseas Chinese communities. Traditional medicine certainly constitutes this. Dr. Wu, perhaps exaggerating for emphasis, referred to "over 100,000" overseas traditional doctors. This figure must be far too high, but the 1957 *Chinese Medicine Yearbook* from Hong Kong lists 3,668 traditional doctors residing in twelve countries where Chinese communities are to be found. Many of them are organized into local associations. This figure certainly understates, for it does not include druggists, omits certain countries, and only partly reports others.

52. Modern medicine's disappointment with this refusal is expressed by Chu Miao-sheng, "Hsiu-kai i-shih fa hou te hsin tsei-i" (The reformed physician's regulations' new bandit doctors), *Taiwan i-chieh* (Taiwan medical society), 6.1–2:11–12 (February 1963).

53. Lin Chen-k'e, "K'an Li-fa Yuan hsieh chi-tao 'ts'ui-ming-fu' " *Wen-hsing,* 82:3–5 (August 1964).

54. "Pien-chi shih pao-kao" (Editorial report) *Wen-hsing,* No. 82:6 (August 1964).

55. Hu Shih, " 'Jen yü i-hsüeh' te Chung-i pen hsü," pp. 16–17; and Fu Ssu-nien, "So-wei 'kuo-i,' " (So-called 'Chinese Medicine'), in *Fu Meng-chen ch'uan chi*, pp. 17–18.

CHAPTER XI: CONCLUSION

1. The implications of science for modern Chinese social thought are treated in D.W.Y. Kwok, *Scientism in Chinese Thought, 1900–1950* (New Haven, 1965).

2. This common preoccupation with increasing national power runs through the Chinese response to the West in fields as disparate as medicine and the British liberal political thought discussed in Benjamin Schwartz, *In Search of Wealth and Power: Yen Fu and the West* (Cambridge, Mass., 1964).

3. See Robert Worth, "Institution Building in the People's Republic of China: The Rural Health Center," *East-West Center Review*, 1.3:19–34 (February 1965).

BIBLIOGRAPHY

Ackerknecht, Erwin. "Problems of Primitive Medicine,"
Bulletin of the History of Medicine, 11.3:503-521 (May 1942).

------A Short History of Medicine. New York, 1955.

Alley, Rewi. "Around Nanyang in Honan," Eastern Horizon,
4.2:23-28 (February 1965).

Balme, Harold. China and Modern Medicine. London, 1921.

Band, Claire and William. Two Years with the Chinese Communists.
New Haven, 1948.

Bodde, Derk. China's Cultural Tradition: What and Whither?
New York, 1957.

Bowers, John Z. Medical Education in Japan: From Chinese to
Western Medicine. New York, 1965.

Briere, O. Fifty Years of Chinese Philosophy, 1898-1950.
London, 1956.

Burchett, Wilfred G. Vietnam: Inside Story of the Guerrilla War.
New York, 1965.

Butterfield, Herbert. The Origins of Modern Science, 1300-1800.
New York, 1957.

Carstairs, G. Morris. "Medicine and Faith in Rural Rajasthan,"
in Benjamin D. Paul, ed., Health, Culture and Community,
pp. 107-134. New York, 1955.

Castiglioni, Arturo. A History of Medicine, tr. E. B. Krumbhaar.
New York, 1958.

Cerny, Jan. "Chinese Psychiatry," International Journal of
Psychiatry, 1.2:229-247 (April 1965).

Chang Chün-mai 張君勵 , Ting Wen-chiang 丁文江, et al.
K'e-hsüeh yü jen-sheng kuan 科学與人生觀
(Science and philosophy of life). Shanghai, 1923.

Chang Hui-chen. Li Shih-chen: Great Pharmacologist of Ancient
China. Peking, 1955.

Chang Ping-lin 章炳麟, "Shang-han-lun tan-lun pen t'i-tz'u"
傷寒論單論本題辭(Discussion of the original text of
the Shang-han lun); Hua-kuo yüeh-k'an 華國月刊 (China
monthly), Vol. 1, No. 6 (February 1924).

------(Chang T'ai-yen 章太炎). "Shang-han-lun chiang-t'zu"
傷寒論講詞 (An introduction to the Shang Han Lun);
Shanghai Kuo-i hsüeh-yüan yüan-k'an 上海國醫學院院刊
(Bulletin of the Shanghai Academy of National Medicine),
1.1:4-9 (1929).

Chang Po-chen 張伯楨, Nan-hai K'ang hsien-sheng chuan 南海
康先生傳(Biography of Mr. K'ang of Nan-hai).
Peking, 1932.

Chang T'ai-yen, see Chang Ping-lin.

Chang Tien-hua 張殿華. "Tsu-kuo i-hsüeh te pao-kuei i-ch'an--
chen-chih" 祖國醫學的宝貴遺産一針灸(The precious
legacy of the medicine of the motherland--acupuncture);
Hsin chien-she 新建設(New construction), 7:72-77
(August 1965).

Chang Tsan-ch'en 張贊臣. Pen-ts'ao kai-yao 本草概要
(Essentials of the pharmacopoeia). Shanghai, 1953.

Chang Tsung-liang, "'Old Style' Versus 'Modern' Medicine in
China: Which Can Do More for the Health and Progress of
the Country, and Why?," Medicine As a Life Work Campaign:
First Prize English and Chinese Essays of the 1926 National
Essay Contest. Shanghai: Council on Health Education, 1926.

Ch'ang-chiang jih-pao 長江日報 (Yangtze daily). Wuhan.

Chao Yü-ch'ing 趙玉青. "Hsin Chung-kuo te Chung-i yao chi-chi wu-chuang ssu-hsiang ts'ai neng tsou hsiang k'e-hsüeh-hua"
新中國的中醫要積極武裝思想
(New China's Chinese-style doctors must arm themselves ideologically); Pei-ching Chung-i 北京中醫 (Peking Chinese medicine), 1.3:11-14 (June 1952).

Chao Yü-huang 趙橘黃. "Chung-yang yen-chiu yüan i she Chung-yao yen-chiu so chi-hua shu" 中央研究院擬設中藥研究所計劃書; I-yao p'ing-lun 醫藥評論 (Medical review), pp. 44-47 (1929).

------"Shuo Chung-yao" 說中藥 (Discussing Chinese drugs); Chung-yang yen-chiu yüan yüan-wu yüeh-pao 中央研究院院務月報(Monthly bulletin of Academia Sinica), 2.1:95-98 (July 1930).

Chen-chiu ju-men 針灸入門 (Introduction to acupuncture). Peking, 1964.

Ch'en, C.C. Scientific Medicine as Applied to Ting Hsien. Nanking, 1933.

Ch'en Kuo-fu 陳果夫. Ch'en Kuo-fu hsien-sheng ch'üan-chi 陳果夫先生全集 (Complete works of Mr. Ch'en Kuo-fu). Hong Kong, 1952.

Ch'en Li-fu 陳立夫. "Kuo-ch'an yao-wu tzu-chi yü min-tsu tzu-chiu" 國產藥物自給與民族自救 (Self-sufficiency in native-produced herbals and national self-sufficiency); Hsi-nan i-hsüeh tsa-chih 西南醫學雜誌 (South-west medical journal), No. 3:3 (1943).

Ch'en Pang-hsien 陳邦賢. Chung-kuo i-hsüeh shih 中國醫學史 (A medical history of China). Shanghai, 1937.

------Chung-kuo i-hsüeh shih 中國醫學史 (A medical history of China). Rev. ed.; Taipei, 1956.

------Chung-kuo i-hsüeh shih 中國醫學史 (A medical history of China). Rev. ed.; Shanghai, 1957.

Ch'en, Theodore Hsi-en. "Science, Scientists, and Politics," in Sidney Gould, ed., Sciences in Communist China. Washington, D.C., 1961.

Ch'en Ts'un-jen 陳存仁. Chin-chin yu wei t'an 津津有味 譚 (Assorted conversational tidbits). Hong Kong, 1957.

Ch'en, William Y. "Science in Communist China: Medicine and Public Health," China Quarterly, 6:153-169 (April-June 1961).

Ch'en Wu-chiu 陳无咎. "Chung-yang Kuo-i-kuan hsüan-yen" 中央國醫館宣言 (Manifesto of the Central Institute for Chinese Medicine); Chung-hsi i-yao 中西醫藥 (Journal of the medical research society of China), 2:104-109 (1936).

Cheng I-cheng 鄭以貞. "Fu hsüeh-hsiao hsi-t'ung ying chia-jih Chung-i hsüeh-hsiao chien-i an" 附學校系統應加入 中醫學校建議案 (Supplement on the case of the proposal to include schools for Chinese medicine in the school system); I-yao hsüeh 醫藥學, 3.1:14-16 (January 1926).

Ch'eng Chih-fan. "Criticize Wang Pin's Erroneous Concept of Despising Traditional Medicine: Correctly Accept the Medical Legacy of the Motherland;" K'e-hsüeh t'ung-pao (Scientific report), No. 6 (1955); in SCMP (supplement), No. 1094:1-6.

Ch'eng Jung-liang 程榮梁. "Chien Kuo Mo-jo hsien-sheng" 械郭沫若先生 (To Mr. Kuo Mo-jo); Hsin Chung-hua i-yao yüeh-k'an 新中華醫藥月刊 (New China medical monthly), 1.2-3:23-24 (April 1945).

Chiang Hui-ming 江晦鳴 .　"Ts'un hu? Fei hu?" 存乎？
廢乎？(Exist or perish?); Chung-hua i-hsüeh tsa-chih
中華醫學雜誌(National medical journal of China),
21.7:755-766 (July 1935).

Chiang Shao-yüan 江紹原 .　"I-hsieh kuan-yü i... Chung-wai
mi-hsin" 一些關於醫⋯⋯中外迷信 (Several Chinese and
foreign superstitions regarding medicine); Kung-hsien 貢獻
(Offerings), 2.8:19-25 (August 1928).

------"Chung-kuo jen tui-yü hsi-yang i-yao ho i-hsüeh te fan-ying"
中國人對於西洋醫藥和醫學的反應(Chinese
reaction to Western pharmaceuticals and medicine); Kung-
hsien, Vol. 4, No. 3 (1928).

------"Kuo-jen tui-yü Hsi-yang fang-yao-i chih fan-ying" 國人
對於西洋方藥醫之反應 (Chinese reactions to Western
drugs and medicine); Kung-hsien, Vol. 2, No. 3; Vol. 4, No. 3
(1928-1929) and K'e-hsüeh yüeh-k'an 科學月刊 (Science
monthly), 1:1-10 (1929).

Chiang Yü-po 蔣玉伯 .　Chung-kuo yao-wu hsüeh chi-ch'eng
中國藥物學集成 (Collected Chinese pharmacological
products). Shanghai, 1935.

Chiao I-t'ang 焦易堂 .　"Chung-kuo te i-hsüeh" 中國的醫學
(China's medicine); Wen-hua chien-she 文化建設
(Cultural construction), 1.1:155-162 (September 1934).

"Chiao Kuan-chang wei ch'uang-pan 'Shou-tu kuo-i yuan' mu-chüan
kao ch'uan-kuo t'ung-pao shu" 焦館長為創辦「首都國
醫院」募捐告全國同胞書(President Chiao's announcement to
fellow countrymen on the founding of "Capital National
Medicine Hospital"); Chung-i hui-k'an 中醫彙刊
(Chinese medicine bulletin), 1.1:178-180 (January 1938).

Chiao Lu-ping 焦陆宾. "Pu hsü chia-chieh ch'i-kung ming-i san shih feng-chien mi-hsin tu-su" 不許假借氣功名義散示封建毒素 (Do not permit usurpation of the name Ch'i-kung to disseminate feudal superstitious poison); Hsin t'i-yü 新体育 (New physical education), 3:25-26 (March 1965).

Chieh-fang jih-pao 解放日報 (Liberation daily). Shanghai.

Ch'ien Hsin-chung 錢信忠. "Jen-chen yen-chiu cheng-li tsu-kuo i-yao i-ch'an" 認真研究整理祖國醫藥遺產 (Conscientiously study and put in order the medical legacy of the motherland); Hsin-hua pan-yüeh pao 新華半月刊 (New China semi-monthly), 7:107-109 (April 1959).

------"Chinese Medicine: Progress and Achievements," Peking Review, 7.9:16-19 (February 1964).

------"Wei-sheng Kung-tso hsiang nung-ts'un ta chin chün te hsü-mo" 衛生工作向农村大进軍的序幕 (Preface to a great advance in medical workers going to the countryside); Hung-ch'i 紅旗 (Red flag), 13.23:1-9 (Dec. 6, 1965).

Chin Ts'ao (pseud.) 勁草. "Hua-pei kuo-i lun-chan shu-chi" 華北國醫論戰述記 (Record of the argument over national medicine in North China); Ming-jih i-yao 明日醫藥 (Tomorrow's medicine), 1.1:5-13 (1935).

China Defence League. In Guerrilla China. Chungking, 1943.

China Medical Commission of the Rockefeller Foundation. Medicine in China. New York, 1914.

"China's Return to Native Medicine," Far Eastern Economic Review, 17.23:814-815 (Dec. 23, 1954).

Chinese Therapeutical Methods of Acupuncture and Moxibustion. Peking, 1950.

Chou li 周禮 (Rites of Chou), chüan 5.

Chow Tse-tsung. The May Fourth Movement. Cambridge, Mass., 1960.

Christie, Dugald. Thirty Years in Moukden, 1883-1913.
London, 1914.

Chu Yen 朱顏. "Wo tui-yü Chung-yao yen-chiu kung-tso te chi-
tien i-chien" 我對於中藥研究工作的幾點意見
(Several opinions of mine regarding research on Chinese drugs);
Hsin-hua yüeh-pao 新華月報 (New China monthly), 9:205
(September 1953).

------Hsin chen-chih hsüeh 新針灸學 (New acupuncture).
Peking, 1954.

------Chung-kuo ku-tai i-hsüeh ch'eng-chiu 中國古代醫學成就
(China'a ancient medical accomplishments). Peking, 1955.

Ch'üan Han-sheng 全漢昇. "Ch'ing-mo te 'Hsi-hsüeh yüan ch'u
Chung-kuo' shuo" 清末的「西學源出中國」說
(Late Ch'ing theories on the Chinese origins of Western
learning); Ling-nan hsüeh-pao 嶺南學報 (Lingnan university
journal), 4.2:57-102 (June 1935).

------Ch'ing-mo hsi-yang i-hsüeh ch'uan-ju shih kuo-jen so-ch'ih te
t'ai-tu" 清末西洋醫學傳入時國人所持的態度
(Chinese attitudes toward the entrance of Western medicine
at the end of the Ch'ing); Shih-huo 食貨 (Food and goods),
3.12:45-47 (May 16, 1936).

------"Ch'ing mo fan-tui Hsi-hua te yen-lun" 清末反對西化的
言論 (Discussions on resisting Westernization at the end of the
Ch'ing); Ling-nan hsüeh-pao, 5.3:122-166 (December 1936).

Ch'üan-kuo teng-chi i-shih ming-lu 全國登記醫師名錄
(National register of physicians). Nanking, 1933.

Chung-i chin-hsiu tsu-chih kuan-li hsüan-chi 中醫進修組織管理
選輯(Selections on the organization and management of improving Chinese medicine). Peking, 1953.

"Chung-i k'e-hsüeh-hua lun-chan t'e-chi" 中國科學化論戰特輯
(A special compilation on the debate over the scientification of

Chinese medicine); Chung-hsi i-yao, 2:91-146 (1936).

Chung-i-yao nien-chien 中醫藥年鑑 (Chinese medicine and
pharmacy year book). Hong Kong, 1957.

Chung-yang jih-pao 中央日報 (Central daily). Nanking and Taipei.

Chung-yang jih-pao i-hsüeh chou-k'an 中央日報醫學週刊
(Central daily news weekly medical supplement).

Clark, Gerald. Impatient Giant: Red China Today. New York, 1959.

Cohen, Paul A. China and Christianity: The Missionary Movement
and the Growth of Chinese Antiforeignism, 1860-1870.
Cambridge, Mass., 1963.

Council on Health Education. First Prize English and Chinese Essays
of the 1926 National Essay Contest. Shanghai, 1926.

Dawson, Percy M. "Su Wen: The Basis of Chinese Medicine,"
Annals of Medical History, 7:59-64 (March 1925).

Elgood, Cyril. A Medical History of Persia and the Eastern
Caliphate. Cambridge, England, 1951.

Faber, Knud. Report on Medical Schools in China. Geneva: League
of Nations, Health Organization, 1931.

Fan Hsing-chun 范行準 . Chung-kuo yü-fang i-hsüeh ssu-hsiang
shih 中國預防醫學思想史 (A history of preventive
medical thought in China). Peking, 1955.

Fan Shih 范遭 , Ming-chi hsi-yang ch'uan-ju chih i-hsüeh 明季
西洋傳入之医學 (Entrance of Western medicine at the
end of Ming). 4 vols.; Shanghai, 1943.

Fang Hsien-chih et al. "The Integration of Modern and Traditional
Chinese Medicine in the Treatment of Fractures," Chinese
Medical Journal, 82.8:493-504 (August 1963) and 83.7:411-429
(July 1964).

Feng Yu-lan 馮友蘭 . "Lun Chung-hsi i-yao" 論中西醫藥
(On Chinese and Western medicine and drugs); Hsing-ch'i
p'ing-lun 星期評論 (Weekly review), 21:3-5 (Apr. 25, 1941).

Field, Mark G. Doctor and Patient in Soviet Russia. Cambridge,
Mass., 1951.

Flexner, Abraham. Medical Education: A Comparative Study.
New York, 1925.

Fox, T. F. "Medical Care in China Today," American Journal of
Public Health, 50.6:28-35 (June 1950).

------"The New China," The Lancet (Nov. 7, 16, and 23, 1957).

Fu Ssu-nien 傅斯年 . Fu Meng-chen hsien-sheng chi 傅孟真
先生集 (Collected works of Fu Meng-chen). 6 ts'e; Taipei,
1952.

Fujikawa, Y. Japanese Medicine, tr. John Ruhrah. New York, 1934.

Gould, Donald. "Galen in China," The Lancet (Sept. 20, 1958),
pp. 633-635.

Grant, John B. "Western Medicine in Pre-Communist China,"
American Journal of Public Health, Special Supplement, 50.6:36-39
(June 1960).

Greene, Felix. China: The Country Americans are not Allowed
to Know. New York, 1961.

Hai-hu (pseud.) 海蠖 . "I-hsüeh yü she-hui chih kuan-hsi"
醫學與社會之關係(The relationship between medicine and
society); Tung-fang tsa-chih 東方雜誌(Eastern miscellany),
2.4:7-10 (April 1905).

Harley, George Way. Native African Medicine: With Special Reference
to its Practice in the Mano Tribe of Liberia. Cambridge, Mass.,
1941.

"Health," China News Analysis, 365:1-7 (Mar. 24, 1961).

"Health Statistics--And a Notable Omission," Union Research Service,
11.25:358-370 (June 24, 1958).

Hei-lung-chiang jih-pao 黑龍江日报 (Heilungchiang daily).
Harbin.

"Herb Medicine," Chinese Medical Journal , 51.4:552-553
(April 1937).

Ho Ch'eng. "Examination of My Mistaken Thinking in Health Work,"
Jen-min jih-pao (Nov. 19, 1955); in Union Research Service,
3.20:280-285.

Hong Kong shih-pao 香港時報 (Hong Kong times).

Hou Tsung-lien 侯宗濂. "Sun Chung-shan hsien-sheng chih chiu-
chih Chung-i" 孫中山先生之就治中醫 (Mr. Sun Yat-sen's
sen's final treatment with Chinese medicine); Min-kuo i-hsüeh
tsa-chih (Republic medical journal), 3.3:164 (March 1925).

Hsi Fu-i 美復一. "Chung-kuo i-hsüeh-yüan ch'eng-li yu kan"
中國醫學院成立有感 (Reactions to the establish-
ment of the Chinese Medicine and Pharmacy Academy); Chung-
kuo i-yao 中國醫藥 (China's medicine and drugs), 1.1:5-6
(January 1959).

Hsiao Shu-hsüan 蕭叔軒. "Tu-ts'ai cheng-chih yü i-hsüeh chien-
she" 獨裁政治與醫學建設 (Autocratic government
and medical construction); Chung-hsi i-yao, 1.1:62-65 (1935).

Hsieh, E.T. "A Review of Ancient Chinese Anatomy," Anatomical
Records, 20:97-127 (January 1921).

Hsieh Ti-yung, ed. 謝滌庸 , Chung-kuo i-yao fu-hsing shih-lu
中國醫藥復興實錄 (A record of China's medical
renaissance). Taipei, 1956.

Hsin-hua jih-pao 新華日報 (New China daily). Chungking.

Hsin-sheng pao 新生報 (New life news). Taipei.

Hsu, Francis L.K. Magic and Science in Western Yunnan: The

Problem of Introducing Scientific Medicine in a Rustic Community.
New York, 1943.

------Religion, Science and Human Crisis. London, 1952.

Hsü Heng-chih 徐衡之 . "Pen yüan ch'uang-pan yüan-ch'i"
本院創辦緣起(The purposes in founding this academy);
Shanghai Kuo-i hsüeh-yüan yüan-k'an, 1.1:1-2 (1929).

Hsü, Immanuel C.Y. "The Reorganization of Higher Education
in Communist China, 1947-1961," China Quarterly, 19:128-160
(July-September 1964).

Hsüeh-hsi 學習 (Study).

Hu Shih. "The Doctor, The Missionary, and The Scientist," National
Medical Journal of China, 17.4-5:667-670 (August-October 1931).

------Hu Shih wen-ts'un 胡適文存 (Collected writings of Hu Shih).
Taipei, 1960.

------ "Jen yü i-hsüeh te Chung-i-pen hsü" 人與醫學的中譯本序
(An introduction to the Chinese translation of Man and Medicine);
in Wen-hsing 文星 (Literary star), No. 61:17-18 (November
1962).

Huang Chia-ssu. "City Doctors Go to the Countryside," China
Reconstructs, 14.10:30-33 (October 1965).

Huang Sheng-pai 黄勝白 . "Lun chiu-i lieh wei hsüeh-k'e chih
miu-wang" 論舊醫列為學科之謬妄 (On the fallacy
of including old medicine in the curriculum); I-yao hsüeh,
2.12:2-10 (December 1925).

Huang-ti nei-ching su-wen 黃帝內經素問 (Yellow emperor's inner
classic, plain questions). Peking, 1956.

Huang Wen 黃文 . San-min chu-i yü i-hsüeh 三民主義與醫學
(San-min-chu-i and medicine). Chungking, 1943.

Huard, Pierre et Ming Wong. La Médecine Chinoise Au Cours Des
Siècles. Paris, 1959.

Hübotter, Fr. Die Chineische Medizin zu Beginn des xx. Jahrhunderts und ihr historischer Ent wicklungsgang. Leipzig, 1929.

Huizenga, Lee S. "Lü Tsu and his Relation to Other Medicine Gods in Chinese Medical Lore," Chinese Medical Journal, 58.9:275-283 (September 1940).

Hume, Edward H. "Medical Education in China: A Survey and Forecast," in Addresses and Papers, Dedication Ceremonies and Medical Conference, Peking Union Medical College, pp. 71-93 Peking, 1922.

------The Chinese Way in Medicine. Baltimore, 1940.

------Doctors East and Doctors West. New York, 1946.

"I-shih fa" 醫師法 (Physicians' law); Chung-hua i-hsüeh tsa-chih, 29.2:219-222 (December 1943).

Jao Cheng-hsi 饒正錫. "Wo-men te ch'i-wang nu-li te fang-hsiang" 我們的期望努力的方向 (The hope toward which we strive); Kuo-fang wei-sheng 國防衛生 (National defense hygiene), 1.1:1-3 (1939).

Jen Ying-ch'iu 任応秋. T'ung-su Chung-kuo i-hsüeh shih-hua 通俗中國医学史話 (A popular history of Chinese medicine). Chungking, 1957.

------Yin-yang wu-hsing 陰陽五行 (Yin-yang and five elements). Shanghai, 1959.

K'ang Yu-wei 康有為. Jih-pen shu-mu chih 日本書目誌 (A Japanese bibliography), Vol. 1, n.d.

------Ta-t'ung shu 大同書 (The great commonwealth). Shanghai, 1935.

K'ang Yu-wei et al. Kung-ch'e shang-shu chi 公車上書記 (The ten-thousand word memorial of 1895). Shanghai, 1895.

Kao Te-ming 高德明. "Hsin Chung-hua i-hsüeh yün-tung te li-lun yü shih-chien" 新中華醫學運動的理論與實踐 (New China's medical movement in theory and practice); Hsin Chung-hua 新中華 (New China), 2.3:63-72 (September 1944).

K'e-hsüeh: Kuo-yao chuan-hao 科學：國藥專號 (Science: special number on national drugs), No. 17:9 (September 1933).

K'e-hsüeh t'ung-pao 科學通報 (Scientific report).

Kinmond, William. No Dogs in China. Toronto, 1957.

Krieg, Margaret B. Green Medicine. New York, 1964.

Ku Hsing-yuan et al. "Survey of Combined Practice (Chinese Native and Western Medicine) Clinics," I-hsüeh-shih yü pao-chien tsa-chih (History of medicine and organization of health services), 2.3:192-197 (Mar. 25, 1958); in Joint Publications Research Service, No. 1480.

Ku Yin 谷音, "Lun Chung-kuo ch'ien-t'u yü i-hsüeh chih kuan-hsi" 論中國前途與醫學之關系 (On the relationship between China's road forward and medicine); Tung-fang tsa-chih, 2.6:107-114 (June 1905).

Kuang-chou jih-pao 廣州日報 (Canton daily).

Kung-jen jih-pao 工人日报 (Worker's daily). Peking.

Kung lun pao 公論報 (Public discussion news). Taipei.

Kung-shang tao-pao 工商導报 (Work and commerce paper). Chengtu.

Kwok, D. W. K. "Wu Chih-hui and Scientism," Tsing Hua Journal of Chinese Studies. New ser., 3.1:160-186 (May 1962).

------Scientism in Chinese Thought, 1900-1950. New Haven, 1965.

Latourette, Kenneth Scott. A History of Christian Missions in China. New York, 1929.

League of Nations, Health Organization. Proposals of the National Government of the Republic of China for Collaboration with the League of Nations on Health Matters. Geneva, 1930.

------Minutes of 17th Session, May 4-8, 1931, pp. 15-17. Geneva, 1931.

Lee T'ao. "Ten Celebrated Physicians and their Temple," Chinese Medical Journal, 58.9:267-274 (September 1940).

------"Medical Ethics in Ancient China," Chinese Medical Journal, 61.2:123-131 (April-June 1943).

Leslie, Charles. "The Rhetoric of the Ayurvedic Revival in Modern India," Royal Anthropological Institute, Proceedings, No. 82:72-73 (May 1963).

Levenson, Joseph R. Liang Ch'i-ch'ao and the Mind of Modern China. Cambridge, Mass., 1953.

------Confucian China and its Modern Fate: The Problem of Intellectual Continuity. Berkeley and Los Angeles, 1958.

Li Ao 李敖. "Hsiu-kai 'i-shih fa' yü fei-chih Chung-i" 修改「醫師法」與廢止中醫 (Reforming the 'physicians law' and abolishing Chinese medicine); Wen-hsing, No. 61:9-15 (November 1962).

Li Mai-mai 李麥麥. "P'ing 'Chung-kuo pen-wei te wen-hua chien-she hsüan-yen'" 評「中國本位的文化建設宣言」 (Criticizing "Manifesto for Cultural Construction on a Chinese Basis"); Wen-hua chien-she, 1.5:27-30 (February 1934).

Li P'ei-san. "Take a Correct Attitude toward the Medical Legacy of the Motherland," Hsüeh-hsi (Study), No. 10 (October 1955); in ECMM, No. 15:1-6.

Li T'ing-an 李廷安. Chung-Wai i-hsüeh shih kai-lun 中外醫學史概論 (A general discussion of Chinese and foreign medical history). Chungking, 1944.

Liang Ch'i-ch'ao 梁啟超 . "I-hsüeh shan-hui hsü" 醫學善
會敘 (Discussing the Medical Society); in his Yin-ping
shih wen-chi 飲氷室文集 (Collected writings from the
ice-drinkers studio), ts'e 23. Shanghai, 1916.

Liang Nai-chin 梁乃津 . "P'i-p'an Yü Yün-hsiu 'hsiao-mieh
Chung-i' te miu-lun" 批判余雲岫「消滅中醫」的謬論
(Criticize Yü Yün-hsiu's nonsense about 'destroying Chinese
medicine'); Kuang-tung Chung-i 廣東中醫 (Kwangtung
Chinese medicine), 1.1:6-13 (September 1956).

Liang Yang. "Integrating Chinese and Western Medicine," Peking
Review, 2.43:21-23 (Dec. 13, 1958).

Liang Yin. "Chinese Medicine Thrives on Modern and Traditional
Methods," Peking Review, 5.3:15-17 (Jan. 19, 1963).

Lockhart, William. The Medical Missionary in China. London,
1861.

Lu Ching-sui 陸錦燧. "Chiao Chung-Hsi-i lun" 較中西醫論
(Comparing Chinese and Western medicine); Hua-kuo yüeh-
k'an, Vol. 1, No. 3 (November 1923).

Lu Hsün 魯迅 . Na-han 吶喊 (War cry). Hong Kong, 1962.

Lu Hsün ch'üan-chi 魯迅全集 (Complete works of Lü Hsün).
Peking, 1956.

Lu Hsün. Selected Works, tr. Yang Hsien-yi and Gladys Yang,
Vols. 1, 2. Peking, 1956.

Lu I-wu 陸以梧 . "Chin-hou Chung-i chieh ying ch'ü chih fang-
chen" 今後中醫界應取之方針 (The road future
Chinese medicine circles should take); Soochow Kuo-i i-yüan
yüan-kan 蘇州國医医院院刊 (Soochow National
Medicine Hospital publication), No.18 (November-December
1939).

Lu Wei-po and Yu Yung-ching. "Learning from Ancient China's
Medicine," China Reconstructs, 8.10:32-34 (October 1959).

297

Lung Yüan-ming 龍達銘. "Yu 'Chung-i hsüeh-hsiao' hsiang-ch'i" 由「中醫學校」想起 (Reflecting on the 'Chinese Medicine School'); Tzu-yu Chung-kuo 自由中國 (Free China), 14.10:336 (May 16, 1956).

MacNair, H. F., ed. Voices from Unoccupied China. Chicago, 1944.

Mann, Felix. Acupuncture: The Ancient Chinese Art of Healing. New York, 1962.

Mao Tse-tung 毛澤東. Hsüan-chi 選集 (Selected works).

Mao Tzu-shui 毛子水, "Lun Li-fa yüan t'ung-kuo 'shou-she chung-i hsüeh-hsiao'" 論立法院通過首設中醫學校 (On the Legislative Yuan's passing the "resolution to establish a school of Chinese medicine"); Tzu-yu Chung-kuo, 14.9:283-284 (May 1, 1936).

------"Wen-hsing tsa-chih liu chou-nien chu-tz'u" 文星雜誌六週年祝詞 (Commemoration of Wen-hsing magazine's sixth anniversary); Wen-hsing, No. 73:11 (November 1963).

Marriott, McKim. "Western Medicine in a Village of Northern India," in Benjamin D. Paul, ed., Health, Culture and Community, pp. 239-268. New York, 1955.

"Medicine in China," China News Analysis, 98:1-7 (Sept. 2, 1955).

"Medicine in Communist China," Current Background, No. 662 (Oct. 3, 1961).

Mei Ju-ao 梅汝璈. "Hsi-i yü Chung-yao" 西醫與中藥 (Western medicine and Chinese drugs); Ching-shih 經世 (Statesman), 1.1:73-75 (January 1937).

Mi Ching-sen. "Ginseng, China's Famous Medicinal Root," China Reconstructs, 13.5:43-44 (May 1964).

Min-tsu wan-pao 民族晚報 (National evening paper). Taipei.

Ming-chi Hsi-yang ch'uan-jih chih i-hsüeh 明季西洋傳入之
醫學 (Late Ming Western medicine entering China). Shanghai,
1943.

Morse, William R.   The Three Crosses in the Purple Mists.
Shanghai, 1928.

------Chinese Medicine.   New York, 1934.

Nan-fang jih-pao 南方日報 (Southern daily).   Canton.

Nathan, Carl F.   Plague Prevention and Politics in Manchuria,
1910-1931.   Cambridge, Mass., 1967.

National Medical Association of China.   Medical Directory.
Shanghai, 1930.

Needham, Joseph.   Science and Civilization in China: History of
Scientific Thought, Vol. 2.   Cambridge, England, 1956.

Needham, Joseph and Lu Gwei-djen.   "Hygiene and Preventive
Medicine in Ancient China," Journal of the History of Medicine
and Allied Sciences, 17.4:429-478 (October 1962).

------"China and the Origin of Examinations in Medicine," Proceedings of the Royal Society of Medicine, 56.2:63-70
(February 1963).

Nei Cheng Pu 內政部 (Ministry of the Interior), Ch'üan-kuo teng-
chi i-shih ming-lu 全國等級醫師名錄 (A national
directory of physicians).   Nanking,

Nguyen, Van Huong.   "Renovation of Traditional Medicine,"
Vietnamese Studies, No. 6:22-25 (1965).

Nieh Ts'ung-k'uan 聶崇寬.   "Chung-Hsi-i chih k'e-hsüeh kuan"
中西醫之科學觀 (A scientific view of Chinese and
Western medicine); Hsien-tai kuo-i 現代國醫 (Contemporary
national medicine), 1.1:16-18 (1931).

Niu Jung-sheng 牛榮聲.   "Chung-i yü Hsi-i" 中醫與西醫
(Chinese medicine and Western medicine); Hsien-tai p'ing-lun

現代評論 (Contemporary critic), 5.114:18-20 (Feb. 20, 1927).

Orleans, Leo A. Professional Manpower and Education in Communist China. Washington, D.C., 1960.

Otori, Ranzaburo. "The Acceptance of Western Medicine in Japan," Monumenta Nipponica, 19.3-4:20-40 (1964).

Otsuka Keisetsu 大塚敬節. "Chung-hua min-kuo kuo-i hsüeh-chieh kuan-chien" 中華民國國醫學界管見 (A view of the national medicine circles in the Chinese Republic); Soochow Kuo-i i-yüan yüan-k'an (November-December 1939).

Pa Chin 巴金. Chia 家 (Family). Shanghai, 1937.

------A Battle for Life. Peking, 1959.

Penfield, Wilder. "Oriental Renaissance in Education and Medicine," Science, No. 141:1153-1161 (Sept. 20, 1963).

P'ing-min i-yao chou-pao 平民醫藥週報 (Common people's medical weekly). Sian, June-November, 1943.

Polgar, Steven. "Health Action in Cross-Cultural Perspective," in Howard E. Freeman, Sol Levine and Leo G. Reeder, eds., Handbook of Medical Sociology, pp. 397-419. Englewood Cliffs, N.J., 1963.

"Present Status and Future of China's Research in Pharmacology"; Sheng-li k'e-hsüeh chin-chan 生理科學進展 (Progress in physiology), 1.1:22-30 (March 1957); in Joint Publications Research Service, No. DL 1134.

"Promotion of Chinese Medicine in Communist China." Union Research Service, 3.20:276-298 (June 8, 1956).

Read, Bernard E. "Chinese Pharmacopoeia," The China Medical
Journal, 44. 6:519-526 (June 1930).

------Chinese Medicinal Plants from the Pen Ts'ao Kang Mu.
Peiping, 1936.

------"Chinese Materia Medica: A Review of Some Work of the
Last Decade," Chinese Medical Journal, 53:353-362
(April 1938).

Report of the Committee on Indigenous Systems of Medicine.
2 vols.; Delhi, 1948.

Report of the Committee to Assess and Evaluate the Present Status
of Ayurvedic System of Medicine. Delhi, 1958.

Schwartz, Benjamin. In Search of Wealth and Power: Yen Fu and
the West. Cambridge, Mass. , 1964.

Sen, Gananatha. "The Spirit and Culture of .Ayurveda," in The
Cultural Heritage of India, II, 410-420. Calcutta,
n. d.

"Senior Medical Personnel and Popular Physicians Go to the
Countryside." Union Research Service, 38.23:340-355
(Mar. 19, 1965).

Shen Kang-ju 沈剛如. "T'an Chung-i wen-t'i" 談中醫問題
(Discussing the Chinese medicine question); Hsing-ch'i
p'ing-lun, No. 33:11-12 (Aug. 5, 1941).

Shen pao i-yao chou-k'an 申報醫藥週刊 (Shen pao, weekly
medical supplement). Shanghai.

Shen-yang jih-pao 沈陽日報 (Shenyang daily). Mukden.

Shen Yen-nan 沈炎南. "Chung-hsi i-hsüeh ho-liu te che-hsüeh
kuan" 中西醫學合流的哲學觀
(A philosophical view of the fusion of Chinese and Western
medicine); Hsin Chung-hua i-yao yüeh-k'an, 1. 2-3:2 (April 1945).

Shih Jo-lin 施若霖. Chung-kuo ku-tai te i-hsüeh chia 中國
古代的醫學家 (China's ancient doctors). Shanghai, 1958.

Shih-pao 時報 (The times). Hong Kong.

Shryock, Richard H. The Development of Modern Medicine.
New York, 1947.

Shu Erh-an 舒而安. "Kuo-jen i fu kuo-yao" 國人宜服國藥
(National drugs suit people of the nation); Soochow Kuo-i yüan
yüan-k'an, 1:5-7 (November-December 1939).

Sieh, Marie. "Medicine in China: Wealth for the State," Current
Scene, 3.5-6 (Oct. 15 and Nov. 1, 1964).

Sigerist, Henry E. A History of Medicine. 2 vols.; New York,
1951, 1961.

------Henry E. Sigerist on the History of Medicine. New York, 1960.

------Henry E. Sigerist on the Sociology of Medicine. New York, 1960.

Singer, Charles and E. Ashworth Underwood. A Short History of
Medicine. Oxford, 1962.

Snow, C.P. The Two Cultures and a Second Look. Cambridge,
Mass., 1964.

Snow, Edgar. The Other Side of the River. New York, 1961.

Stern, Bernard J. Society and Medical Progress. Princeton, 1941.

Sun Wen 孫文. Sun Chung-shan ch'üan-chi 孫中山全集
(Complete works of Sun Yat-sen), Vol. 6. Shanghai, 1929.

Sung Ta-jen 宋大仁. "Chien-she pen-wei te wen-hua yü
Chung-kuo i-hsüeh wen-t'i" 建設本位的文化與中國醫
學問題 (Cultural construction on a Chinese basis and China's
medical problems); Chung-hsi i-yao, 1.1:34-44 and 1.3:235-244
(September and November 1935).

Ta-kung pao 大公報. Tientsin, Peking, and Hong Kong.

Ta-kung pao i-hsüeh chou-k'an 大公報醫學週刊 (Ta-kung pao,
weekly medical supplement). Tientsin.

T'an Chuang 譚壯 . "Tui-yü Chung-kuo mu-ch'ien i-hsüeh te
shang-t'ao" 對於中國目前醫學的商討
(Discussion of China's present medicine); Kuo-fang wei-sheng,
2.3-4:7-16 (December 1941).

T'ang Erh-ho 湯爾和 . "Hsüeh fa-cheng te jen k'e-i pu tung hsieh
i-hsüeh ma?" 學法政的人可以不懂些醫學嗎?
(Can those who study jurisprudence remain totally ignorant of
medicine?); Hsin chiao-yü 新教育 (New education),
2.3:295-303 (November 1919).

------"Kuan-yü Sun Chung-shan ping-chuang te i-wen" 關於孫
中山病狀的疑問 (Doubts on the illness of Sun Yat-sen);
Min-kuo i-hsüeh tsa-chih, 3.2:32-33 (February 1925).

T'ang Tsung-hai 唐宗海 . Chung-hsi hui-t'ung i-ching ching-i
中西匯通醫經精義 (Combining the essential meaning
of Chinese and Western medical classics). Shanghai, 1908.

Teng Chia-tung 鄧家棟 "Wo-men yao p'i-p'an kuo-ch'ü 'hsieh-
ho' te i-ch'ieh" 我們要批判過去「協和」的一切
(We must criticize everything about Peking Union Medical
College in the past); I-yao hsüeh, 5.1:3-4 (January 1952).

Teng Ssu-yu and J. K. Fairbank. China's Response to the West.
Cambridge, Mass., 1954.

Thompson, Laurence G., tr. Ta T'ung Shu: The One-World Philosophy
of K'ang Yu-wei. London, 1958.

T'ien-min (pseud.) 天民 . "Chung-kuo tsui ku fa-ming chih chen-
chiu hsüeh" 中國最古發明之針灸學
(China's most ancient art of acupuncture and moxibustion);
K'e-hsüeh te Chung-kuo 科學的中國 (Scientific China),
2.1:4-5 (July 1933).

T'ien-wen-t'ai pao 天文台報 (Observatory post). Hong Kong.

Ting Chung-yu, see Ting Fu-pao.

Ting Fu-pao 丁福保. I-hsüeh chih-nan hsü-pien 醫學指南
續編(Continued medical compass). Shanghai, 1908.

------(Ting Chung-yu) 丁仲祐. Chung-hsi i-fang hui-t'ung 中西
醫方會通(Combining Chinese and Western prescriptions).
Shanghai, 1910.

Tong, Hollington K., ed. China Handbook, 1937-1945. New York,
1947.

"Toward a New Science of Medicine," China News Analysis,
No. 269:1-7 (Mar. 20, 1959).

"Training in Medicine," China News Analysis, No. 577:1-7
(Aug. 20, 1965).

Travert, André. "The Attitude of the Communist Party Toward
China's Cultural Legacy," in E. F. Szczeparik, ed., Symposium
on Economic and Social Problems of the Far East. Hong Kong,
1962.

Ts'ang Lin 蒼霖. "I-yao yü min-sheng" 醫藥與民生
(Medicine, drugs, and livelihood); Min-sheng i-yao 民生醫
藥 (Livelihood medicine), 1.1:2-3 (August 1934).

Tseng Chüeh-sou 曾覺叟. "Chung-i wu hsü k'e-hsüeh-hua"
中醫無須科學化 (Chinese medicine has no need of
scientification); Chung-hsi i-yao, 2:99-103 (1936).

Tsingtao jih-pao 青島日報(Tsingtao daily).

Ts'ui I-t'ien 崔義田. "Jen-min wei-sheng kung-tso che te
ssu-hsiang kai-tsao" 人民衛生工作者的思想改造
(Thought reform of people's health workers); I-wu sheng-huo
醫務生活 (Medical affairs), 1:1 (1952).

Veith, Ilza, tr. Huang Ti Nei Ching Su Wen: The Yellow Emperor's
Classic of Internal Medicine. Baltimore, 1949.

------"Some Philosophical Concepts of Early Chinese Medicine,"
in Transactions of the Indian Institute of Culture, No. 4

(December 1950).

------"Psychiatric Thought in Chinese Medicine," Journal of the
History of Medicine, 10.3:261-268 (1955).

------"Acupuncture Therapy--Past and Present," The Journal of
the American Medical Association, No. 180:478-484 (May 12,
1962).

------"The Supernatural in Far Eastern Concepts of Mental Disease,"
Bulletin of the History of Medicine, 37.2:139-158 (March-
April 1963).

Wallnöfer, Heinrich and Anna von Rottauscher. Chinese Folk
Medicine, tr. Marion Palmedo. New York, 1965.

Wang Chao-lin. "Medicine Town Revived," Peking Review,
6.7:17-18 (Feb. 15, 1963).

Wang Ching-wei 汪精衛. "Hsing-cheng yüan Wang Yüan-chang
tui i-hsüeh chieh chih hsi-wang" 行政院汪院長對醫
學界之希望 (The hopes of Executive Yuan President Wang for
the medical world); Chung-hua i-hsüeh tsa-chih, 20.4:453-455
(April 1934).

Wang Te-ch'üan 王德焄. "Tu Kuo Mo-jo hsien-sheng Chung-i
k'e-hsüeh hua i-i" 讀郭沫若先生中醫科學化擬議
(Ideas from reading Mr. Kuo Mo-jo on the scientification of Chinese
medicine); Hsin-Chung-hua i-yao yüeh-k'an, 1.1:34-35
(February 1945).

Wartman, William B., ed. Medical Teaching in Western Civilization.
Chicago, 1961.

Way, E. Leong. "Pharmacology," in Sidney H. Gould, ed.,
Sciences in Communist China, pp. 363-382. Washington, D.C.,
1961.

Wei-sheng t'ung-chi 衛生統計 (Health statistics). Nanking, 1938.

Wen-hui pao 文滙報. Hong Kong and Shanghai.

Whitmore, Clara B. "A History of the Development of Western Medicine in China." Ph.D. thesis; University of Southern California, 1934.

"Wo-men mu-ch'ien te chin-chi jen-wu" 我們目前的緊急任務 (Our present urgent responsibility); Hung-sze wei-sheng 紅色衛生 (Red hygiene), 2:2-6 (June 1933).

Wo Wo-sheng (pseud.) 我我生. "Lun kuo-chia i-hsüeh chih hsing-chih" 論國家醫學之性質 (On the nature of state medicine); Hsin-min ts'ung-pao 新民叢報 (New people's miscellany), No. 60:63-67 (1905).

Wong, K. Chimin and Wu Lien-te. History of Chinese Medicine. Tientsin, 1932.

Worth, Robert M. "Institution-Building in the People's Republic of China: The Rural Health Center," East-West Center Review, 1.3:19-34 (February 1965).

Wu Chi-fu 吳基福. "Ts'ung huo-luan t'an-tao 'pien-fa'" 從霍亂談到「變法」(From a discussion of cholera to "legal reform"); Wen-hsing, No. 59:3-6 (September 1962).

------"T'ou-shih Taiwan i-chieh te 'ta tsa-yüan'" 透視台灣醫界的「大雜院」(A peek into the Taiwan medical world's assorted grab-bag); Wen-hsing, No. 61:4-8 (November 1962).

Wu Chiang 吳江. "Wen-hua i-ch'ang te hsüeh-hsi ho p'i-p'an wen-t'i" 文化遺產的学习和批判問題 (The problem of studying and criticizing the cultural legacy); Hung-ch'i, No. 6:18-23 (Mar. 16, 1961).

Wu Lien-te. "Medical Progress in China Since the Revolution," National Medical Journal of China, 6.2:125 (June 1920).

------"A Hundred Years of Modern Medicine in China," Chinese Medical Journal, 50.2:152-154 (February 1936).

------"Chung-kuo i-hsüeh chih fu-hsing" 中國醫學之復興
(Renaissance of China's medicine); K'e-hsüeh (Science),
20.4:259-266 (April 1936).

------Plague Fighter: Autobiography of a Chinese Physician.
Cambridge, England, 1959.

Wu, S.C. "Chinese Medicine," Chinese Recorder: Journal of the
Christian Movement in China, 56.11:733-741 (November 1925).

Yang Ch'ao 楊超. "T'an-t'an i-hsüeh k'e-hsüeh-hua, Chung-kuo-
hua yü ta-chung-hua" 談談醫學科學化中國化與大眾化
(On medicine's scientification, Sinicization, and popularization);
Kuo-fang wei-sheng, 1.2:40-44 (March 1940).

Yang-ch'eng wan-pao 羊城晚报 (Canton evening newspaper).

Yang Chi-chou 楊繼洲. Chen-chiu ta-ch'eng 針灸大成
(Complete treatise on acupuncture). Peking, 1965.

Yang Chi-shih 楊濟時. "Hsi-i shih shen-mo?" 西醫是什麼？
(What is Western medicine?); Min-kuo i-hsüeh tsa-chih,
3.6:1-7 (June 1925).

Yeh Ch'ing-ch'iu 葉勁秋, ed. Chung-i te hsüeh-hsi tzu-liao
中醫的學习資料(Materials for the study of Chinese medicine).
Shanghai, 1950.

Yen Hsi-shan 閻錫山. "Hui-chang Shansi Yen tu-chün chien sheng-
chang ti-i tz'u k'ai-hui yen-shuo" 會長山西閻督軍兼省長第
一次開會演説(Inaugural speech of the society's president,
Governor of Shansi, Yen); I-hsüeh tsa-chih
(Medical journal), 1.1:11-14 (July 1921).

Yen Kung-ch'en 顏公辰. "Tu 'Shen-shu kuan-yü Chung-i
k'e-hsüeh-hua te wen-t'i' hou" 讀「申述關於中醫科學化
的問題」後(After reading Shen Shu on Chinese medicine's
scientification); Hsin Chung-hua-yao yüeh-k'an, 1.5-6:20-24
(July 1945).

Yin Kuei-t'ien 尹桂田. "Tsen-yang li-yung Chung-yao" 怎樣利
用中藥 (How to use Chinese drugs); Kuo-fang wei-sheng,
1.1:45-47 (November 1939).

Yü Feng-pin 余鳳彬. "Pao-ts'u ku i-hsüeh chih shang-liang"
保守古醫學之商量 (A discussion on preserving old medicine);
Chung-hua i-hsüeh tsa-chih, 2.1:4-6 (1916).

Yü Yen 余巖 (Yü Yün-hsiu 余雲岫). "Chiu-i hsüeh-hsiao hsi-
t'ung an po-i" 舊醫學校系統案駁議 (Rejection of
old medicine in the school system); Min-kuo i-hsüeh tsa-chih,
4.3:1-4 (March 1926).

Yü Yün-hsiu 余雲岫. "K'e-hsüeh te kuo-ch'ang yao-wu yen-chiu
chih ti-i pu" 科學的國產藥物研究之第一步
(First step in scientifically studying nationally produced drugs);
Hsüeh-i 學藝, Vol. 2, Nos. 4, 5 (July and August 1920).

------"Hsüeh-hsiao hsi-t'ung chia-jih Chung-i hsüeh-hsiao t'i-an
chih po-i" 學校系統加入中醫學校提案之駁議
(Rejection of proposal to include Chinese medicine in the school
system); I-yao hsüeh, 2.10:13-19 (October 1925).

Yueh, Sung-sheng. "A Traditional Medicine Shop"; China Reconstructs,
11.3:41-43 (March 1962).

Zimmer, Henry R. Hindu Medicine. Baltimore, 1948.

Chang Chi-ch'un 張際春

Chang Ching-chiang 張静江

Chang Chung-ching 張仲景

Chang Tsung-liang 張宗良

Chang Tzu-ho 張子和

Ch'en Chao-ying 陳肇瑛

Ch'en Shih-kung 陳實功

ch'i 氣

ch'i-kung 氣功

Ch'i-shih jih-pao i-yao wei-sheng chuan-k'an 濟世日報醫衛專刊

Chia I 賈誼

chih-che pu shuo, shuo-che pu chih 知者不說, 說者不知

chih ch'i jan pu chih ch'i so-jan 知其然不知其所然

ching-shen 精神

Ch'ing shih kao 清史稿

chiu 酒

chiu-i 舊醫

Chou-kuan hsin-i 周官新義

Chou Tso-jen 周作人

Chu P'ei-te 朱培德

Chung-i 中醫

Chung-i hui-k'an 中醫会刊

Chung-kuo hsin-wen 中國新聞

Chung-yao 中藥

Fan Wen-chung 范文忠

fu-ku 復古

Han-i 漢醫

Ho Ch'eng 賀誠

Ho Ping-yüan 何炳元

Hou-Han shu 後漢書

Hsi-i 西醫

Hsi-yao 西藥

Hsiao-lin kuang chi 笑林廣記

hsien-tai hua 現代化

Hsin-wen p'ing-lun 新聞評論

hsing 形

hsiu-ts'ai 秀才

hsüan-hsüeh 玄學

Hu Han-min 胡漢民

Hua-nien 華年

Hua T'o 華佗

Huang Ch'ing-ch'eng 黃慶澄

Huang-ti 黃帝

Huang-ti nei-ching 黃帝内經

Hung Jen-kan 洪仁玕

Hung sze wei-sheng 紅色卫生

i 醫

309

i-sheng 醫生
i-shih 醫師
I-wen 醫文

Ju-i 儒醫
Ju-men shih ch'in 儒們事親
ju pien i, ts'ai pien chiu
儒變醫, 菜變齏
Juan Yuan 阮元

K'ang-hsi 康熙
Kao Kang 高尚
Ke-hsin Chung-i 革新中醫
k'e-hsüeh hua 科學化
Ku Chieh-kang 顧頡剛
ku-wen 古文
Kuan-tzu 關子
Kuan Yü 關羽
Kung-ch'e shang shu-chi
公車上書記
Kuo-i 國醫
Kuo-i kuan 國醫館
Kuo-i yüan 國醫院
kuo-nao 國腦

Lei-kung 雷公
Li Huan-ying 李煥燊
Li Shih-tseng 李石曾
Ling-shu 靈樞
Liu T'ing-cheng 劉廷楨

min-tsu hua 民族化
Mo-ching 脉經
Mu-tan t'ing 牡丹亭

pa-tao 霸道
Pen-ts'ao 本草
Pen-ts'ao ching 本草經
Pen-ts'ao kang-mu 本草綱目

san-chiao 三焦
Shang-han lun 傷寒論
Shanghai Kuo-i hsüeh-yüan yüan-
    k'an 上海國醫學院院刊
Shao Yuan-chung 邵元冲
shen 神
Shen Ching-fan 沈瑩凡
Shen-nung 神農
Shen T'ung-sheng 沈桐生
Shih-chi 史記
shih-tai hua 時代化
Shih Ying 石瑛
Su-wen 素問

ta-t'ung 大同
t'ai-chi-ch'uan 太極拳
T'ai-p'ing kuang-chi
太平廣記
Taiwan i-chieh 台灣醫界
T'an Ch'in 覃勤
T'an Yen-k'ai 譚延闓
T'ang Ssu 唐俟

t'i-yung 體用

Ting Chung-ying 丁仲英

Tseng Chi-tse 曾紀澤

Tu Tzu-liang 杜子良

Tung-pei wei-sheng 東北衛生

T'ung-wen kuan 同文館

Tzu-yu jen san-jih k'an

自由人三日刊

Wai-k'e ching-yao 外科精要

Wai-t'ai pi-yao 外台秘要

Wan-kuo yao-fang 萬國藥方

Wang An-shih 王安石

Wang Ching-i 王景沂

Wang Hsien-ch'ien 王先謙

Wang Jen-chün 王仁俊

Wang Pin 王斌

Wang Shu-ho 王叔和

Wang Ta-hsieh 汪大燮

wang-tao 王道

Wang T'ao 王燾

Wang Yün-wu 王雲五

Wo Jen 倭仁

Wong Fun (Wang Fang) 王方

wu 巫

Wu Ju-lun 吳汝綸

Wu To 巫燁

Yeh Ch'u-cheng 葉楚傖

Yu Hsien 猷先

INDEX

Index

315

Index

Index

Index

Index

Index

Index

Index

226. *See also* "United Clinic" ("United Hospital")

Prescriptions, for Chinese native drugs, 32, 190, 246–247n49

Progress, law of universal, 112–115 passim; Yü Hsiu on, 152–153

Progress, medical reform for national, *see* Strength, concern for national

Psychiatric care, technical Chinese medicine as a substitute for, 273n6. *See also* Mental illness

P'u Ju, 259n44

Public health, 43; early government measures for, 45–47 passim; efforts of national government, 53–55 passim. *See also* Strength, concern for national

"Public Health Centers," *see* "United Clinic" ("United Hospital")

"Public Health Workers Associations," 163

Publicity, given to successful physicians, aid to medical missionaries, 41–42

Pulse-taking, 21–22, 64

Quackery, 51–52, 140–141, 182–183, 208, 223

Read, Bernard E., 243n17, 263n28

Red, Chinese and expert, 185

"Red doctors," 173–174

Red over expert, 186

Red versus expert, 173

Re-examination of traditional medical literature, *see* Literature, medical, textual research in ancient

Reform, criticism and thought, *see* Ideological reform and criticism movement

Research, institutes of medical, 48; Chinese Medicine Research Institute, 178, 185; Research Society for the Improvement of Chinese Medicine, 87–89 passim; in Taiwan, 214–221 passim. *See also* Drugs, Chinese native as field for scientific research; Literature, medical, textual research in ancient; Medical experience,

China's own to be scientifically studied

Resources, China's medical, 52, 235, 236

Retraining of Chinese traditional doctors, *see* Improvement Schools

Rockefeller Foundation, a pilot project by, *see* Peking Union Medical College

Rural health center, *see* Health centers; "United Clinic" ("United Hospital")

Schools of medicine: during Ch'ing era, 43–45, 63–64; "Emergency Services Training Schools" for war needs, 55; Imperial College of Medicine, 28; of the Indian Army medical service, 63; and the Kuomintang, 139–145 passim, 263n17; started by missionaries, 38–39, 48–49; provincial (Chinese managed), 47–48, 49, 50–51; "Special Medical Schools" recommended by League of Nations, 54–55, 139–140; in Taiwan at Taichung, 212–219 passim, 221

and the policies of the Peoples Republic: colleges as part of government education system, 180–181, 193; facilities for the various minority peoples, 198–199; Improvement Schools, 159, 161–162, 163, 180; Western doctors to study Chinese medicine, 166, 179–180, 183, 185, 197–198, 201–202, 208

See also Disciple system

Schwartz, Benjamin, 282n2

Science, modern: China's acceptance of, 229–230, 233–234 passim; Chinese medicine had in embryo the essentials of, 84–85, 98–99, 220, 279–280n33; as great liberating force from the authority of traditional culture, 115; less accepted in India, 233; pessimism about future of in China, 116–117; and progress, 71–78 passim

quotes on: Ch'en Tu-hsiu, 70, 71–72; Chou Shao, 109, 115–116; Fu Ssu-nien, 105; Hu Shih, 84

322

Index

Index

Index

325

Date Due